ENGINEERING

The Profession and

Elementary Problem Analysis

FRONTISPIECE

Engineering is making it possible for man to explore outer space in much greater detail than ever before. Even though he may embark on interstellar adventures, the boundless reaches of outer space will always lie beyond as a challenge to his ingenuity. As an example of the vastness of the universe, the galaxy in the constellation of Andromeda is only one of many island universes of stars. Here the stars are so clustered together that the galaxy blazes like a whirling Fourth-of-July pinwheel. Andromeda's galaxy is considered a twin of the Milky Way galaxy that holds the earth and its sun. Actually turning in space, it is 9 quintillion miles from earth and from one of its edges to the other is over 130,000 light years. Two dwarf satellite galaxies flank it like very bright stars. (© National Geographic Society—Palomar Observatory Sky Survey.)

ENGINEERING

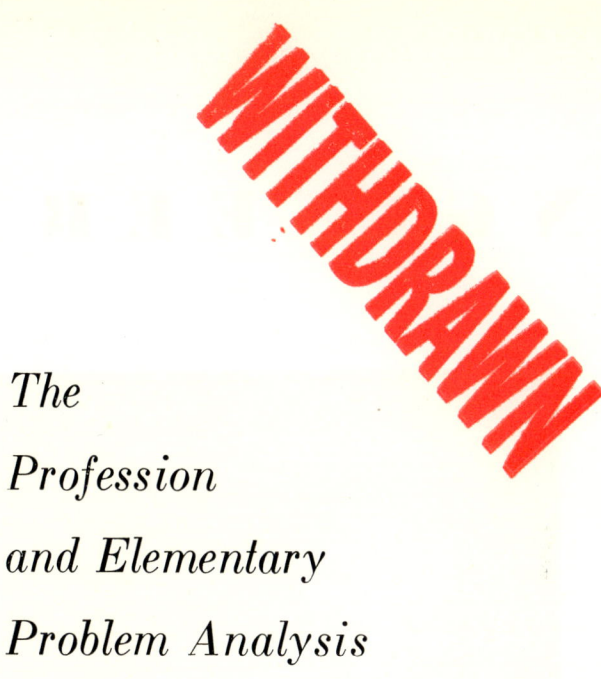

The Profession and Elementary Problem Analysis

H. W. LEACH, P.E.
Instrumentation Engineer
Bell Helicopter Corporation

GEORGE C. BEAKLEY
P.E., Ph.D.
Professor of Engineering
Arizona State University

Second Edition of
Elementary Problems in Engineering

New York: The Macmillan Company

© H. W. Leach and George C. Beakley 1960

All rights reserved—no part of this book may be reproduced in any form without permission in writing from the publisher, except by a reviewer who wishes to quote brief passages in connection with a review written for inclusion in magazine or newspaper.

First Printing

Library of Congress catalog card number: 60-5314

The Macmillan Company, New York
Brett-Macmillan Ltd., Galt, Ontario

Printed in the United States of America

Material included from *Elementary Problems in Engineering*, *The Slide Rule*, and *Engineering Analysis* copyright © H. W. Leach and George C. Beakley 1949, 1951, 1953, 1959

PREFACE

This book has been prepared with the realization that the impact of the newest concepts in engineering education are producing a profound revolution in course content and in teaching objectives in engineering courses. In accordance with recent reports and recommendations of committees from the American Society for Engineering Education, courses in engineering analysis have received increased emphasis. To keep abreast of the latest concepts in engineering education, this text has been completely rewritten and revised. The previous edition appeared under the title *Elementary Problems in Engineering*. While most of the basic types of problems have been retained, many new problems have been added which will challenge the more advanced student. Some of the more difficult problems are marked with an asterisk.

Considerable emphasis has been given to the engineering method of analysis and to the use of *idealized model systems* which serve as the basis for all engineering analyses. Solved examples of realistic situations have been included throughout the book to furnish guidance for the student in his study.

Additional orientation material has been prepared to outline more fully the role of the engineer in our modern age. In addition, this material serves to show how the engineer has been instrumental in the development of our civilization since the dawn of time and how he will continue to play a strategic part in the space age.

For those who desire it, the authors have compiled a workbook of problems to supplement those given in the text. The problems are prepared so that a minimum of layout work needs to be done by the student. This provides more time for practice in slide rule technique and problem analysis. The pages are perforated so that they can be turned in as separate assignments. These workbooks may be secured from the authors.

In preparing this revision, the authors have drawn upon the experience of many professors who have been teaching engineering problems and analysis courses in all parts of the United States. Their comments and suggestions have been of the greatest aid. In particular, we are indebted to Dr. Lee P. Thompson, Dr. Warren Rice, Dr. Phil Cobb, Dr. Ed Wallace, Dr. Alfred Stafford, and Dean H. C. Doremus for their inspiring suggestions and constructive criticisms. To the many others who have given the authors the benefit of their recommendations we wish to express our sincere thanks.

H. W. Leach
George C. Beakley

CONTENTS

Introduction   1

I. Engineering—An Art and Science

1. Engineering in the World of Yesterday   6
2. Engineering in the World of Today   30
3. Engineering in the World of Tomorrow   34
4. Engineering Fields of Specialization   46
5. The Engineering Profession   70

II. Preparation for Problem Solving

6. Presentation of Work   81
7. Scientific Presentation of Data   88
8. Graphs and Curve Plotting   100
9. Mathematical Tools Useful in Problem Solving   124
   - A. Algebra   124
   - B. Logarithms   132
   - C. Trigonometry   145
   - D. The Slide Rule   162
10. Unit Systems and Dimensional Analysis   210
11. The Engineering Method of Analysis   226

III. Applications of the Engineering Method of Analysis

12. Problem Analysis   250
13. Analysis in Static Mechanics   272
14. Analysis in Motion   316
15. Analysis in Work, Power, and Energy   330

IV. Appendix and Tables   360

Index   391

Introduction

The Engineers Council for Professional Development has proposed the following definition of engineering:

Engineering is the profession in which a knowledge of the mathematical and physical sciences gained by study, experience, and practice is applied with judgment to develop ways to utilize, economically, the materials and forces of nature for the progressive well being of mankind.

The work of the engineer may be said to include:
1. The control and utilization of the forces, materials, and energy of nature.
2. The organization of human effort for such purposes.
3. The estimation of costs and appraisal of values, both economic and social, involved in these activities.

Engineering plays such an important part in our national growth and industrial development that it is logical to assume that as our civilization develops more complex problems, the engineer will be called on to aid in their solution. When we stop to consider the extent of our dependence on machinery and mechanical devices, we understand why there will be an increasing demand for engineers.

Practically every modern convenience is the result of engineering development; it is through contact with these that a person gains basic ideas of engineering work. Students starting an engineering course should visit and observe construction jobs, operation or maintenance of engineering works, and in other ways thus pick up as much firsthand knowledge as possible.

The successful, practicing engineer is primarily a scientist, though his field is broader than that usually assigned to the specialist in science. His training implies a knowledge of a great body of scientific facts and an ability to apply their principles to fields in which he is working.

Achievements of engineering are too numerous to mention in a book of this type. The engineer has been responsible largely for our transportation systems, which in turn were such a large factor in the development of the interior of our country. In the communication field the telephone, telegraph, radio, and television are commonplace items, though they were unheard of not too many years ago. The knowledge of design of structures has enabled us to erect bridges and skyscrapers, to build aircraft and missiles, and to perform great subsurface works. Furthermore, modern scientists, with the help of engineers, are on the threshold of a new era of power which will radically modify our present power machinery. All these achievements indicate the part that engineering plays in the development of any civilization.

QUALITIES REQUISITE FOR SUCCESS IN ENGINEERING

Qualities necessary for success in engineering do not differ greatly from those required for other vocations; integrity, industry, initiative, perseverance, personality, and other such characteristics. Results of questionnaires to employers regarding desirable traits in prospective engineers show that a vast majority place character first.

The engineer deals with human beings as well as material elements. He must be able to get along with people and to direct their energies and efforts to secure maximum results. Engineers are responsible for the expenditure of large sums of money, frequently in the form of the savings of many persons. Therefore, it is incumbent on them to see that such expenditures are made in the most effective manner.

For students wishing to predetermine probability of success in college engineering work, there are some essentials which may be considered. Chief of these is a facility in mathematics and the physical sciences. Engineering applies mathematics as a tool, and beyond that it uses the same type of analytical reasoning in setting up problems as it does in their solution.

Since mathematics is so vital in engineering education, it is reasonably safe to predict that a high school student who does not make above average grades in mathematical subjects is unlikely to get along well in engineering subjects.

Engineering is based on the natural sciences, and therefore another measure of engineering aptitude is an interest and talent in physics, chemistry, and science. After mathematics and science, English ranks high as an important preparatory course. Without the ability to read and understand printed information and to transmit ideas to others, the prospective engineer will be hindered in his profession.

Engineering is brain work applied to practical things. Interest and skill in the construction of models are significant in indicating initiative and a desire to create, but absence of these does not indicate an unfitness for the profession. A desire to tinker and perform manual operations is not always a true indication of adaptability to engineering.

As is to be expected, the engineer is not a standardized product. Different positions require different qualifications, and no one man may meet all requirements. The profession calls for men of temperate habits, morally sound, with good health and pleasing manners. They should also be ambitious, industrious, clearheaded, and possessed of common sense.

OBJECTIVES OF ENGINEERING EDUCATION

An engineer has obligations as a professional person in our present-day society, and he must meet the demands for the continual improvement of

Introduction

man's material environment. He can do this only by striving to improve his own education and by working steadily to push back the frontiers of knowledge of the profession.

His activity usually has a direct bearing on the welfare and safety of numbers of people. He must therefore work with the limitations of the state of his art and decide which one of several possibilities will provide the best solution to a given problem.

Engineering is a creative profession, and it is only by continuing to increase our knowledge of basic science that we are able to open new areas of engineering endeavor. Because of the vision and determination of engineers, we have achieved our dominent role in industrial superiority and in providing for a high standard of living.

In order to continue to move forward, our educational system must be set up with two objectives in mind. The first is a technical education which will prepare the engineer in such manner that he can analyze and design creatively and be able competently to perform the functions of construction, production, and operation of a project because of his mastery of the fundamental scientific principles associated with his specialty.

The second objective is a broad goal of engineering education which includes not only the general education of the individual but also a development of leadership ability and an instillment of a deep sense of professional ethics. This objective is set up to aid the engineer to take his place in society, not only as a technically trained person but also as a well-rounded citizen in his community and in his nation. A knowledge of history, sociology, psychology, languages, and an appreciation of cultural fields is as desirable as technical competence.

The integration of the past and present, of technology and culture, and of economic and ethical factors are desirable in an engineering education to provide the individual with an inspiration to launch out on his own initiative both before and after graduation.

ENGINEERING ANALYSIS AND DESIGN

As part of his education the engineer must be taught methods of attacking problems as practice for later professional endeavor. In most engineering curricula at least one-fourth of the total undergraduate program is devoted to engineering analysis and design, including the necessary technological background. Engineering research offers one of the best methods of expressing initiative and creative ability, and the use of problems of varying degrees of difficulty provides a means of practicing methods of analysis.

Problems encountered both in college and, especially, in professional life will involve situations which are beyond the class of routine handbook approaches. Therefore the student should welcome opportunities to practice the solving of problems on unfamiliar situations and to develop new methods rather than merely to adapt old ones. The capacity to design creatively involves a willingness to attack a situation never seen before and for which data are often incomplete. Also involved is an acceptance of responsibility for securing a solution to the best of one's ability.

In this course, and in many of the student's other courses, problems will be encountered which may at first seem to be without possibility of solution. The fact should be borne in mind that a positive numerical answer is not always possible. However, the engineer is obligated to provide the best answer which his level of education and experience will permit.

By consciously pushing always to explore every avenue of approach, an ability to analyze and synthesize can be developed which will be of inestimable benefit in later professional life. If the student will welcome new and untried problems as challenges to his ability, rather than as a task to be avoided, he will soon develop a keen ability to analyze problems, and he will experience the joy of accomplishment in the conquering and solving of unfamiliar situations.

PART ONE
an art and science

Ewing Galloway

Man's desire to create and build enduring monuments is exemplified in the pyramids of Egypt.

chapter one

Engineering in the World of Yesterday

Many people think that engineering is a new science. Actually engineering, although not always called by that name, is the oldest of the sciences and has existed since the beginning of time. As soon as man contrived to manipulate the materials and forces of nature for his own use, he began the practice of engineering. This knowledge has been handed down through all generations to provide us with our modern engineering science.

In order to acquaint the student with the ways in which engineering has developed as an art and science since the dawn of history and to outline the place which the engineer has held in various civilizations, the following sections are presented.

THE BEGINNINGS OF ENGINEERING: 6000 B.C.–3000 B.C.

A close examination of the social life of mankind reveals that in every age, engineering in some form has been one of the basic means by which civilization has advanced. In fact the history of engineering may be regarded as coinciding with the history of civilization. In early times the practice of engineering was directed to two main purposes, the first being to the development of tools for the struggle for existence of an individual or a group, and the second being to mutual protection against warlike neighbors. Thus the earliest engineering was principally either civil or military.

The beginning of engineering may be considered to have occurred probably in Asia Minor or in Africa some 8000 years ago. About this time man began to domesticate animals and to cultivate plants. As a result, he built permanent-type houses in groups and formed communities. Prior to this time, man's chief occupation was gathering food. He hunted animals, fished in streams, and picked edible plants wherever he could find them. The families and tribes were nomadic, followed sources of food supply, and lived in the most primitive types of dwellings.

When the domestication of animals and plants began, there also arose a need for methods of providing for increased production to feed a stable and growing population. The first engineers or craftsmen were those people who devised methods to divert streams for irrigation of crops and who constructed permanent buildings to form cities. The new style of living posed problems concerning hydraulics, transportation, structures, and metallurgy. It was during this period that the effectiveness of food production permitted men time to engage in other activities. Some became rulers, some priests, and many became artisans, whom we may call the first engineers.

It is generally agreed among historians that it was during this period that the region in the river valleys of the Euphrates, the Indus, and the Nile became the birthplace of civilization. These late Stone Age people used fire for preparing food, and likely some observing person saw the greenish rocks used around his camp fire would form beads of copper upon being heated. First he used the copper for ornaments, but later he found it was a better material for tools than the sharpened rocks he had been using. It is fortunate that ores of tin also occur near deposits of copper ore. This probably led to the discovery of the first alloy, bronze, which permitted the construction of even better tools.

In addition to the discovery of methods to produce fire at will, another great achievement in ancient engineering was irrigation. The tasks of draining swamps and digging canals required efforts beyond that of a single individual. Thus the development of an agricultural group was necessary. The influence of irrigation also stimulated mathematics. Fields had to be measured and boundaries established. Surveyors had to calculate masses of earth to be moved to make canals and dams. The carrying on of such works required organization of the efforts of other men and the establishment of a system of supervisors, foremen, and workers. As a result, a class society began to develop which produced craftsmen who had the time to manufacture clothing, tools, and utensils for trade.

The appearance of groups of artisans who could produce items desired by others led to the need for trade and commerce, and vice versa. This, of course, meant that roads were needed and that the engineering necessary to provide trade routes was in demand. These prehistoric highway engineers have left a few examples of their work in recently unearthed archeological discoveries in the Tigris-Euphrates region. The advent of roads stimulated a desire for better methods of transportation than the primitive sled-type vehicle first used.

The inventor of the wheel and axle is lost in antiquity, but it is certain that this was one of the fundamental inventions preceding the beginning of machines. By the time of the appearance of the earliest Egyptian and Mesopotamian picture writing some 5000 years ago, the wheel had been developed in a crude state, although it was at least 1000 years later that extensive use was made of two-wheeled carts pulled by horses. An early application of the wheel was in the manufacture of pottery. As soon as man found he could stabilize clay utensils by firing, he cast about for methods of making containers and soon discovered the possibilities of the potter's wheel. References to the potter's wheel are contained in some of the earliest of written records.

A final result of developments in the earliest civilizations was a need for a better method of communication and recording of ideas. The development of writing is a study in itself, but certainly the early engineers needed writing

MESOPOTAMIA

Mesopotamia, often called the "Cradle of civilization", could also be said to have nurtured engineering in its infancy. Clay tablets, such as the ones shown on this page, have been unearthed which show city plans, irrigation, and water supply systems, and what appears to be, road maps. Although no engineering tools have been discovered among the remains of ancient Mesopotamia, the evidence unearthed of their remarkable architecture; construction indicates that they used measuring tools, which, even though primitive, aided in producing engineering of a high degree for this period. Their cities, with their water supply, irrigation systems, and road networks, were among the wonders of the ancient world.

Many outstanding contributions of mathematics were made by the Mesopotamians. It has been proven that they had knowledge of the sexagesimal system, in which they divided the circle into 360 degrees, the hour into 60 minutes and the minute into 60 seconds.

Courtesy Maddox and Hopkins

Fig. 1-1. Mesopotamia, often called the cradle of civilization, also may be said to have begun engineering. Excavations have revealed their extensive architecture, irrigation systems, roads, and land planning. In this picture is shown a party of surveyors using tools for measurement which, for the period, were remarkably accurate.

Engineering in the World of Yesterday

and writing materials and were instrumental in their development. In order to record the growing accumulation of knowledge of mathematics and engineering, the early engineer in the Mesopotamia region made use of soft clay on which cuneiform characters were incised. These were then baked to provide permanent documents, which are legible even today. In some regions such as the Nile Valley, the inner part of a reed was carefully split and laid into parallel sections with a binder, to form a sort of paperlike material called *papyrus*. In other parts of Asia Minor the treated skins of animals were used to form parchment. Infrequently other materials such as thin sheets of stone or wood slabs were employed as writing materials. In many places the type of writing that developed depended upon the writing material available. For example, the incised characters in soft clay differed from brush stroke characters that were best used on papyrus.

In engineering work a source of energy is necessary. This requirement led to the enslavement and subsequent use (until comparatively recent times) of numbers of humans as a primary source of energy. The construction of all early engineering works has almost without exception been performed in all civilizations, whether they be Oriental, Mediterranean, or American Indian, by human labor. The development of mechanical sources of power did not occur until near the end of the period of history known as the Middle Ages.

ENGINEERING IN EARLY CIVILIZATIONS: 3000 B.C.–600 B.C.

After about 3000 B.C., enough records were made on clay tablets, on papyrus, on parchment, on pottery, and as inscriptions on monuments and temples to provide us with many records of ancient civilizations. From these records are revealed the urban civilizations of Egypt, Mesopotamia, and the Indus Valley. The stories of the growth of villages into cities, and the development of a class society of craftsmen, merchants, soldiers, and government officials, is clearly presented.

The Mesopotamians did not leave us enduring monuments as the Egyptians did, but thousands of clay tablets have been uncovered in the deserts of the Euphrates Valley, many of which deal with problems in practical mathematics, that disclose the knowledge of Babylonian engineers. From these writings we know that they computed land areas and volumes of excavations. They solved simple algebraic problems which arose in their work. They developed a number system based on 60 instead of 10, which today is the basis of our measurement of angle and time.

The engineers of Babylon also made use of drawings and diagrams. A statue of the ruler Gudea depicts him seated and holding a proportionally divided scale and a drawing on his lap. The ruins of the cities themselves show a high degree of knowledge of building materials. Since stone was scarce, dried or baked brick was commonly used. Even today we find bricks, bearing the seal of Nebuchadnezzar, that have been removed from their ancient ruins and built into the walls of houses of present day Iran.

Primitive arch forms were developed in many brick structures, including some of the early hydraulic works. The design of canals for bringing water to the cities and of conduits for removal of storm water and wastes reached a surprising state of development. Highway bridges to span rivers were constructed which used stone piers with wooden stringers to carry the roadway. Also, a naturally occurring asphalt was used to surface some of their roads, a method of construction which was not used again until late in the nineteenth century.

It was the ancient Egyptians who made those remarkable monuments, the pyramids, that impress the traveler even today. The Pyramid Age, starting about 3000 B.C., witnessed the rise in Egypt of the art of cut-stone masonry. It began with a sand heap covered with stone and progressed through constantly improving masonry techniques to the Great Pyramid, which was begun about 2900 B.C. This period of a little over 100 years was a period when there was rapid development, not only in building but also in art, literature, and religion. This accelerated development persisted for several centuries, and it is truly called the Golden Age in Egypt.

Apparently the vast human resources of this ancient land were the key to Egypt's remarkable constructions. Of the now recognized six basic machines,* the Egyptians are known to have used only the lever, the inclined plane, the wedge, and the wheel. The huge blocks of granite used in construction were quarried by laboriously chipping channels around the native rock, using balls of harder rock as tools. By this method blocks weighing 15 tons or more were cut out for use in masonry structures. All the processes used for construction needed human labor in vast quantities. It has been estimated that about 100,000 persons labored twenty years to build the Great Pyramid. This means that the Egyptians were the world's greatest organizers and directors of labor, for this great army of workers had to be fed, and even though most of them probably were slaves, reasonable attention had to be paid to their human needs.

The engineers and architects of Egypt were exceptional men. They held a high place in the Pharaoh's court, and their names as builders were recorded in the ancient writings. Imhotep, a designer of one of the large pyramids, was so revered for his wisdom and ability that he was included as one of the Egyptian gods after his death. The builders of the structures possessed great skill in transferring plans from drawings to the building site. For example, the base of the Great Pyramid is square to within about 1 in. in a distance of about 756 ft, and its angles are in error by only a few minutes. This becomes more remarkable when it is remembered that the structure was built on a sloping rocky ledge.

* The six basic machines are the lever, wheel and axle, pulley, inclined plane, wedge, and screw.

Engineering in the World of Yesterday

EGYPT

In ancient Egypt warfare and strife delayed the development of engineering; however, with the unification of Upper and Lower Egypt, the science of measurement and construction made rapid progress. Buildings, city planning, and irrigation systems show evidence of this development. Good judgment and reasonable engineering design resulted in sound and durable structures. The Pyramids are engineering marvels both in design and construction.

That the Egyptians advanced mathematics is attested to by papyrus scrolls, dating back to 1500 B.C., which show that the Egyptians had knowledge of the triangle and were able to compute areas and volumes. They also had a device to obtain the azimuth from the stars.

The annual floods of the Nile afforded ample practice in measurement surveying. This may well have been the first example of the importance of re-surveys. The rope, used as a measure was first soaked in water, dried, and then coated heavily with wax to insure constant length. Probably some crude surveying instruments were devised, but none have been found.

Courtesy Maddox and Hopkins

Fig. 1-2. In Egypt the science of measurement and construction developed rapidly. The pyramids are engineering marvels both in design and construction. Papyrus scrolls show that the Egyptians had knowledge of the triangle and were able to compute areas and volumes.

No pictures have been discovered to show with certainty how the huge blocks of stone were moved into place during the building of a pyramid. The best theory is that a ramp or inclined plane which spiraled around the structure as it was built provided a means for lifting the blocks into place. Perhaps a different method was used at the Great Temple of Amon at Karnak to place the huge stone beams weighing 60 or 70 tons on the 10-ft diameter, 69-ft high stone columns. It is believed today by engineers that the space between the columns was filled with sand and the beams were then dragged up the inclined surface to a place on top of the columns. The sand was subsequently removed, leaving the beams in place.

The Egyptians also were active in irrigation works. Each autumn as the Nile floods came, bringing their load of silt, water was diverted into canals and finally into fields where it was allowed to stand to deposit its silt. The dikes and canals were remarkable in themselves. For example, an ancient writing has been recovered which awarded a contract to an engineering contractor for what would be (today) about 50 miles of dikes.

In addition to irrigation works, the Egyptian engineers laid out and built a canal connecting the Red Sea and the Mediterranean. This was used for over a thousand years before it was allowed to silt up and fall into disuse.

A question may be asked today concerning why the Egyptians, who made such vast strides in science and engineering in a relatively short time, failed to maintain their leadership. The reasons are many, but there are a few major causes for this apparent stagnation of development.

A fixed political, social, and economic life developed early. A powerful ruling class dominated the land and endeavored to avoid change. This discouraged progress, and there was no public demand to improve the living conditions of the vast majority of people because they exercised no part in the government.

Technically the conditions were favorable for maintaining conditions as they were. The Nile served most transportation needs, and it furnished a yearly renewing of the cultivated land. Construction materials were readily available and ample supplies of labor could be procured. There was little need to invent, since most of the daily requirements were being satisfied.

A third reason may be found in the character of the scientists of that time. Apparently there was little curiosity among those who held places of leadership. They were content to know *how* to do a thing as contrasted with later civilizations who asked *why* a thing was true. Man had not yet learned to think in terms of abstract principles. This came with the Greeks.

SCIENCE OF THE GREEKS AND ROMANS: 600 b.c.–a.d. 400

The history of engineering in Greece had its origins in Egypt and the East. As the Egyptians had developed their buildings and canals, they also had

GREECE

The outstanding progress made by the Ancient Grecians in architecture and mathematics and their contribution to the advancement of engineering demand our admiration.

Aristotle contended that the world was a spheroid. He stated that observations of the various stars showed the circumference of the earth to be about 400,000 *stadia* (400,000) miles.

Erathosthenes, of Cyrene, observed that the sun's rays, when perpendicular to a well at Alexandria, cast a shadow equal to one fiftieth of a circle at Syene (Aswan) five hundred miles away. Thus he established that the circumference of the earth was fifty times five hundred miles or 25,000 miles.

The Greeks constructed many buildings and structures of large size, which show engineering skill and excellent architectural design. One tunnel, which was built to bring water to Athens, measured eight feet by eight feet and was forty-two hundred feet in length. The construction of such a tunnel necessitated extremely accurate alignment both on the surface and underground.

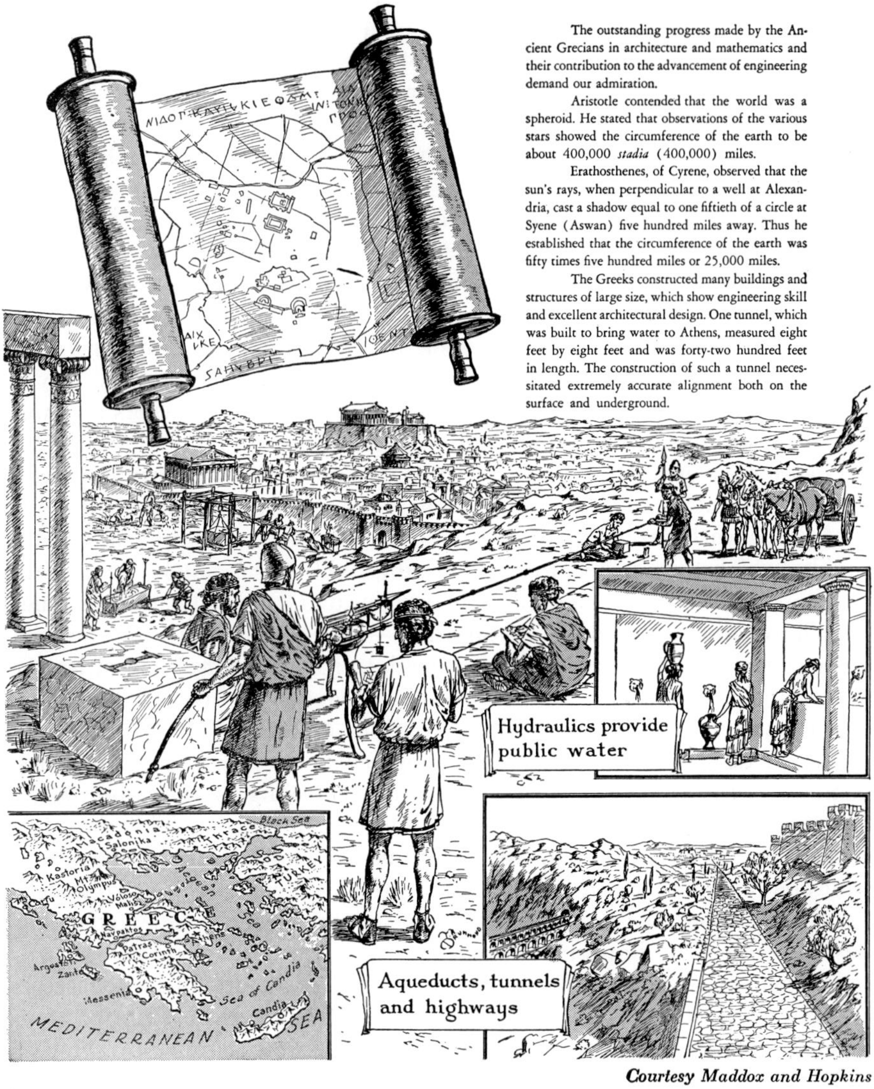

Courtesy Maddox and Hopkins

Fig. 1-3. The Greeks constructed many buildings of unusual beauty which show a high degree of engineering skill and architectural design. Their cities had municipal water supplies which required dams and aqueducts to bring water from the mountains. This picture shows a builder laying out a building foundation, using a divided circle, a plumb bob, and a knotted rope.

developed trade with nearby Mediterranean neighbors. One of these groups lived on the island of Crete, where a vigorous civilization had emerged. These people borrowed a knowledge of stone work from the Egyptians and added architecture in brick and terra cotta. Following the decline of Crete as a cultural center about 1400 B.C., first trade and subsequently learning gradually shifted to an ancient city on the mainland of Greece called Mycenae. To this city, Crete passed on not only scientific learning but also the early Greek language.

The engineers and craftsmen of Mycenae utilized the column and beam construction of the Egyptians, but they also developed the corbeled arch to a high state of effectiveness. In addition they developed an outstanding system of canals for the water supply of cities.

The Greeks of Athens and Sparta borrowed heavily from the culture of the Mycenaeans, which had in turn come principally from Egypt by way of Crete. They were quick to turn to use the discoveries of others and were known better for development than for invention.

Greece developed as a series of city-states, since the topography divided the country into somewhat isolated areas. From the beginning they were confronted with problems of city planning for transportation and water supply, which they solved with remarkable skill. The Greek engineer was capable in the use of labor and materials, and he established technical procedures that endured for centuries.

However, the very division of Greece into somewhat isolated cities prevented the formation of a strong government, and since most of the population were slaves, no organized body of public opinion existed to encourage continual development. Another strong factor retarding higher development of Greek engineering was a widespread feeling in the country that anything resembling manual labor was fit only for slaves. This prevented much of the abstract thought of the famous Greek philosophers from being subjected to experimentation and verification. Thus, in spite of outstanding contributions of Greece's philosophers and mathematicians, technology never became an important part of Greek life. Plato (427–347 B.C.) mentioned that science was a mental exercise that should not be debased by practical use. Even Archimedes (287–212 B.C.), famous for his inventions, seems to have been apologetic for performing experimentation. Archimedes did develop, and perhaps invent, the water screw, the compound pulley, and the plunger pump. Another famous Greek scientist was Hero, who is credited with inventing the first reaction turbine. Of all the contributions of the Greeks to the realm of science, perhaps the greatest was the discovery that nature has general laws of behavior which can be described in words.

The best engineers of antiquity were the Romans. Within a century after the death of Alexander, Rome had conquered many of the eastern Mediterranean countries, including Greece. Within two more centuries Rome held

Engineering in the World of Yesterday

ROME

The Romans excelled in the building of aqueducts. Many of these carried water for great distances with perfect grade and alignment. The key design in this type of construction was the arch which was also used in bridges, tunnels, buildings, and other construction.

Evidence of the Romans' knowledge and understanding of basic geometric principles is further shown by their River and Harbor construction and the scientific approach to navigational problems.

Sanitary systems, paved roads, magnificent public buildings, water supply systems, and other public works still in evidence today, stand as monuments to the Roman development of engineering as a key to the raising of the standard of living.

The rise of the Roman Empire was attributable to the application of engineering principles applied to military tactics. Invincibility of the Roman legions was the result not only of the valor of the fighting men but also, and perhaps more strongly, to the genius of the Roman military engineers.

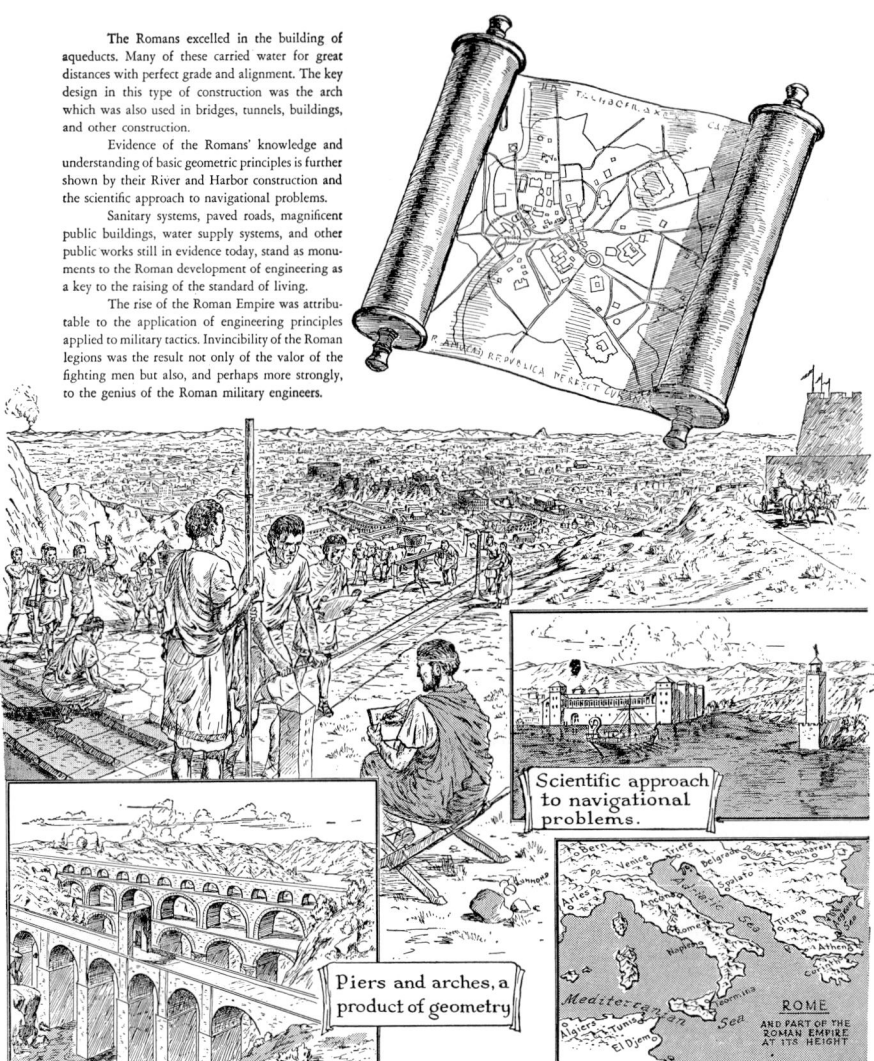

Courtesy Maddox and Hopkins

Fig. 1-4. The rise of the Roman Empire was attributed to the application of engineering principles to military tactics. This picture shows a construction party as they build a section of the famous Roman highways. Notice the heavy foundations which exist to this day.

dominion over all of what was known as the civilized world. Borrowing heavily from all cultures of the countries it had conquered, Rome adapted much of Greek science to its own purposes. First, in producing engines of war and then in carrying out public works, the Roman engineer, while lacking originality of thought, was superior in the application of techniques.

Roman roads were models of engineering skill. Rome had learned from history how important it is to have a good system of communication to hold together a great empire. At the peak of Roman sovereignty, the road network comprised over 180,000 miles of improved roads that extended as far east as the Euphrates and as far west as France and Britain.

In addition to road building, Roman engineers were famous for the construction of aqueducts and bridges. At first the Roman bridges were constructed of wood erected on piles. In 55 B.C. Julius Caesar recorded the building of a wooden bridge about 1400 feet long across the Rhine. When the Roman engineers turned to the use of stone, they exhibited unusual skill in erecting bridge-type structures, many of which still exist today. One outstanding example is the famous Pont du Gard near Nimes, France, which is 150 ft high and over 900 ft long. It carries both an aqueduct and a roadway. Although the Romans discovered a durable cement which they called *pozzuolana*, they had difficulty in building forms to contain the concrete mixture. Consequently it was used principally as a mortar for their stone masonry. The arch, inherited from the Etruscans, became an outstanding feature of Roman masonry construction.

While the rudiments of iron smelting were known early in recorded history, little use was made of it until Roman times. By the beginning of the Christian era, iron refining had been developed to the point where it was used for small items of building hardware, as tips on spears, and as axes, saws, and other tools. However, the methods of smelting usually resulted in over half of the metallic iron being thrown away in the slag.

Many reasons have been advanced for the decline of Roman civilization. Although excelling in law and civil administration, distant colonies were never fully a part of the Empire, and the necessary expansion of frontiers created a need for better communications than were then available. Roman science seemed to lack the curiosity and imagination necessary to create vastly improved scientific techniques to keep pace with the geographic expansion. Discontent and disorganization within the empire itself finally led to the fall of Rome to a far less cultured invader.

ENGINEERING IN THE MIDDLE AGES: 5TH–16TH CENTURIES

While it took about a thousand years for Western civilization to reach a stage of development approximating that of the Romans, the science of Greece and Rome had shifted to the East where it infused with Oriental culture and learning. In western Europe, much of the learning was dispersed in local groups, principally under the control of religious orders. However, it was not until the twelfth and thirteenth centuries when scholars began to translate Arabic scientific works that any widespread interest was evident in science.

It was during this time that the name *engineer* was first used. Historical writings of about A.D. 200 tell of an *ingenium*, an invention, which was a sort of battering ram used in attacks on walled defenses. Some thousand years later we find that an *ingeniator* was a man operating such a device—the beginning of our modern title, engineer.

During the Middle Ages, some worthwhile advancements were made despite the lack of incentives for scientific growth. Also, it was during this period that several of the world's outstanding masonry constructions were made. Medieval castles and the Gothic cathedrals are examples of structural engineering of that time. Canals and water systems also were further developed, and in spite of only a rudimentary knowledge of sanitation, sewage disposal systems were installed in several of the larger cities.

One great technical advance made during this period was the development of improved iron foundries. It was discovered that wood charcoal, with a suitable air blast, could be used to produce excellent grades of iron. Casting methods improved, and with the invention of gunpowder, cannon were made which changed the nature of warfare.

The introduction of the compass, whose invention is credited to the Chinese, fostered sea navigation and made the exploration of distant lands less hazardous.

Other realms of scientific growth were taking place in chemistry and allied sciences. The Arabs possessed considerable knowledge of chemistry and devoted much time to the practical applications of chemical processes. Arabian trade with China provided a means for learning of a Chinese process for making paper. Within a few years the Arabs had established a paper mill and were making paper in large quantities. The cheapness of paper contributed much to the communication of ideas, since it eventually replaced expensive papyrus or parchment.

Arab scientists also discovered processes for sugar refining, soap making, and perfume distilling. The discovery of gunpowder about the fourteenth century had rapid and far reaching results. The chemists of this era also developed new processes for making glass, and outstanding examples of their art may be seen today in the magnificent windows of medieval buildings.

A major factor affecting science and engineering in the Middle Ages was religion. Prior to this time in history, human labor performed practically all work that was accomplished. The few machines that had been developed served as a meager supplement to the masses of slaves. However, with the growth of Christianity, an aversion to slave labor developed. This necessitated a search for other sources of power and most certainly was an important factor in the development of engines in the centuries following the Middle Ages.

Significant developments in power sources during the Middle Ages were in the use of the horse, the water wheel, and the windmill. Curiously enough, it was not until the ninth century that a horse collar was invented which would allow a horse to exert any appreciable pull without choking.

The Bettman Archive

Fig. 1-5. The invention of printing by using movable type meant that scientific information could be made available to many more people. Here Johann Gutenberg is examining a proof sheet, the first ever produced from movable type.

This development, insignificant as it may at first seem, was a means of securing appreciable power from other than human sources. The water wheel and windmill, known long before to the Persians, was rediscovered during this period.

About 1454, Gutenberg, using movable type, produced the first books printed on paper. This revolutionary development meant that the knowledge of centuries which previously was recorded laboriously by handwriting now could be disseminated in great quantities. Knowledge which formerly was available only to a few was spread to scholars everywhere. The inven-

Engineering in the World of Yesterday

tion of paper and the development of printing served as fitting climaxes to the Middle Ages.

THE REVIVAL OF SCIENCE: 17TH AND 18TH CENTURIES

Following the invention of printing, the self-centered medieval world changed rapidly. The changes appeared in literature, ethics, and philosophy and in practically every other field of human endeavor. Led by a group of

The Bettman Archive

Fig. 1-6. Galileo is considered one of the foremost scientists of his time. Many inventions and discoveries have been credited to him, including the first telescope. By using his telescope, Galileo discovered the moons around the planet Jupiter. This picture shows Milton in the observatory of Galileo looking through a telescope.

outstanding educators such as Grosseteste and Roger Bacon,* the universities and colleges began to develop a positive science of physics, chemistry, and mathematics. A new concept of testing replaced the older practice of establishing physical principles by whomever could argue more forcefully.

At first the departure from medieval philosophy was filled with danger. Galileo was persecuted for his advanced ideas, and Bruno was burned at the stake in 1600 for his revolutionary ideas about the structure of the universe. Slowly, however, freedom of thought was encouraged, and by the time of

* See page 227.

Newton and Leibnitz the whole domain of nature was under the scrutiny of science.

Four men of this period made discoveries and formulated laws which have proved to be of great value to engineering. They were Boyle, Huygens, Hooke, and Newton. Robert Boyle experimented with gases and formulated a basic law relating pressures and volumes of gases.

Christian Huygens investigated the effects of gravitational pull and devised, among other things, a pendulum to measure the acceleration of gravity.

Robert Hooke experimented with elastic properties of materials and formulated basic laws relating to the distortion of materials under stress.

Isaac Newton is famous for his three basic laws of motion. The statements of the principles, simple as they seem, were formulated from a maze of wordy speculations and concepts that seemed always to cloud any attempt at concise thinking in that day. In fact much of the difficulty encountered by all researchers was due to lack of concise and unambiguous words to express their ideas.

Newton also was famous for his part in the development of the basic mathematics called *calculus*, which has been a valuable mathematical tool for engineers since his time. Other mathematical developments of this era included the invention of logarithms by Napier about 1600, the adaptation of logarithms to a base of ten by Briggs, and finally the first crude slide rule made by Oughtred about 1622.

Considerable improvement was made in road networks at this time. However, the greatest strides in communication and transportation resulted from advances in the construction of canals, docks, and harbors. Sometime in the fourteenth century the canal lock was invented in Holland, and by the seventeenth century many miles of navigable canals had been built in Italy, France, and England. Prior to the coming of the railroad, the canal was the most important means of providing inland transportation.

Sanitation was still in a primitive state in most cities. A shallow ditch located in the center of the street was the drain for waste materials of all kinds. Water for flushing the sewer ditches was frequently inadequate. There was little knowledge of the dangers of unsanitary conditions, and public funds to remedy the conditions were usually not available.

Advancements also were made in spinning and weaving. About the beginning of the seventeenth century, Jurgen of Brunswick introduced a machine method of twisting the yarn into a thread. Shortly thereafter improvements were made in looms by Hargreaves, Crompton, and Arkwright, which vastly increased the output of woven cloth of all kinds.

The development of chemical technology was hampered by the lack of basic information on the nature of matter. Scientists such as Boyle tried to correlate the fundamental laws of chemistry, but it was not until the period

Engineering in the World of Yesterday

of the Industrial Revolution that chemistry was able to cast aside the veil of alchemy and formulate positive laws.

The search for sources of power to take the place of human labor was still going on. Windmills had reached a fairly advanced stage of development, particularly in Holland and Germany where they were used to pump water from the lowlands, to grind grain, and to saw wood. Water wheels, undershot or overshot, were a primary source of power in certain locations in England and France. Animal labor was beginning to be widely used, particularly in agriculture, as a replacement for human labor.

About 1687 the French inventor Papin designed a steam engine that operated on the principle of introducing steam into a cylinder and then condensing the steam. The resulting vacuum caused a piston to move in the cylinder, thus providing mechanical motion from steam. Papin died before he had completed more than a prototype, and Newcomen, an Englishman, made the first workable engine using Papin's basic ideas. Newcomen's engine operated slowly and it was wasteful of energy, due to alternate heating and cooling of the cylinder, inefficient because of crude machining of mating surfaces, and dangerous, since the knowledge of strength of materials was meager.

However, Britain had turned toward industry, and the roar of machinery and the hiss of steam, were destined to guide the future of her economy.

BEGINNINGS OF MODERN SCIENCE: 19TH CENTURY

If a person were to have to select two engineering developments which were outstanding in the nineteenth century, these would likely be the production of iron and the use of steam power.

Iron works had been established in Britain as early as the sixteenth century, but malleable iron was still too expensive for wide use. Henry Cort, about the beginning of the nineteenth century, developed a puddling process for making large quantities of malleable iron from cast iron, which made the metal available at reasonable cost. As soon as wrought iron could be manufactured cheaply, it was adopted for structures where wood or stone was formerly used. This century ushered in a vast program of bridges, machines, ships, and transportation systems using iron as a basic material. When the demand increased for better grades of iron, other men of science (such as Bessemer, who in 1856 invented the converter to make steel; Siemens, who patented a regenerative furnace in the same year; and Thomas, who developed in 1878 an alkali process of refining) contributed greatly to efficient methods of manufacture.

Following the invention of a working steam engine by Newcomen, many attempts were made to improve its operating characteristics. Of all the early efforts to improve the engine, James Watt made the most outstanding contribution. His basic patent about 1776 was the true beginning of an age of mechanical power, for his engine used the expansive force of steam to drive the piston and required no cooling between strokes. Since his engine was originally adapted to pumps to dewater mines, his engines were rated corresponding to the number of horses that a given engine would replace. Thus Boulton and Watt standardized a *horsepower* as being equivalent to 33,000 ft-lb per minute, in order to classify their engines for sale. This same standard of conversion is used today.

The fabrication of suitable iron products encouraged the development of the machine tool industry for the building of parts for machines of all kinds. The machines of this age can be classified as machines of power, machines of production, machines of construction, and machines of transportation.

In addition to the reciprocating steam engine developed by Watt and others, there were improvements made in water wheels. In place of the inefficient undershot wheel, the reaction turbine and the impulse wheel came into common use to provide power for many of the textile mills in England and Germany. Another development in the field of power was the invention of the electric generator and motor. Following the discoveries of Benjamin Franklin, Coulomb, Volta, Oersted, and Faraday, Thomas Davenport of Vermont made what was probably the first electric motor to be powered by batteries which could be used for performing industrial work. The first electromagnetic generator that was commercially successful was installed in France in 1873 by Gramme. By 1890 Westinghouse had installed alternating-current generators, and Tesla had invented alternating-current motors, which established electricity as an outstanding source of power. To power electric generators, De Laval, Parsons, and Curtis developed steam turbines which had many advantages over reciprocating steam engines. By the end of the century, steam turbines were rapidly replacing other types of steam engines.

Like the development of electric power and communication during the last half of the nineteenth century, the growth of transportation was a large factor in the changes in our political, social, and economic life. Without great transportation systems, it would not have been possible for the civilized countries of the world to support their large cities because the problems of supply would have been too great. The types of transportation systems of this era were principally water, railroad, and highway.

Sailing ships of the early years of the nineteenth century were replaced by steam engines by the 1860's. The first ships carried both sails and steam engines, since the fuel consumption was too high to permit oceanic trips on steam alone. Rapid developments in design soon made sails obsolete, and by 1894 ships using Parson's turbine were in service.

Railroads were in operation in England by 1830, and the first appeared in the United States a few years later. By 1869 a transcontinental railroad

Engineering in the World of Yesterday

was completed. The first locomotives used were adaptations of Watts early engines, but Stephenson's 7 1/2-ton Rocket of 1829 contained practically all the major improvements in design that had been used on the most recent steam locomotives built. Electric locomotives began commercial service

Courtesy Southern Pacific Company

Fig. 1-7. This remarkable picture, taken in 1877 when the high Secrettown trestle in the Sierra Nevada mountains of California was being filled in with dirt by the Central Pacific, now the Southern Pacific Railway, shows the meager tools with which the builders had to work in blasting a trail over and through the rugged mountains for the rails of the first transcontinental railroad. In those days there were none of the power implements that are so common to modern construction. Scrapers were not even used in the grading. Dynamite had been invented but was not in general use during the years the railroad was being built in 1863–69. Chinese "coolies" did the work with pick and shovel, one-horse dump carts, wheel barrows, and back power. At times it was necessary to lower the workmen over cliffs in baskets to ledges where they could level off a grade in the mountainside.

about 1880, and by 1900 both electric street railways and intercity electric trains were common.

Highways in 1800 were built for slow-moving carriages and foot traffic. Most of the movement of heavy articles was over waterways. Within a few years, however, the experiments of English and French engineers showed that good roads were feasible by properly contouring the road bed and by sealing the surface with asphalt. As smoother roads became common, the speed and weight of horse-drawn vehicles increased. The greatest impetus to road building came with the invention of the automobile, credited to Benz, in 1885. The requirements of grade and smoothness to accommodate automobile traffic presented great challenges to civil engineers of the late nineteenth century.

The Bettman Archive

Fig. 1-8. During the eighteenth century scientific research began to provide more answers to men's questions concerning natural laws. In this picture, Foucault, who devised a pendulum to demonstrate the effect of the earth's rotation, shows his new development to a group of scientists of that time.

During this growth of the machine age there was also a change in the methods of the scientist. His success in learning the secrets of nature gave him increased confidence, and his discoveries began to cover wider and wider fields. Research, both pure and applied, brought more answers to man's questions concerning the secrets of nature. Britain, the foremost industrial nation at the beginning of the century, received serious competition from Germany by 1850 and finally relinquished her leadership to the United States by the end of the nineteenth century.

One of the most important reasons for American success was the unusually close cooperation between science and technology. It was becoming more evident that discoveries by research scientists could be the beginnings of new industries and that money spent for research eventually returned many times its value.

Not to be overlooked was the growth of the engineering schools in the United States. In 1840 there were only two, but in 1870 there were about seventy. The first engineering courses consisted of little more than vocational work and most of the emphasis was on very practical applications. It was not until the pressures of war indicated the need that a more scientific approach to engineering courses was made in the United States.

TWENTIETH CENTURY TECHNOLOGY

As the twentieth century came into being, a number of inventions emerged which were destined to have far reaching effects on civilization. The beginnings of the automobile have already been mentioned. Further advancements were made in internal combustion engines by the introduction of the diesel engine. Following the inventions of Edison and De Forest in electron tube applications, electricity began to play an increasingly important role. The Wright brothers' first flight in a powered aircraft was the forerunner of air travel, a type of transportation long dreamed of by man.

Courtesy of North American Aviation, Inc.

Fig. 1-9. Exemplifying twentieth century technology is today's modern assembly line. Mass-production techniques make possible the rapid and economical assembly of consumer goods. In this picture is shown an assembly line for the production of the world's first supersonic aircraft.

These basic inventions were part of a vast number of developments which took form in the early part of the century. So fast has been the growth of science, with one discovery coming on the heels of another, that it is difficult

Courtesy Bureau of Reclamation

Fig. 1-10. The twentieth century ushered in a time of intense growth and development of engineering construction. Large public works projects were built such as that shown in this picture of Hoover Dam and Lake Mead. Hoover Dam, which is 726 ft high and 1200 ft long, is the highest dam in the United States. Behind the dam is Lake Mead, the largest man-made lake in the world. This lake, which is about 115 miles long, stores water for flood control, irrigation, and for the generation of electric power. This project was completed in 1936.

to evaluate properly their relative importance, although we may certainly realize their impact on our life.

Until late in the nineteenth century, engineering as an applied science was divided into two principal groups, civil and military. Mining and metallurgy was the first group to be recognized as a separate branch, and the American Institute of Mining and Metallurgical Engineers was founded in

1871. In 1880 the American Society of Mechanical Engineers was founded, and in 1884 the American Institute of Electrical Engineers was founded. In 1908, the American Institute of Chemical Engineers was founded. The organization of each of these groups together with the founding of other engineering societies marked the beginnings of our present separate groups whose objectives are peculiar to specialized fields of engineering endeavor.

An outstanding characteristic of this century is the vastly increased use of power by man. In 1954 it was estimated that the average family in the United States used about 2550 kilowatt-hours (kwh) of energy per year. This would be the equivalent of the energy output of over thirty laborers per day to supply the household power requirements, truly a long step from the days of the Egyptians and Greeks.

Even more impressive is the control of power wielded by locomotive enginemen who operate 5000-horsepower (hp) engines, by airplane pilots, and by generating station dispatchers. For example, the newer jet planes develop a power output of more than 35,000 hp, the equivalent of over 700,-000 human beings. The dispatcher of a large electrical generating station has at his fingertips the controls of over 1,000,000 hp.

A significant development in engineering early in the century was the movement to the United States of numbers of prominent engineers from Europe. Lindenthal, an Austrian, was an outstanding bridge designer and builder. A Norwegian, Singstad, was an authority on underwater tunnels. Many others emigrated about the same time, and in addition a number of educators brought with them the ideas of the necessity of a firm theoretical background for engineering students in their college work. Such men as Timoshenko, who made many contributions in the field of mechanics and stress analysis, and von Kármán, who was an authority on aeronautical problems, are examples of these outstanding educators.

With the political, economic, and scientific disorganization in Europe following World War II, the United States has placed increased dependence upon scientists and engineers who recently have emigrated to this country, as well as upon her own scientists and engineers, for continuing advancements in the basic understanding of natural laws on which the improved techniques of the future will be based.

chapter two

Engineering in the World of Today

Courtesy Leeds & Northrup Company

Teamwork is the key to the success of modern engineering endeavor. In this picture a team of engineers and technicians is working together to acquire data from electric strain gauges which are attached to the fuselage of an aircraft undergoing static tests. As the data are collected by the technicians using electrical indicating equipment, the engineers evaluate the information and determine its usefulness for future design studies.

chapter two

Engineering in the World of Today

It is difficult to specify a time at which modern engineering can be said to have started. Writers differ in their delineation of the modern engineering period. However, we may say broadly that modern engineering had its beginnings not more than a century ago. By the year 1900 the pace of discovery and invention was such that we certainly can class the subsequent years as the start of the modern engineering period.

Since that time engineers have developed the electron tube with its many variations, new processes for obtaining chemical materials—including metals, plastics, and organic products—the use of nuclear processes, and improved methods of communication and transportation—including exploration of outer space.

In modern times, engineering endeavor has changed drastically from so-called scientific procedures in the time of Imhotep, Galileo, and Ampere. Formerly, engineering discovery and development was accomplished principally by individuals. With the increasing knowledge available and the widening of the realm of engineering to include so many diversified branches, it is usual to find groups or teams of scientists and engineers working on a single project. Formerly, an individual could absorb and make individual use of practically the whole universe of engineering knowledge, but the degree of complexity is such today that it is now impossible for any one engineer to be proficient in all fields. As a result, an engineering team, composed of engineers who have special knowledge, training, and skills, is frequently needed to carry a project to completion.

This intensive specialization has contributed greatly to rapid advances in recent years in improvements in metallic alloys, in solid state physics, in power plant design, and in nuclear applications. Engineering teamwork is proving to be very successful in industry, not only in making improvements in existing processes but also in the field of pure research, where no one is able to predict the ultimate direction to which the unexplored paths may lead.

An outstanding example of engineering teamwork is in the development of nuclear power. Growing from a mere suggestion of a possibility in the 1930's, the research phase of nuclear power was crowned with success within little more than a decade. The utilization of teams of highly skilled specialists working together is a primary reason for the significant results that have been achieved in such a short time.

Another example of teamwork is in the development of computers. Beginning with primitive forms that were in use in the early 1900's, teams of

Courtesy Space Technology Laboratories, Inc.

Fig. 2-1. Research and development, as in the field of missiles, rockets, and space craft, has become an all important part of today's advancing technology. In many devices such as space craft it is imperative that thousands of components, working simultaneously or in controlled sequence, operate perfectly under extremes of environment. Since such a vehicle may contain over 100,000 components, the problems to be solved are tremendous. This photograph shows the launching of one of the first United States missiles to be guided into orbit around the earth.

engineers have worked steadily to improve computing machines. By adapting every new invention or technique that was suitable, these engineering teams have developed the modern computer to a marvel of complexity. Yet it is a machine which an operator can learn to use within a relatively short period of time and which eliminates much of the tedium of repetitious mathematics from the computations of engineers.

Everyone is familiar with some of the more dramatic phases of missile work. The "count-down" and "blast-off" are commonplace expressions as a result of use in television programs and newspaper articles. Yet in the background and in much of the untold story are the teams of engineers who design, construct, test, and finally launch the missile. The complexity of the problems and the wide range of variables involved in preparing any given missile for launching makes it impractical, if not impossible, for this feat to be performed by other than teams of engineering specialists.

Another application of the engineering team principle is used in the relatively recently organized field called *operations research*. Operations research deals with a study of managerial problems, particularly in relation to engineering, and is concerned with providing a basis for sound decisions to solve problems. Many of the principles discussed under management engineering and industrial engineering are applicable in operations research. In addition, studies are made of technological and social problems that affect operation of any given activity. Teams of specialists, utilizing mathematics, experimentation, models, and statistics, analyze and evaluate the available alternatives which will solve a problem. Finally they recommend a decision based on the best knowledge of all facts at hand.

Several universities recently have instituted graduate courses in phases of operations research which stress research skill, an ability to team with other specialists, and communication with management.

All indications point more and more to the use of teams of engineers as the sum total of scientific knowledge becomes greater, and there is an increasing emphasis upon fundamentals of mathematics and science to undergird specialization by an individual in a certain engineering field.

chapter three

Engineering in the World of Tomorrow

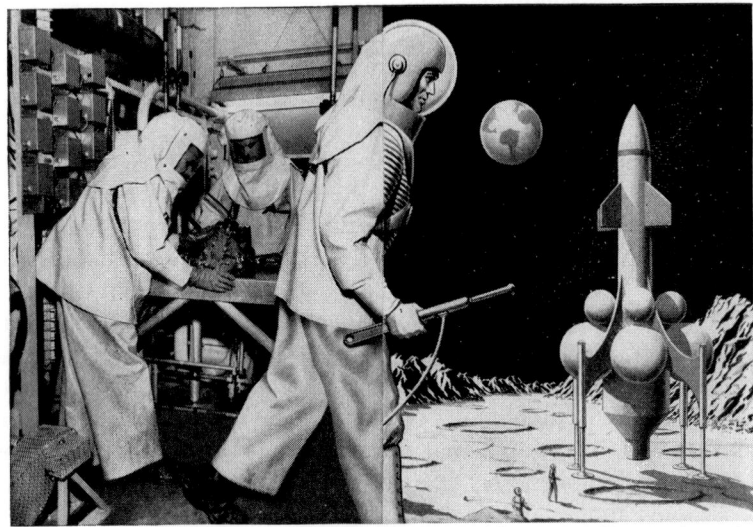

Courtesy Hamilton Standard Division, United Aircraft Corporation

Engineering in our world of tomorrow will require a continuous flow of uninhibited ideas which will be used in the development of useful products. The creative abilities of engineers will continue to push back the frontiers of learning. Such ability takes imagination, vision, and a high degree of technical skill to develop systems which can be used in exploring new frontiers. The above picture exemplifies this as the engineer of today steps into tomorrow costumed for flight into space.

chapter three

Engineering in the World of Tomorrow

Advances in science and engineering knowledge follow a logarithmic pattern in that each discovery or invention opens many additional areas for exploration. Science, as distinguished from the arts, makes use of prior discoveries to advance its knowledge. Each new development widens the horizon of possible achievement just as a person in an airplane views enlarging horizons as the plane gains altitude.

Starting with the invention of the wheel in the predawn of recorded history, developments have increased at an accelerated pace despite the occasional setbacks of social and economic upheavals. The same process is still going on, with the fantasies of a few years ago becoming the possibilities of today and the realities of a few years hence.

Less than a century ago Jules Verne was virtually the only prominent person making predictions of scientific achievements to come. Since then, the rapid expansion of science has permitted many of his fictional devices to become reality. In fact so many of the fanciful inventions of science fiction of a few years ago are possible today that it seems almost everyone is now becoming an amateur prognosticator. From a civilization that was amazed when scientific predictions were fulfilled, now we are tending to believe that any prediction is fact. The man not well informed on scientific matters may even think that the scientist is behind the times when predictions are not immediately transformed into articles for our use.

There is almost always a time lag, sometimes large and sometimes small, between a discovery and practical applications of the discovery. For example, in 1905 Lee deForest could not foresee more than a few applications of his three-element vacuum tube. Actually he was tried in court, several years after the invention was announced, for attempting to defraud the public by selling stock in his company. The prosecutor of the court stated that deForest had even claimed that it would be possible to transmit the human voice across the Atlantic Ocean, thereby misleading the public with absurd and impossible claims.

The tendency today is exactly reversed. An announcement of a discovery results in an immediate demand for articles employing the discovery. As an example, a recent announcement of the discovery of a light amplifier brought quick speculation as to applications such as flat-screen television and spectacular display advertising. We must remember that successful applications of discoveries take time to develop. The basic principles of television were known as early as 1920, but widespread use of television did not occur until some thirty years later. There are many discoveries made

Engineering in the World of Tomorrow 35

Courtesy Rocketdyne, a Division of North American Aviation, Inc.

Fig. 3-1. Progress in the development of million-pound thrust chemical rockets and nuclear rocket engines may lead to practical considerations of space stations weighing as much as this 250,000-lb vehicle. Requiring nearly 15,000,000 lb of thrust to lift from the earth, such a vehicle could be used as a scientific laboratory in space for astronomy, weather control, fusion research, space physics, and television relay. To carry a crew of fifty men, the station would be about 60 ft in diameter and spin gently in space to create an artificial gravity between 0.2 and 0.8 of earth's gravity. The design shown here would orbit at an altitude of 22,300 miles.

for which no practical uses have yet been developed but which doubtlessly may provide future gadgets for our enjoyment.

We must recognize also that there are many misunderstandings as to the nature of research. Science is not just a new nuclear reactor, a color TV set, a miracle drug, or an "almost human" computing machine. These are technological end products of research. Yet most people tend to evaluate scientific progress in terms of usable articles, whereas the true progress is in terms of extension of the boundaries of human knowledge.

However, in the team of scientists the one whose work contributes most intimately to the benefit of mankind is the engineer. The engineer, in our modern usage of the term, is concerned principally with utilizing the great fundamental discoveries for the welfare of civilization. In fact our twentieth century probably will be noted by historians as the first age in which engineering has made the benefits of discoveries available to the entire human race.

When we come to making predictions as to the nature of discoveries and developments in the future, we look into a crystal ball that becomes more and more cloudy as we push the scientific frontier into the years beyond. We may with some semblance of certainty predict things that will be available to the public in ten years because they will be mostly applications of principles already known. When we attempt to look twenty years into the future, our predictions become more nearly an educated guess as to discoveries which are now perhaps only in the planning stage. Beyond twenty years even a guess at what projects will be then undergoing research is mere speculation. However, from the dreams of engineers and men of science, we may describe some of the discoveries and developments which can be feasibly based on the direction of our scientific advances during the last fifty years.

OUTER SPACE

As man begins in earnest his exploration of outer space, the engineer truly faces one of his most challenging tasks. Our present knowledge indicates that we are on the threshold of greater discoveries in the vast outer space into which we are sending the first inquisitive invaders. The problems to be solved and the dangers involved are far beyond those ever encountered at any time in past history. Here teams of engineers must work on many parts of a program in order to maintain our position in research.

Our outer space program involves the knowledge and use of practically every scientific development of our time. In addition, invention and development of materials and processes will be necessary to such an extent that it taxes our credulity.

The programs already outlined include manned vehicles to the moon and

Engineering in the World of Tomorrow

Courtesy Convair Astronautics, a Division of General Dynamics Corporation

Fig. 3-2. To avoid expensive and hazardous landings of supply ships on the moon, a cargo drop technique may be developed to deliver food and material for lunar bases. This picture shows how supply ships could be used for this purpose. The vehicle in the background is approaching the moon tail first in order that its rocket thrust will push against the weak lunar gravity. Supplies and cargo are carried in a case at its top. In the foreground another ship has dropped its supply package from a height of several hundred feet. Such a system would permit the use of comparatively cheap and relatively simple space-ferry craft which would be able to shuttle between the moon and a "warehouse satellite." Thus, it would never need the additional structure and instrumentation required for landings and take-offs. Such a method of lunar logistic supply is possible because the moon gravity is only about one-sixth that of the earth.

unmanned reconnaissance of Mars and Venus. Farther in the future are man-carrying rockets to other celestial bodies. Some of the most fantastic science fiction of a decade or so ago has become sober fact today as the frontiers of knowledge in engineering and science are steadily advanced.

MANUFACTURING PROCESSES

One promising field of research has been opened recently in the chemical industry. For decades chemical processes have been carried on by controlled applications of heat, pressure, and catalysts. Now another method of promoting chemical reaction has been added—atomic radiation. We have known for years of the chemical effects of light radiation, but the use of electron beams presents us with a new chemical process.

One recent use of this process is in the manufacture of irradiated polyethylene. Experiments are now under way to evaluate radiation in the processing of other chemical materials. Research is also being carried on to utilize irradiation in the sterilization of foodstuffs and in eliminating the need for refrigeration to preserve many perishable foods. In extensive research now going on in the petroleum industry, irradiation effects on fuels and lubricants hold promise of providing products from crude oil which will have vastly improved properties. Experiments also show that irradiation may change the crystal arrangement in solid materials, with an accompanying change in energy. For example, graphite that has been irradiated has been found to burn with a hotter flame.

COMMUNICATIONS

The growth of the radio and television industry is well known to all. Yet few realize the planning which had to go into this part of our communication system many years ago. For example, in the early 1940's provision was being made to include TV circuits in telephone cables. This was done at a time when television was still a laboratory device. From A. G. Bell's first telephone nearly a century ago to our modern system, which now includes dialing equipment that permits a customer to dial any of millions of phones in the United States, the engineer has at times had to work so far in the future that he had to plan on using equipment which had not then been invented. This seemingly unusual condition continues to exist as requirements are projected farther and farther in the future and hypothetical characteristics of communication equipment are discussed in engineering planning groups.

One obvious development that may be expected in the near future is the televisiphone. Such a device is well within the realm of application of present knowledge; and doubtlessly within a few years you will be able to see as well as hear the person to whom you are talking.

Engineering in the World of Tomorrow

Our postal system will likely be changed so that letter mail will be scanned by photocell devices and automatically will be routed to destinations. Helicopter transport for short distances, airplanes for intermediate distances, and rockets for long distances will speed mail from originator to destination in a matter of hours.

A machine similar to a teletype will make possible the reception of news in the home as it occurs. In addition a facsimilie device will print advertising drawings and furnish comics for the children.

Much library material will be on microfilm or microcards, and a book may be read by simply projecting these small photographs on a viewing screen. Schools will be able also to add greatly to their instruction by having access to broadcast programs conducted by research organizations and to view history in the making by receiving worldwide television broadcasts. Television programs will also be recorded on magnetic tape so that they may be displayed at any convenient time in 3-D and color.

Just as planning years ago was required for our present-day communication systems, so it is necessary for our planning now to provide for developments in communication to keep pace with the growth of other industries.

TRANSPORTATION

Transportation systems are undergoing rapid changes now, and engineers plan even more radical changes in the near future. Automobiles will be engineered with a view toward safety. Automatic controls may someday relieve the driver of much of the attention now needed on long trips. Electronic devices will cause the vehicle to follow a preset route, and by means of radar-type devices, use the brakes to avoid colliding with other vehicles. Turbine-type engines will probably become common because of their reliability and light weight. Polarizing glass in windshields will reduce night glare from the headlights of oncoming vehicles. A series of buttons on the dash will operate such gadgets as jacks at each wheel to facilitate servicing, and a panel of warning lights will indicate troubles in the engine or transmission.

Helicopter cars may make their appearance also to fulfill the dream of a personal flying machine for each family. Certainly airplanes and trains will improve their equipment to provide faster, safer, and more comfortable riding.

For the shopper, city planners are even now proposing zoned areas in business districts which have loop freeways around them with automatic multi-story garages for parking. No vehicles will be permitted within the zoned areas, and a series of conveyor-belt sidewalks will move people effortlessly from place to place.

ENERGY SOURCES

Another problem that will have to be solved is the problem of providing adequate amounts of energy. We need energy, usually in the form of heat, to process materials in industry, to help generate electric power, and to provide motive power for transportation of all kinds. Our principal sources of energy now are fossil fuels, such as coal and petroleum, and water power. Research indicates that in the future we may have atom-powered plants large enough to power huge generators and also have plants small enough to power airplanes and automobiles.

The question of the cost of producing electric power from nuclear power plants has arisen as a limiting factor. At present the most optimistic estimates are that electricity from nuclear power plants will cost about 2 mills to 5 mills per kilowatt-hour more than electric power from fossil-fuel powered plants. Even though the present cost of producing electric power from nuclear plants is almost double the cost of power from conventional plants, private industry is spending millions of dollars on research which will provide the engineering information necessary to change from fossil fuel to nuclear fuel power when the supply and cost picture changes. Our known reserves of conventional fuels will not likely last beyond 1990 at the present rate of usage. Consequently, the change-over to plants making use of other energy sources must begin within the next two decades.

Another source of energy which is available to us is the sun. Experiments have been conducted to determine methods of absorbing and storing solar energy for the heating of buildings and to provide power for undeveloped areas. These experiments show that it is possible for a field of about 50 acres to provide the energy requirements for a city of 10,000 persons. However, present methods of using the sun's energy preclude such high efficiencies. Perhaps improved methods of producing electricity by thermocouples and solar batteries will enable us to replace our present power sources used in producing electricity.

The question naturally arises as to why solar power is not already being used, since it is in a sense "free." The answer is that it is a matter of economics. At present, the cost of energy from carbon-bearing fuels is less than would be the cost of space and equipment essential in capturing the heat from the sun. As the cost of carbon fuels becomes higher, and the exhaustion of fossil fuels approaches, research is certain to provide better methods of storing and transforming heat from the sun.

In addition to atomic and solar heat sources, another source that may be employed is the heat within the earth's interior. In Italy a power plant has been in operation for over twenty years which uses the heat from steam that issues from fissures in an area of volcanic activity. It also is possible that

Engineering in the World of Tomorrow

by drilling deep wells, we may be able to tap the heat of the interior of our earth.

Other power sources that have been incompletely explored or utilized are power from ocean tides, ocean currents, different water temperatures in the ocean, and power from prevailing winds.

NUCLEAR POWER

The invention of processes to utilize nuclear power for peacetime applications offer vast possibilities. Experiments have been conducted which

Courtesy Wittich D. Holloway

Fig. 3-3. Power from nuclear explosions. Underground "heat reservoirs" may eventually supply much of our electricity. Water from a lake may be pumped down to the area of a nuclear blast where trapped heat will turn it into steam to run a power plant on the surface.

show that it is feasible to perform great excavation jobs with nuclear explosions. This offers the possibility of creating harbors and excavating canals with nuclear explosions in a manner impossible with conventional explosives.

As a result of recent tests in Nevada, it appears that a nuclear explosion deep underground may enable one to trap the heat of the blast. Water, which can be later introduced to the site of the explosion, may produce steam for heat and power. Also, the heat of subterranean explosions may be used to melt tars and heavy oils in certain underground formations and to permit the recovery of petroleum not otherwise available.

In a similar manner, properly placed nuclear explosions could be used to blast the cover from ore deposits and permit strip mining in places where only shaft mining has been practical.

ELECTRONICS

Modern communication systems are closely tied to electronics because electronics affords a relatively sure and speedy method of carrying information from one place to another. However, electronics covers a much broader field of applications than communications alone. In the future it is probable that improved electronics devices will be developed that will provide revolutionary changes, just as a newcomer, the transistor, has radically affected circuit design.

In the years to come, our day may begin with a breakfast of pre-prepared foods which have been cooked completely in a few seconds in an electronic oven. The house will be air conditioned by an electronic air conditioner which will be portable and will require no motor or moving parts. To light the rooms, the entire walls may be covered with a material which will glow brilliantly in response to a tiny current.

At an office, an executive may dictate to a machine which will type directly from the voice sounds in a microphone. Other machines may transcribe and translate messages into foreign languages.

The transistor, hardly a decade old, is the forerunner of other improvements in electronic circuits. The success of the transistor has produced an emphasis on the study of solid-state physics that will probably lead to such things as a metal that stores electricity, much as iron retains magnetism, and an improved television camera that will be about the size and weight of a photographic camera. Several large companies are now allocating as much as 25 per cent of their research money to investigate the uses of solid-state materials, with a view to their application to electronics.

COMPUTERS

In the field of computers, the possibilities of developing machines which can think and reason are approaching reality. So far, computing machines may be considered as half-witted prodigies. However, discoveries made recently in the realm of computing machines indicates that a machine with creative ability and the ability to learn is entirely possible. Such a machine could duplicate, in certain fields, everything that a human being can do.

A machine could be built to do semi-routine tasks such as traffic control or minor administrative work. It could conceivably be taught to do such work as operate a lathe, compose music, or perform surgical operations.

MATERIALS

Research in the development of alloys and studies of the crystal structure of metals is steadily improving the materials which are available for the development of new machines. Indications are that a new field is rapidly being opened in the use of ceramic-like materials. These materials will have properties of strength and heat resistance far beyond materials now available. Such exotic materials will be capable of being heated to a white heat without oxidizing or softening.

We need not fear the depletion of our natural resources as long as engineering ingenuity exists. The resources of the mind and of the universe are unlimited, and what we now need is vision to see beyond the horizon of present knowledge.

Mankind is moving steadily forward, and each gain in technology and science increases the certainty of still further advances. The future of engineering is determined only by the problems to be solved and by the possibilities to be explored.

chapter four

Engineering Fields of Specialization

One of the most important responsibilities of the professional engineer is his obligation to his client to insure that construction performed meets the design criteria. Here the engineer is discussing with the contractor certain features of the construction of this large aqueduct.

chapter four

Engineering Fields of Specialization

THE WORK OF THE ENGINEER

Much of the change in our civilization in the past hundred years has been due to the work of the engineer. We hardly appreciate the changes that have occurred in our environment unless we attempt to picture the world of a few generations ago without automobiles, telephones, radios, electronics, transportation systems, aircraft, machine tools, electric lights, and all the modern appliances in our homes. In the growth of all these things, the role of the engineer is obvious.

Development in the field of science and engineering is progressing so rapidly at present that within the last ten years we have acquired materials and devices which we now consider commonplace but which were unknown to our parents. Through research, development, and mass production, directed by engineers, ideas are made into realities in an amazingly short time.

The engineer is concerned with more than research, development, design, construction, and operation of technical industries, however, for many are engaged in businesses which are not primarily concerned with production. Formerly, executive positions were held almost exclusively by men whose primary training was in the field of law or business, but the tendency now is to utilize engineers more and more as administrators and executives.

No matter what type of work the engineer may do, he will find opportunities not only in technical activities but also in other functions such as cost accounting, budgeting, rate analysis, purchasing, marketing, personnel, labor relations, and industrial management. In a few instances engineers may even perform highly specialized work in such fields as teaching, writing, patent practice, and work with the military establishment.

Courses of study outlined under various engineering curricula leading to a degree in engineering are planned to provide instruction in mathematics and sciences and to furnish training in the application of these subjects to the solution of technological problems in various engineering fields. The subjects in engineering curricula are not training courses for mechanical skills such as are given in trade schools but are planned to provide preparation for research, design, operation, management, testing, and maintenance of engineering projects.

The principal branches of engineering as they now exist are discussed below.

Engineering Fields of Specialization   47

AERONAUTICAL ENGINEERING

In recent years the manufacture of aircraft and the operation of airlines have become important parts of American industry, and the demand for persons trained in these fields has increased greatly.

The principal subdivisions of this branch of engineering are aerodynamics, structures, power plants, and airplane components. Aerodynamics studies deal with the performance, stability, control, and design of various types of

Courtesy North American Aviation, Inc.

Fig. 4-1. An aeronautical engineer working with an industrial model of a jet aircraft makes final adjustments of mounting and instrumentation prior to test in a supersonic wind tunnel.

planes and other devices that fly; the determination of loads on airplane structures; and the use of wind tunnels to determine performance and control characteristics.

Structures include studies in the design of various members in an airplane and the calculation of their strength; the estimation of weight and balance of airplanes, propellers, and airplane structural parts; and laboratory testing of the strength of various components of an airplane.

Studies in airplane power plants include engines, turbo-jets, and rockets. The course in testing and operation of various types of power plants is frequently combined with engines courses given by mechanical engineering departments.

Airplane components include the hydraulic, mechanical, and electrical equipment, gauges, meters, controls, and indicators that are part of the auxiliary equipment of an airplane.

Although aeronautical engineering is one of the newer fields, it offers many possibilities for employment. The rapidly expanding network of airlines, both national and international, provide many openings for the engineering graduate. Since the demand for increasing numbers of aircraft of various types exists, there are opportunities for work in manufacturing plants and assembly plants and in the design, testing, and maintenance of aircraft and their component parts. The development of new types of aircraft, both civilian and military, requires the efforts of well-trained aeronautical engineers, and it is in this field that the majority of positions exist. Employment opportunities exist for specialists in the design and development of fuel systems using liquid oxygen propellants and solid propellants. Control of the newer fuels involves precision valving and flow sensing at very low and very high temperatures. Air traffic control is a problem that is becoming increasingly more complex, and trained people are needed here.

The design of ground and airborne systems that will permit operation of aircraft under all kinds of weather conditions is a part of the work of aeronautical engineers. Formerly the aeronautical engineer was limited to the design of aircraft which operated only within the earth's atmosphere, but now he designs space vehicles to operate in the boundless reaches of interstellar space.

AGRICULTURAL ENGINEERING

The courses in agricultural engineering train the student for a career in the application of engineering principles to the field of agriculture. The curriculum prepares a student for design or sales work with farm equipment, machinery, and buildings; superintendency of farms and ranches where machinery and buildings, irrigation, drainage, and erosion control are important parts of their management; teaching or extension work with various agricultural colleges; engineering work with landholding or management companies or with the government on soil conservation and projects having engineering applications. The agricultural engineer must also be familiar with such diverse subjects as metallurgy, hydraulics, and sanitation.

The main divisions of agricultural engineering are as follows:

1. Farm Power and Machinery

This division deals with tractors and stationary engines, farm implements, and the various machines used in agricultural production.

Engineering Fields of Specialization 49

2. Farm Structures

This division deals with all buildings and building equipment used on a farm or ranch and includes animal shelters and buildings, barns and storage buildings, and farm dwellings and their modernization.

3. Farm Electrification

This division is concerned with the various uses of electricity on the farm.

4. Soil and Water Control and Conservation

This division consists of irrigation, drainage, water management, and soil erosion control.

Many agricultural engineers are employed by companies which serve agriculture, and some are employed by firms which serve other industries. Development, advertising, and sales work with manufacturers of farm equipment and machinery provide openings for agricultural engineers. State

Courtesy Allis-Chalmers Manufacturing Company

Fig. 4-2. Agricultural engineers apply fundamental engineering principles of analysis and design to improve our methods of food production and land utilization. The above picture shows an example of engineering technique as applied to an irrigation project.

agricultural colleges and their extension services and experiment stations and federal agencies employ many agricultural engineers.

In order that the agricultural engineer may understand the problems of agriculture and the application of engineering methods and principles to their solution, instruction is given in agricultural subjects as well as in basic engineering. Agricultural research laboratories are maintained at schools for research and instruction using various types of farm equipment for study and testing. The farm boy who has an analytical mind and a willingness to work, together with an interest in the engineering aspects of agriculture, will find the course in agricultural engineering an interesting preparation for his life's work.

ARCHITECTURAL ENGINEERING

The architectural engineer is primarily interested in the selection, analysis, design, and assembly of modern building materials into structures that are

Courtesy A. M. Kinney, Inc.

Fig. 4-3. The architectural engineer may work either in an engineering firm or architectural firm. Here, as part of a team of engineers, he combines fundamental principles of architecture and engineering in the design of structures to harmonize both beauty and utility.

safe, efficient, economical, and attractive. The training he receives in college is designed to teach him how best to use modern structural materials in the construction of tall buildings, manufacturing plants, and public buildings.

The course in architectural engineering differs from courses in architectural design and construction in that less creative ability is needed in engineering than is needed in design. The architectural engineer is trained in the sound principles of engineering and at the same time is given a background which enables him to appreciate the point of view of the architect. The architect is concerned with the space arrangements, proportions, and appearance of a building, while the architectural engineer is more nearly a structural engineer and is concerned with safety, economy, and sound construction methods.

Opportunities for employment will be found in established architectural firms, in consulting engineering offices, in aircraft companies, and in organizations specializing in building design and construction. Excellent opportunities await the graduate who may be able to associate himself with a contracting firm or who may form a partnership with an architectural designer. In the field of sales an interesting and profitable career is open to the type of individual who is able to present his ideas clearly and convincingly.

CHEMICAL ENGINEERING

A chemical engineer is trained to apply scientifically the principles of chemistry, physics, and engineering to the design and operation of plants for the production of materials that undergo chemical changes during their processing.

The courses in chemical engineering cover inorganic, analytical, physical, and organic chemistry in addition to the basic engineering subjects; and the work in the various courses is designed to be of a distinctly professional nature and to develop capacity for original thought. The industrial development of our country makes large demands on the chemical engineer. The increasing uses for plastics, synthetics, and building materials require that a chemical engineer be employed in the development and manufacture of these products. While well trained in chemistry, the chemical engineer is more than a chemist in that he applies the results of chemical research and discovery to the use of mankind by adapting laboratory processes to full-scale manufacturing plants.

The chemical engineer is instrumental in the development of the newer fuels for turbine and rocket engines. Test and evaluation of such fuels and means of achieving production of suitable fuels are part of the work of a chemical engineer. This testing must be carefully controlled to evaluate the performance of engines before the fuel is considered to be suitable to place on the market.

Opportunities for chemical engineers exist in a wide variety of fields of manufacture. Not only is he in demand in strictly chemical fields but also in nearly all types of manufacturing. The production of synthetic rubber, the uses of petroleum products, the recovery of useful materials from what was formerly considered waste products, and the better utilization of farm

Courtesy E.I. du Pont de Nemours & Company

Fig. 4-4. Chemical engineers work with elaborate chemical apparatus to study minute details of materials in order to reveal structural secrets that cannot be uncovered by any other means. Here a team of engineers and technicians makes adjustments on an involved distillation apparatus.

Engineering Fields of Specialization

products are only a few of the tasks that will provide work for the chemical engineer. While the first professional work of a graduate chemical engineer may be in production, other opportunities exist in the fields of engineering design, research and development, patents, and sales engineering.

CIVIL ENGINEERING

Civil engineering is one of the oldest branches of the engineering profession and deals with the art and science of directing the great sources of power in nature for the use and convenience of man. Specialization has brought the grouping of engineers into electrical, mechanical, chemical, and so on, but underlying all these groups is the work of the civil engineer.

Courtesy State of California Department of Public Works

Fig. 4-5. An important phase of civil engineering is the planning for orderly growth and development of urban areas to include transportation systems. This picture shows a four-level interchange in downtown Los Angeles where several freeways intersect. Such freeways play an increasingly important role in making it possible to handle tremendous volumes of traffic in minimum time.

Civil engineering covers such a broad field that it has been divided into several branches. The major subdivisions are: construction, highway and railroad, municipal and sanitary, surveying and mapping, and hydraulic engineering. Construction engineering deals with the design and supervision of construction of bridges, buildings, tunnels, and dams. Highway and railroad engineering includes the planning, design, and construction of roads, streets, and thoroughfares. Municipal and sanitary engineering is concerned with the planning of urban centers for the growth and development of business and residential areas and the design and construction of water supply systems, sewerage systems, and systems for the disposal of wastes. Surveying and mapping deals with the measurements of distances over the earth's surface and the location of structures, right of ways, and property boundaries. Hydraulic engineering is concerned with the improvement of water resources, harbor and river development, flood control, irrigation, and drainage.

Civil engineers engage in technical, administrative, or commercial work with manufacturing companies, construction companies, transportation companies, and power companies. Other opportunities for employment exist in consulting engineering offices, in city and state engineering departments, and in the various bureaus of the federal government.

COMPUTER ENGINEERING

One of the newer branches of engineering, computer engineering, is now being taught as a separate specialization in several universities. Such a need arose after World War II for scientists and engineers who could do design work and supervise the construction and operation of computing machines. The increase in the complexity of computers has created a need for specialists in the field who can adapt existing knowledge of mechanical and electrical devices to extend the capabilities of computers.

Computers at present can only provide answers to a specific set of questions and cannot provide an analytical solution because they are not now thinking machines. However, engineers have designed them for a variety of purposes, and computers drastically reduce the time necessary to explore a number of concepts of a design or a process.

The computer engineer is concerned with the application of sound engineering principles, both mechanical and electrical, in the design and construction of computers. He must be familiar with the basic requirements of a computer so that he can design to provide for the necessary capabilities.

The computer engineer must strive in design to build a machine that will furnish solutions of greater and greater problem complexity and at the same time have a means of introducing the problem into the machine in as simple a manner as possible.

Engineering Fields of Specialization

Although there are relatively few companies that build elaborate computing machines, employment possibilities in the design and construction part of the industry are not limited. Many industrial firms, colleges, and governmental branches are setting up computers as part of their capital equipment, and opportunities exist for employment as computer applications engineers who serve as liaison between computer programmers and engineers who wish their problems evaluated on the machines. Of course, in a field

Courtesy Burroughs Corporation

Fig. 4-6. Computer engineers are used in logic design and in scientific application of computer systems, both digital and analog. In this picture, computer engineers are checking the intricate wiring system of a unitized digital electronic computer. Such equipment is of inestimable value in solving highly complex mathematical problems in a fraction of the time that would have been required by conventional methods.

such as computers which is expanding rapidly, increasing numbers of employment opportunities become available. Doubtlessly more and more dependence will be placed on the use of computers in the future, and an engineer trained in this work will find ample opportunity for advancement.

ELECTRICAL ENGINEERING

Electrical engineering is concerned, in general terms, with the utilization of electric energy, and it is perhaps more far-reaching in its contacts with human endeavor than any of the other branches of engineering. Electricity used in one form or another reaches nearly all our daily lives and is truly the servant of mankind. Electrical engineering is divided into the two broad fields of power and communications.

Power engineering deals with the design, construction, and operation of systems that produce and transmit large amounts of electric energy. When

Courtesy E.I. du Pont de Nemours & Company

Fig. 4-7. The electrical engineer works with many types of apparatus both electronic and mechanical. One of the newer fields is servo-electronics in which electrical and mechanical components are synthesized into a single system. Here a team of electrical engineers work with a color co-ordinate computer which will permit the scientific matching of colors.

it is considered that the capacity of generating stations has been steadily increasing and now exceeds 50,000,000 hp in the United States, the importance of having engineers trained to work with large amounts of power is readily seen.

In the field of communication engineering, the amounts of power used are small, and the engineer is concerned primarily with phenomena associated with the various frequencies of electric waves. The applications of electrical communication equipment range from the early telegraph through the telephone, radio, moving pictures, television, and radar.

Engineering Fields of Specialization

Other branches of electrical engineering that may include either, or both, power or communication activities are illumination engineering which deals with lighting using electric power, electronics which has applications in both power and communications, and such diverse fields as X-ray, acoustics, and seismograph work.

Employment opportunities in electrical engineering are extremely varied. Electrical manufacturing companies use large numbers of engineers for design, testing, research, and sales. Electrical power companies and public utility companies require a staff of qualified electrical engineers, as do the companies which control the networks of telegraph and telephone lines and the radio systems. Other opportunities for employment exist with oil companies, railroads, food processing plants, lumbering enterprises, biological laboratories, chemical plants, and colleges and universities as teachers or research workers. The aircraft and missile industries use engineers who are familiar with circuit design and employment of flight data computers, servomechanisms, analog computers, vacuum tubes, transistors, and other solid-state devices. There is scarcely any industry of any size that does not employ one or more electrical engineers as members of its engineering staff.

The engineering graduate must be familiar with the various sciences, but it is especially desirable that he be well versed in the fundamental principles of physics, chemistry, and mathematics. A thorough understanding of the underlying phenomena is necessary if the engineer is to direct the forces of nature to the best advantage. In addition to basic science courses, the electrical engineer will take courses in machinery, electronics, communication, and wave phenomena. As in other engineering courses, the demand for breadth and culture is met by studies in history, literature, economics, English, and public speaking.

INDUSTRIAL ENGINEERING

The field of industrial engineering or, as it is frequently called, *management engineering* is a wide and all-inclusive field. Whereas other branches of engineering tend to specialize in some particular phase of science, the realm of industrial engineering may include parts of all engineering fields. The industrial engineer then will be more concerned with the larger picture of management of industries and production of goods than with the detailed development of processes.

The work of the industrial engineer is rather wide in scope, so it is difficult to designate any specializations that the industrial engineer may choose. His general work is with men and machines, and as a result he is trained in both personnel administration and in the relations of men and machines to production.

The industrial engineer must be capable of preparing plans for the arrangement of plants for best operation and then organizing the workers so that their efforts will be coordinated to give a smoothly functioning unit. In such things as production lines, the various processes involved must be perfectly timed to insure smooth operation and efficient use of the worker's efforts. In

Courtesy E.I. du Pont de Nemours & Company

Fig. 4-8. The industrial engineer works with many phases of industry. One of the subjects with which he is concerned is methods and motion analysis. A new technique to aid in such analysis is illustrated in this picture. Here an operator is photographed at his work while he has small incandescent light bulbs attached to his wrists. The resulting streaks of light which appear on the photograph will enable the industrial engineer to evaluate the operator's motions and to recommend methods of improving the speed and economy of a manipulation.

addition to coordination of plant activities, the industrial engineer is concerned with cost accounting, handling of stocks of raw and finished products, worker relationships with organized groups and with managements, time and motion study, and pay of workers.

Opportunities for employment exist in almost every industrial plant and in many businesses not concerned directly with manufacturing or processing goods. In many cases the industrial engineer may be employed by depart-

Engineering Fields of Specialization

ment stores, insurance companies, consulting companies, and as engineers in cities. The industrial engineer is trained in fundamental engineering principles, and as a result may also be employed in positions which would fall in the realm of the civil, electrical, or mechanical engineer.

The courses prescribed for the student of industrial engineering follow the pattern of the other branches of engineering by starting with a thorough foundation in the engineering sciences. The engineering courses in the later semesters will be of a more general nature, and the curriculum will include such courses as economics, psychology, business law, personnel problems, and accounting principles.

MECHANICAL ENGINEERING

Mechanical engineering deals with power and the machines used to generate power and apply it to useful processes. The range of work that may be classed as mechanical engineering is wider than that in any of the other branches of engineering, but it may be grouped generally under two heads: work that is concerned with power-generating machines, and work that deals with machines that transform or consume this power in accomplishing their particular tasks.

Some of the general subdivisions of mechanical engineering are as follows: Power or combustion engineers deal with the production of power from fuels. Machine designers may work with parts which vary in size from the tiniest part of the most delicate instrument to the massive parts of heavy machinery. Railway engineers work with the complex railway equipment which is part of our transportation system. Automotive engineers work constantly to develop new vehicles and engines which improve on those we now have. Heating, ventilating, air-conditioning, and refrigeration engineers deal with the design of suitable systems for making our buildings more comfortable and for providing proper conditions in industry for good working conditions and efficient machine operation.

Employment may be secured by mechanical engineering graduates in almost every type of industry. Manufacturing plants, power-generating stations, public utility companies, transportation companies, airlines, and factories, to mention only a few, are examples of organizations that need mechanical engineers. Experienced engineers are needed in the missile industry in the design and development of gas turbine compressors and power plants, air-cycle cooling turbines, electrically and hydraulically driven fans, and high-pressure refrigerants. Mechanical engineers are also needed in the testing of airborne and missile fuel systems, servovalves, and mechanical-electrical control systems. In addition, an engineer may be employed as a salesman, a research worker, a teacher, or in the governments of cities, states, and the nation.

Courtesy Allis-Chalmers Manufacturing Company

Fig. 4-9. The mechanical engineer has courses in such basic engineering subjects as thermodynamics, fluid mechanics, heat transfer, machine design, and vibrations. Using principles learned, he is able to design specialized equipment and machines such as this 75-mw tandem-compound, double-flow steam turbine. Modern designs of high-pressure, high-temperature machines require the use of new and improved alloys unknown a few years ago.

Engineering Fields of Specialization

The courses in mechanical engineering include courses both in power and in machine principles. Courses include thermodynamics, machine design, engines, electricity, vibrations, kinematics, and so on. In the senior year elective courses may enable one to specialize in any of the various fields of mechanical engineering.

MINING AND METALLURGICAL ENGINEERING

As the name implies, this branch of engineering deals with the work of the engineer in the field of mining of materials and the work of the engineer as related to the production and use of metals. In many schools, since the work is closely related in the two fields, a combined degree is given in mining and metallurgical engineering.

In mining, the engineer is concerned with the problems associated with the removal from the earth of ores, fuels, or products such as building stones, either by underground passages or by stripping away the layers of soil covering the desired materials. Also, he deals with mine locations and surveys, tests and analyses of samples, and efficient operation of mining processes.

Metallurgical engineering may be divided into two branches. One branch deals with the location and evaluation of deposits of ore, the best way of mining and concentrating the ore, and the proper method of refining the ore into the basic metals. The other branch deals with the fabrication of the refined metal or metal alloy into various machines or metal products.

The metallurgist performs pure and applied research on vacuum melting, arc melting, and zone refining to produce metallic materials having unusual properties of strength and endurance. In addition the metallurgist in the aircraft and missile industries is called upon to recommend the best materials to use for special applications and is frequently called on to give an expert opinion on the results of fatigue tests of metal parts of machines.

In addition to the two branches listed above, ceramic engineering is frequently included as a branch of this type of engineering. Requirements for the design of inorganic materials that will be flexible at $-60°$ centigrade or have strength at $2000°$ centigrade have given impetus to the study of ceramic engineering. In addition some materials may need to have properties that will not be changed by exposure to high concentrations of radioactivity. Use is made of the newer techniques of sintering in the field of high-temperature inorganic materials, some of which are unusual blends of ceramic and metallic materials. An example of one of the newer uses of ceramics in industry is in the manufacture of the parts of turbine and rocket engines which are exposed to hot gases. These frequently are protected with refractory ceramic materials which have been developed by research teams.

Ceramic engineering also deals with the problems of production of pottery, chinaware, porcelain, building brick, sewer pipe, drain tile, firebrick, spark plugs, electric insulators, and so on. In some schools, ceramic engineering may be included in the chemical or mechanical engineering departments.

Courtesy Avco, Research and Advanced Development Division

Fig. 4-10. Mining and metallurgical engineers as specialists in mineral and metallic materials are striving to develop new materials with vastly improved properties. Requirements for substances which will withstand elevated temperatures have led to the development of methods of testing refractories such as this plasma jet apparatus which produces a temperature of over 20,000°F.

NAVAL AND MARINE ENGINEERING

Students who desire to prepare for a professional career in the design and building of ships, ship propulsion machinery, and the allied industries may elect to take courses leading to a degree in naval and marine engineering.

Naval architecture, as a subdivision of this branch of engineering, includes

Engineering Fields of Specialization 63

such considerations as stability, subdivision of ship hulls, freeboard and tonnage, ship motions in waves, steering, powering, and structural design.

Marine engineering includes many of the courses given in mechanical engineering and includes courses which cover steam machinery, diesel and gasoline engines, electric drive equipment, instruments and control equipment, and auxiliary equipment used in marine power plants.

Along much of our coast line and in some inland waterways, companies have erected shipbuilding installations, and it is in these that the naval and

Courtesy Newport News Shipbuilding and Drydock Co.

Fig. 4-11. Naval and marine engineers work with the design, construction, and repair of all types of vessels. In this picture, modern dry-dock facilities are shown which provide means for maintenance and repair of sea-going ships.

marine engineer will find the best opportunities for employment. The construction of ships, both for industry and for the government, requires the services of numbers of well-trained engineers. In addition to these plants which deal usually with large construction, the companies which design and construct smaller craft will furnish additional employment opportunities. Other companies operate salvage and repair services and do specialized marine construction that will require trained engineers. In addition opportunities exist in the field of technical sales and as employees of the state and federal government.

The courses in naval and marine engineering include the basic engineering subjects of physics, chemistry, mathematics, and English for the first part of the curriculum. Later, courses in strength of materials, fluid mechanics, electricity, and thermodynamics provide general engineering knowledge. Special courses in dynamics of hull design, ship structures, marine engines, and ship propulsion are included in the latter part of the curriculum.

NUCLEAR ENGINEERING

This is one of the newest branches of engineering to be recognized by industry. A need has arisen within the last few years for engineers educated to cope with problems which are associated with the uses of nuclear power. While much work in the field of nucleonics at present falls within the realm of pure research, a growing demand for people educated to utilize recent discoveries for the benefit of mankind has led many colleges and universities to offer courses in nuclear engineering. The nuclear engineer is familiar with the basic principles involved in both fission and fusion reactions, and by applying fundamental engineering concepts, he is able to direct the enormous energies involved in a proper manner. Work involved in nuclear engineering includes the design and operation of plants to concentrate nuclear reactive materials, the design and operation of plants to utilize heat energy from reactions, and the solution of problems arising in connection with safety to persons from radiation, disposal of radioactive wastes, and decontamination of radioactive areas.

The wartime uses of nuclear reactions are well known, but of even more importance are the less spectacular peacetime uses of controlled reactions. These uses include such diverse applications as electric power generation and medical applications. Other applications are in the use of isotopes in chemical, physical, and biological research, and in the changing of the physical and chemical properties of materials in unusual ways by subjecting them to radiation.

Recent advances in the knowledge of controlled nuclear reaction have enabled engineers to build power plants using heat from reactions to drive machines. Submarine nuclear power plants, long a dream, are now a reality, and experiments are being conducted on smaller nuclear power plants that can be used for airborne or railway applications.

At present, ample opportunities for employment of nuclear engineers exist in both privately owned and government-operated plants where separation, concentration, or processing of nuclear materials is performed. Nuclear engineers are also needed by companies that may use radioactive materials in research or processing involving agricultural, medical, chemical, metallurgical, and petroleum products.

Courtesy Westinghouse Electric Corporation

Fig. 4-12. The nuclear engineer is a member of one of the newer branches of engineering. As a part of his work he explores all possible methods of utilizing nuclear energy for the benefit of mankind. This picture shows the design features of the four-story high reactor for the nation's first full-scale nuclear power station. Here safety must be a primary consideration, as the limits on output are set only by the ability of the heat exchanger to remove power. Analytical treatment of the thermal stresses in combination with pressure and mechanical stresses is particularly difficult because of complex structural geometries and nonuniform radiation heating. Other design problems include materials, operational reliability, warpage, tolerances, alignments, and maintenance.

PETROLEUM ENGINEERING

Petroleum engineering deals with all phases of the petroleum industry, from the location of petroleum in the ground to the ultimate delivery to the user. Petroleum products play an important part in many phases of our everyday life in providing our clothes, food, work, and entertainment. Because of the complex chemical structure of petroleum, we are able to make

Courtesy Shell Oil Co.

Fig. 4-13. One of the tasks of the petroleum engineer is to locate oil deposits and to devise methods for oil recovery. In some cases deposits lie in places which are remote from easy accessibility. This picture shows an oil-drilling rig in the bayou country of Louisiana. Other drilling locations are in the open waters of the Gulf of Mexico and in the Pacific Ocean off the California coast. These off-shore locations may be a considerable distance from shore and frequently are serviced by helicopter.

Engineering Fields of Specialization 67

an almost endless number of different articles. Owing to the wide demand for petroleum products, the petroleum engineer strives to satisfy an ever-increasing demand for oil and gas from the ground.

The petroleum engineer is concerned first with finding deposits of oil and gas in quantities suitable for commercial use, in the extraction of these materials from the ground, and the storage and processing of the petroleum above ground. The petroleum engineer is concerned with the location of wells in accordance with the findings of geologists, the drilling of wells and the myriad problems associated with the drilling, and the installation of valves and piping when the wells are completed. In addition to the initial tapping of a field of oil, the petroleum engineer is concerned with practices that will provide the greatest recovery of the oil, considering all possible factors that may exist many thousand feet below the surface of the earth.

After the oil or gas has reached the surface, the petroleum engineer will provide the means of transporting it to suitable processing plants or to places where it will be used. Pipe lines are providing an ever-increasing means of transporting both oil and gas from field to consumer.

Owing to the expanding uses for petroleum and its products, the opportunities for employment of petroleum engineers are widespread. Companies concerned with the drilling, producing, and transporting of oil and gas will provide employment for the majority of engineers. Because of the widespread search for oil, employment opportunities for the petroleum engineer exist all over the world; and for the young man wishing a job in a foreign land, oil companies have crews in almost every country over the globe. Other opportunities for employment exist in the field of technical sales, research, and as civil service employees in the national government.

The curriculum in petroleum engineering includes courses in drilling methods, engines, oil and gas recovery, storage and transportation, and geology.

chapter five

The Engineering Profession

Courtesy United Engineering Center Project
The New Engineering Societies Building in New York City.

This building houses the headquarters of a majority of the major engineering societies in the United States. In addition to offices for the societies it also has space for conference rooms, auditoriums, exhibits, and the engineering societies library.

chapter five

The Engineering Profession

A profession is an occupation or calling to which one devotes himself. It is usually the vocation to which a person applies most of his time and from which he makes his living. The word "profession" implies more than just a vocation, however. It implies a period of education, of training, and of experience in work of a specialized nature. A person who is a professional is expected to possess above average competence and to be one of a group which is characterized by high moral and ethical standards.

As part of the education which is given to engineering students, studies in the humanities are made a part of the curriculum in order to develop a well-rounded individual, both technically and socially. Perhaps this is one of the greatest differences between engineering courses and trade school courses where purely technical skills are emphasized. Since the engineer will most certainly have to deal with other people in the practice of engineering, he must be trained both for technical competence and for working with other people.

The engineering profession has many organized societies to aid the individual engineer in his work as a professional. These societies provide the requirements to maintain professional growth following graduation from college. By means of publications and committees, they furnish technical information to help the engineer keep abreast of new developments, and they offer social and economic contacts which are helpful in relations with clients and with other engineers.

A brief outline of a few of the engineering societies is given below as well as some of the things which apply to engineering as a profession.

ENGINEERING SOCIETIES

American Society of Civil Engineers (ASCE)

Early in the life of the United States, engineers had begun to build canals, buildings, bridges, and machinery. In 1852 a group of engineers organized the first engineering society in the United States and named it "American Society of Civil Engineers and Architects." From this beginning with forty-eight charter members have come the many engineering societies that cover the field today.

In 1857 a separate body, the American Institute of Architects, was founded, and in 1868 the word "Architects" was dropped from the name of the society. Later other specialized groups such as the American Institute of Mining and Metallurgical Engineers, the American Society of Mechanical Engineers, and the American Institute of Electrical Engineers were formed from the original ASCE.

The ASCE carries on its technical work through fourteen technical divisions. These divisions are Air Transport, City Planning, Construction, Engineering, Mechanics, Highways, Hydraulics, Irrigation and Drainage, Power, Sanitary Engineering, Soil Mechanics and Foundations, Surveying and Mapping, and Waterways. Members contribute papers for dissemination of information in the society publications.

American Institute of Mining and Metallurgical Engineers (AIME)

Originally a part of the ASCE, the American Institute of Mining Engineers formally organized their society in 1871 with the objective of promoting more economical production of useful minerals and of working for the safety and welfare of those engaged in industry. In 1918 the American Institute of Metals joined the Mining Institute to form the American Institute of Mining and Metallurgical Engineers. The abbreviation AIME was retained after the consolidation.

The principal branches of this society are mining, metals, and petroleum. A monthly journal is published for each of the branches to furnish up-to-date technical information to the members.

American Society of Mechanical Engineers (ASME)

The American Society of Mechanical Engineers was organized in 1880 to promote the art and science of mechanical engineering, to encourage original research and to foster engineering education, and to promote exchange of technical information between engineers to broaden the usefulness of the profession.

Expansion of knowledge in mechanics, power plants, machine design, transportation, and materials engages the activities of an ever-increasing number of mechanical engineers and demands a thorough preparation in mathematics and the physical sciences. In the new fields created by the advent of nuclear power, many of the problems faced lie within the province of the mechanical engineer. The ASME through its committees, local sections, and publications strives to keep its membership abreast of the new developments and to discuss technical problems of concern to mechanical engineers.

American Institute of Electrical Engineers (AIEE)

The American Institute of Electrical Engineers was organized in 1884 as a society of electrical engineers interested in encouraging electrical developments and applications. The objectives of the society have been expressed as "the advancement of the theory and practice of electrical engineering and of the allied arts and sciences, and the maintenance of a high professional standing among its members."

The AIEE has worked steadily to promote standards in the electrical industry to the extent that there is now a great deal of uniformity in all kinds of manufactured electrical products. The Institute publishes a monthly magazine carrying articles of a technical nature, and in addition, a "Transactions" publication in three parts covering electronics and communication, industry and general applications, and power.

Other Societies

Four of the engineering societies form what are known as the Founder Societies. They are ASCE, AIME, ASME, and AIEE. These four societies have co-operated to build an Engineering Societies Building in New York City. Since they were the first established, they formed a pattern for the organization of other technical societies. From the beginning of four major societies in the nineteenth century, we now have over 100 technical societies, each of which deals with some specialized engineering field. As the discovery of some phenomenon or the improvement of a technique occurs, there is a tendency of some segment of an existing society to withdraw and create a group primarily interested in the speciality—thus a new society is born.

Some of the larger societies are listed below with the dates of their organization.

    The American Association of Petroleum Geologists (AAPG), 1917
    American Institute of Architects (AIA), 1857
    American Institute of Chemical Engineers (AIChE), 1908
    American Institute of Industrial Engineers (AIIE) 1948
    American Standards Association (ASA), 1918
    American Society of Agricultural Engineers (ASAE), 1907
    The American Society for Engineering Education (ASEE), 1893
    The American Society of Heating, Refrigerating, and Air Conditioning Engineers (ASHRAE), 1895
    American Society for Metals (ASM), 1920
    The American Society of Naval Engineers (ASNE), 1888
    American Society of Tool Engineers (ASTE), 1932
    American Society for Testing Materials (ASTM), 1898
    Institute of the Aeronautical Sciences (IAS), 1932
    Illuminating Engineering Society (IES), 1906
    Institute of Radio Engineers (IRE), 1912

Instrument Society of America (ISA), 1946
Society of Automotive Engineers (SAE), 1905

National Society of Professional Engineers (NSPE)

The National Society of Professional Engineers was founded in 1934 for the purpose of promoting the professional, social, and economic interests of the professional engineer. It has only one membership grade, and its membership is limited to those registered to practice the profession of engineering according to the laws of the various states.

The headquarters of the NSPE is in Washington, D.C., and it is active in working with congressional committees on legislative items which concern engineers.

In addition to the national society, the states have their respective state societies which have the same objectives as the national societies except they are more concerned with problems at a local level. Chapter meetings of the state societies in the larger cities provide opportunities for registered professional engineers to meet socially and discuss problems of general interest. Many of the chapters also provide for student membership to give college engineering students an opportunity to be in contact with practicing engineers during their college years.

Engineers Joint Council (EJC)

The Engineers Joint Council is a federation of professional societies dedicated to the betterment of the nation and to the professional and sociological development of the engineer. The EJC represents the engineer's broad profession and works to promote sound public recognition of him.

The nation's engineers, through EJC, bring their constructive thoughts to bear on national manpower policy, employment conditions for engineers, science and engineering education, national resource policies, labor-management relations, and nuclear energy applications.

The Engineers Joint Council was created in 1941 to co-ordinate activities of the professional societies on matters of co-operation with the government, postwar adjustments, intersociety coordination, and relations with international groups. It has continued to grow until it now represents about twenty engineering societies. Its officers are appointed from the governing bodies of the constituent engineering societies, and the EJC works closely with the Engineers' Council for Professional Development. It holds annual meetings, at which time matters of common concern to all engineering branches are discussed.

Engineers Council for Professional Development (ECPD)

The Engineers Council for Professional Development is sponsored by eight of the major engineering societies. It was organized in 1932 for the purpose of enhancing the professional status of the engineer. It also promotes efforts to raise the standards of engineering education and practice and to study problems dealing with the technical, social, and economic phases of engineering.

ECPD operates at the local level through the participating societies by means of committees. One comittee of special interest is the one which works with engineering colleges to study the engineering curricula and to accredit a curriculum when it has been demonstrated that certain standards have been met. Graduates from engineering courses accredited by ECPD may not, in some states, have to take the engineer-in-training part of the examination for professional registration.

The sponsoring societies are AIChE, AIEE, AIME, ASCE, ASEE, ASME, EIC, and NCSBEE. Of these societies, seven are in the United States and one is in Canada. As an exercise, the student should determine the full name of each society.

REGISTRATION OF ENGINEERS

The first engineering registration law was passed in Wyoming in 1907. By 1950 all states had enacted laws providing for registration of engineers, and the majority of practicing engineers today are registered under laws of the various states.

The need for registration goes back to the necessity in our modern civilization to regulate the practice of persons whose activities deal with the protection of life, health, rights, and property. Three professions—medicine, law, and engineering—are primarily entrusted with these responsibilities, and the exclusion or elimination of those unqualified to practice in these fields is desirable. The public expects a profession to maintain high standards of qualification and to disown those unfit by reason of character or lack of training.

Protection of the public in the practice of engineering justifies the legislative steps taken by the various states to enact laws providing for registration of engineers meeting specified educational and experience requirements. Regulation is achieved in two ways, either by protecting the use of the title or by regulating the actual practice of the profession. A model law provides that the practice of engineering shall mean any professional service or creative work requiring engineering education, training, and experience, and the application of special knowledge of the mathematical, physical, and engineering sciences to such professional work as consultation, investigation,

The Engineering Profession

evaluation, planning, design, and supervision of construction for the purpose of assuring compliance with specifications and design, in connection with any public or private utilities, buildings, machines, equipment, processes, works, or projects.

Requirements differ in various states concerning the educational and experience requirements for registration. For example, in some states an examination on technical subjects is mandatory, while in others, graduation from an approved school of engineering is sufficient evidence of technical competence. Usually laws provide that a person who has not graduated from an approved engineering college may secure registration by submitting evidence of experience in responsible charge of engineering works for a specified period of time and, in addition, by passing a written examination.

Every engineer should consider the desirability of registering in the state in which he is practicing. By registering, an engineer gains two important benefits. First, he receives authority to practice his profession before the public, and second, he establishes his professional standing on the basis of legal requirements. Although registration laws require compliance only for those who offer their services to the public as professional engineers, the great majority of those who have obtained registration, while not required to do so, have voluntarily subscribed to registration to identify themselves legally as professional engineers.

Registration is not easily obtained, and when an engineer receives his certificate attesting to the fact that he is a professional engineer, he may take justifiable pride in a real accomplishment.

ENGINEER-IN-TRAINING CERTIFICATE

Most state engineering registration laws provide for the granting of a preregistration certificate to those persons who have not yet attained the requisite experience for full registration. This program is generally known as "Engineer-in-Training" registration. The requirements usually are graduation from an accredited engineering curriculum plus the successful completion of an examination on fundamental engineering subjects. This program is designed so that those who have recently graduated from an engineering course may take the first step toward registration while the subjects are still fresh in mind.

The successful applicants for EIT status are granted a certificate upon completion of the examination. After acquiring the necessary experience (usually four years) required under state law and after passing the second portion of the examination relating to a particular specialty, the engineer in training will be eligible to full registration and will be authorized to practice as a professional engineer.

Details of the laws relating to EIT vary in the individual states, but essentially the state boards of registration are interested in knowing that the applicant has acquired the basic knowledge to insure his technical competence as implemented by later experience.

ENGINEERING ETHICS

Ethical standards change with the times, and ethical conduct is the middle road between man's inner nature of selfishness and socialistic pressure for completely unselfish behavior. We are not self-sufficient, and with the growth of specialization we depend more and more on each other. This dependency involves a trust of each other—a trust of skills and of performance.

The engineer, since he deals with machines, construction, or processes that affect public welfare, health and safety, is in a position where he must trust others, and he must himself be completely trustworthy. This must come from within, for experience has shown that the legislation of ethics is a poor way of securing proper conduct.

The importance of proper conduct in the engineering profession is brought out by surveys which show that most of the state boards of examiners for registration for engineers include ethical considerations in their decision as to the fitness of an applicant for registration.

The National Society of Professional Engineers has published a brochure on "Ethics for Engineers" which contains the Canons of Ethics of the Engineers Council for Professional Development. These canons include rules for the engineer in his professional life, in relations with the public, in relations with clients and employers, and in relations with other engineers. These rules have been taken largely from the ethical codes of the various engineering societies.

Canons of Ethics for Engineers*

Honesty, justice and courtesy form a moral philosophy which, associated with mutual interest among men, constitutes the foundation of ethics. The engineer should recognize such a standard, not in passive observance, but as a set of dynamic principles guiding his conduct and way of life. It is his duty to practice his profession according to these Canons of Ethics.

As the keystone of professional conduct is integrity, the engineer will discharge his duties with fidelity to the public, his employers and clients, and with fairness and impartiality to all. It is his duty to interest himself in public welfare and to be ready to apply his special knowledge for the benefit of mankind. He should uphold the honor and dignity of his profession and avoid association with any enterprise of

* Prepared by Engineers Council for Professional Development and adopted by Board of Directors, National Society of Professional Engineers, Oct. 28, 1946.

The Engineering Profession

questionable character. In his dealings with fellow engineers he should be fair and tolerant.

A typical code of ethics for professional engineers is given below:

Code of Ethics*

It shall be considered unprofessional and inconsistent with honorable and dignified bearing for any Professional Engineer:

1. To act for his client, or employer, in professional matters otherwise than as a faithful agent or trustee, or to accept any remuneration other than his stated recompense for services rendered.
2. To attempt to injure falsely or maliciously, directly or indirectly, the professional reputation, prospects, or business of anyone.
3. To attempt to supplant another Engineer after definite steps have been taken toward his employment.
4. To compete with another Engineer for employment by the use of unethical practices.
5. To review the work of another Engineer for the same client, except with the knowledge of such Engineer, or unless the connection of such Engineer with the work has terminated.
6. To attempt to obtain technical services or assistance without fair and just compensation commensurate with the services rendered.
7. To advertise in self-laudatory language, or in any other manner derogatory to the dignity of the profession.
8. To practice in any field of engineering in which the registrant is not proficient.

* All applicants for engineering registration in Texas, under oath, subscribe to and agree to exemplify this code of ethics.

PART TWO
preparation for problem solving

A.M. Byers Company Illustration

The engineer's work is distinguished by clarity of thinking, systematic analysis, and conciseness of presentation. These are trade-marks of his profession.

Fig. 6-1. Vertical Lettering.

chapter six

Presentation of Work

In problem solving, both in school and in industry, considerable importance is attached to a proper analysis of the problem, to a logical recording of the problem solution, and to the over-all professional appearance of the finished calculations. Neatness and clarity of presentation of the problem solution is a way by which the engineer's work may be distinguished. Students should strive always to practice professional habits of problem analysis and to make a conscious effort to improve the appearance of each paper, whether it is submitted for grading or included in a notebook.

The computation paper used for most calculations is 8 1/2 by 11 in. in size, with lines ruled both vertically and horizontally on the sheet. These lines usually divide the paper into five squares per inch, and the paper is commonly known as cross-section paper or engineering calculation paper. Many schools use paper that has the lines ruled on the reverse side of the paper so that erasures will not remove them.

The problem work shown on the paper should not be crowded, and all steps of the solution should be included.

Engineers use slant or vertical lettering (see Fig. 6-1), and either is acceptable as long as there is no mixing of the two forms. The student should not be discouraged if he finds that he cannot letter with great speed and dexterity at first. Good lettering comes with long hours of patient practice. Use a well-sharpened H or 2H pencil and follow the sequence of strokes recommended on model lettering sheets.

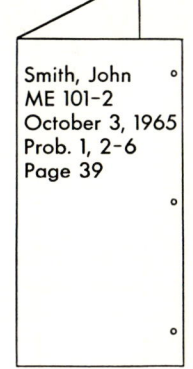

Fig. 6-2

When the work is finished, the paper may be folded and endorsed on the outside or may be submitted flat in a folder. Items that appear on the endorsement should include the student's name, and the course, section, date, problem numbers, and any other prescribed information. An example of a paper that has been folded and endorsed is shown in Fig. 6-2.

Several styles of model problem sheets are shown in Figs. 6-3 to Fig. 6-6. Notice in each example that a sequence is followed in which the known data are given first, followed by a brief statement of the requirements, and then a solution in orderly steps.

	Problem 1 (Algebra) Smith, Bill

  a. $(x^n)^4 (x^2) = \underline{\underline{x^{4n+2}}}$

  b. $\dfrac{x^7}{x^2} = \underline{\underline{x^5}}$

  c. $(y^4)(y^3) = \underline{\underline{y^7}}$ |
| | Problem 8 (Logarithms)
  $\qquad\qquad\qquad\qquad$ GIVEN:
  a. $(35)(6) =$ Ans.
  b. $\dfrac{(400)}{(75)} =$ Ans. |
| | $\qquad\qquad\qquad$ SOLUTION:
  a. log ans. = log 35 + log 6
   log 35 = 1.5441
   log 6   = 0.7782
   log ans. = 2.3223
   ans.   = $\underline{\underline{210}}$
  b. log ans. = log 400 − log 75
   log 400 = 2.6021
   log 75 = 1.8751
   log ans. = 0.7270
   ans.   = $\underline{\underline{5.33}}$ |

Fig. 6-3. **Model Problem Sheet, Style A.** This style shows a method of presenting short, simple exercises.

Presentation of Work

Margin line should be drawn in

Problem No.

SKETCH

Wt. = 71 lb.

Show last name first

Name

GIVEN:

Show as much of the given data as possible on the sketch. Show all dimensions, weights, and other pertinent information which might aid the student in solving the problem. List any other data which cannot be shown on the sketch

FIND:

a.   List here all required answers

b.

SOLUTION:

a.   Show completely all steps necessary for the solution. Double underline required answers. Everything is printed using either slant or vertical letters

b.

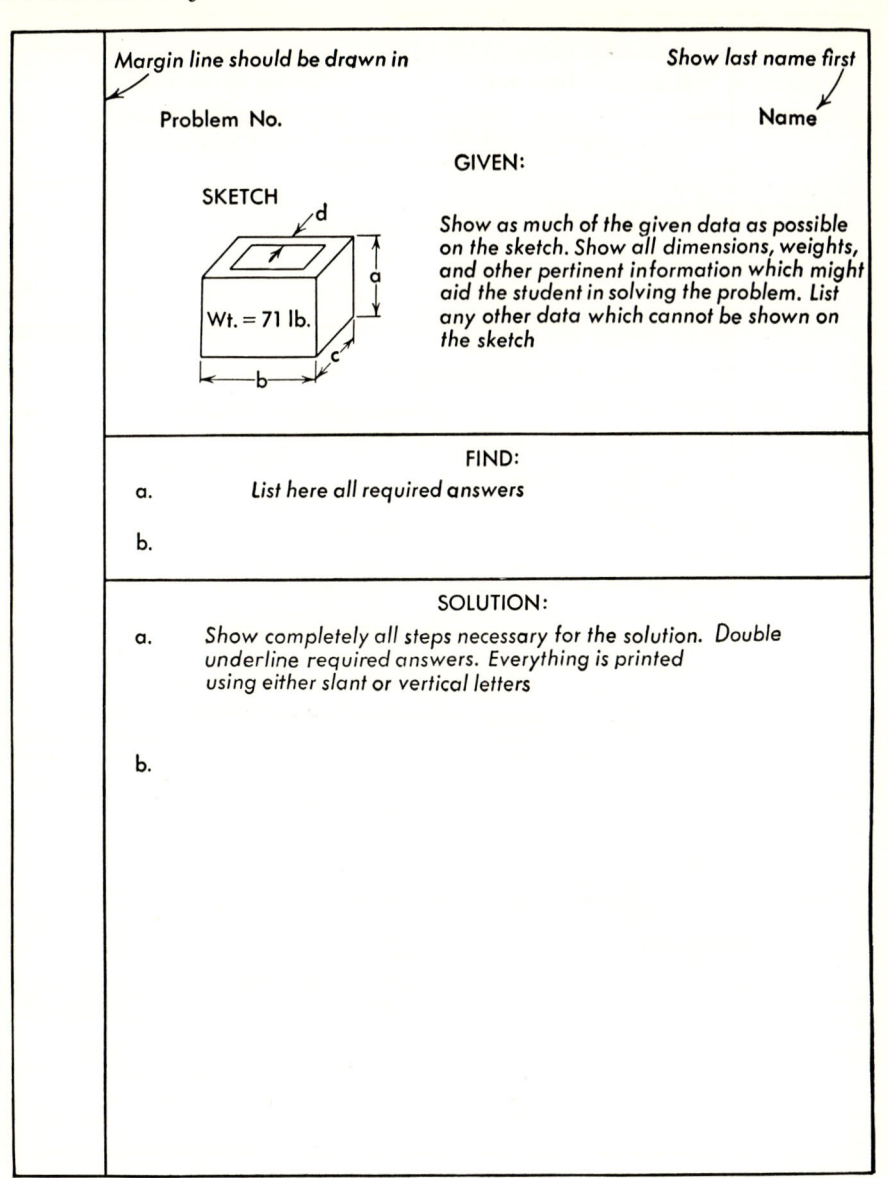

Fig. 6-4. Model Problem Sheet, Style B. This style shows a general form which is useful in presenting the solution of mensuration problems.

| MH 81-12 | SEPT 18, 1965 | ASGT. NO. 10 | SMITH, J.C. | 2/5 |

PROBLEM NO. 8-2 — Date due
Course & number

Number of this sheet
Number of sheets in this assignment

Block A (1000 lb) on 30° incline connected via rope over pulley at B to block B (600 lb) on horizontal surface with force P applied. $\mu = 0.20$ for all surfaces.

DATA

Determine magnitude of force P to prevent block A from sliding down the plane.

REQ'D

FREE BODIES ON LEFT | **CALCULATIONS ON RIGHT** | **SOL'N**

Show all steps in solution

Free body of A (1000 lb) with 30° angle, showing T, F_A, N_A:

$\Sigma F_y = 0$
$N_A - 1000 \cos 30° = 0$
$N_A = 866$ lb
$F_A = \mu N_A = 0.20(866) = 173.2$ lb
$\Sigma F_x = 0$
$T - 1000 \sin 30° + 173.2 = 0$
$T = 500 - 173.2 = 326.8$ lb

Free body of B (600 lb) showing T, P, F_B, N_B:

$\Sigma F_y = 0$
$N_B - 600 = 0$
$N_B = 600$ lb
$F_B = \mu N_B = 0.20(600) = 120$ lb
$\Sigma F_x = 0$
$P + F_B - T = 0$
$P + 120 - 326.8 = 0$
$\underline{\underline{P = 206.8 \text{ lb}}} \rightarrow$

Double underline answers, and state units

Show direction of vector quantities

Index answer

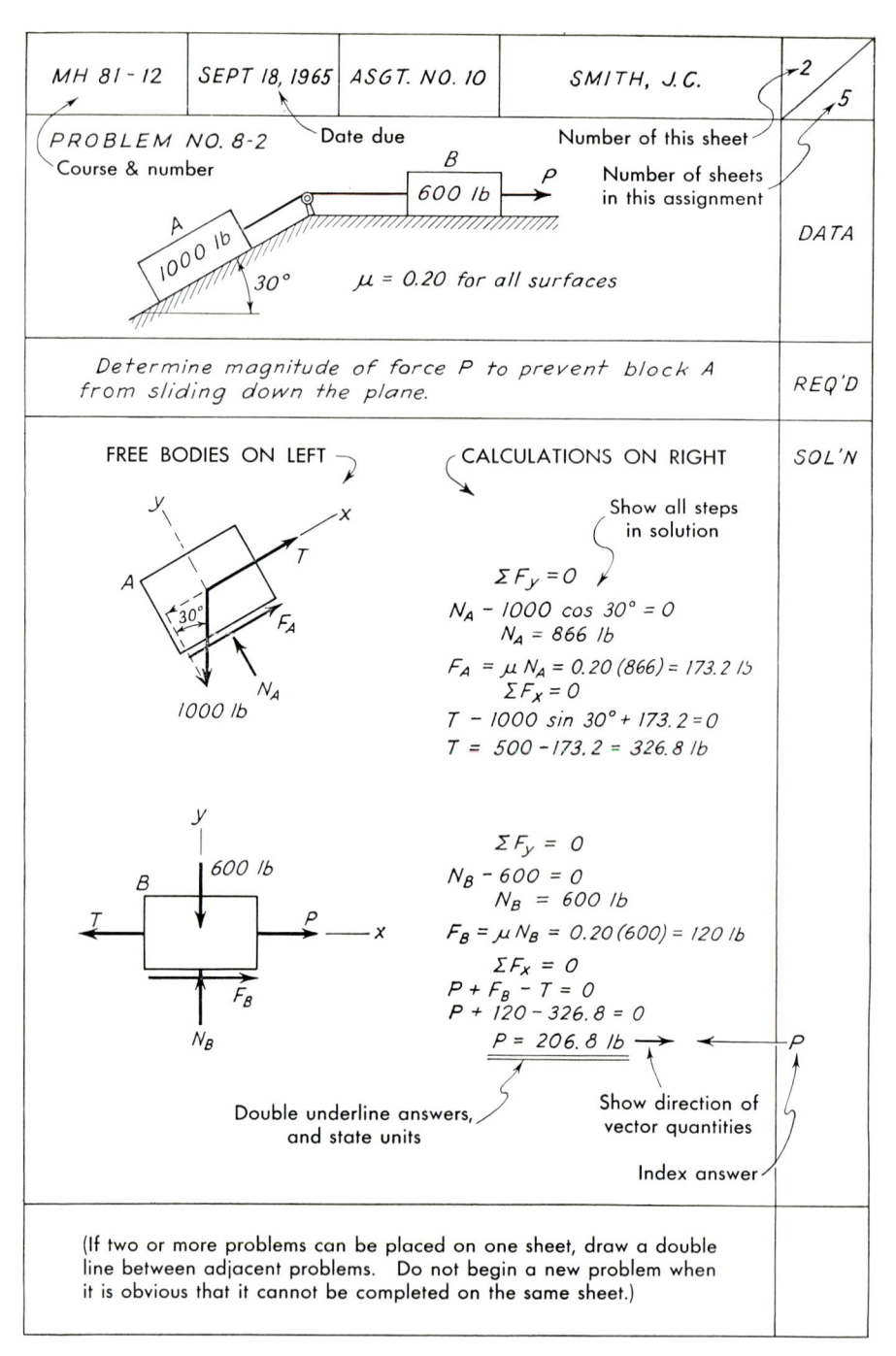

(If two or more problems can be placed on one sheet, draw a double line between adjacent problems. Do not begin a new problem when it is obvious that it cannot be completed on the same sheet.)

Fig. 6-5. Model Problem Sheet, Style C. This style shows a method of presenting stated problems. Notice that all calculations are shown on the sheet and that no scratch calculations on other sheets are used.

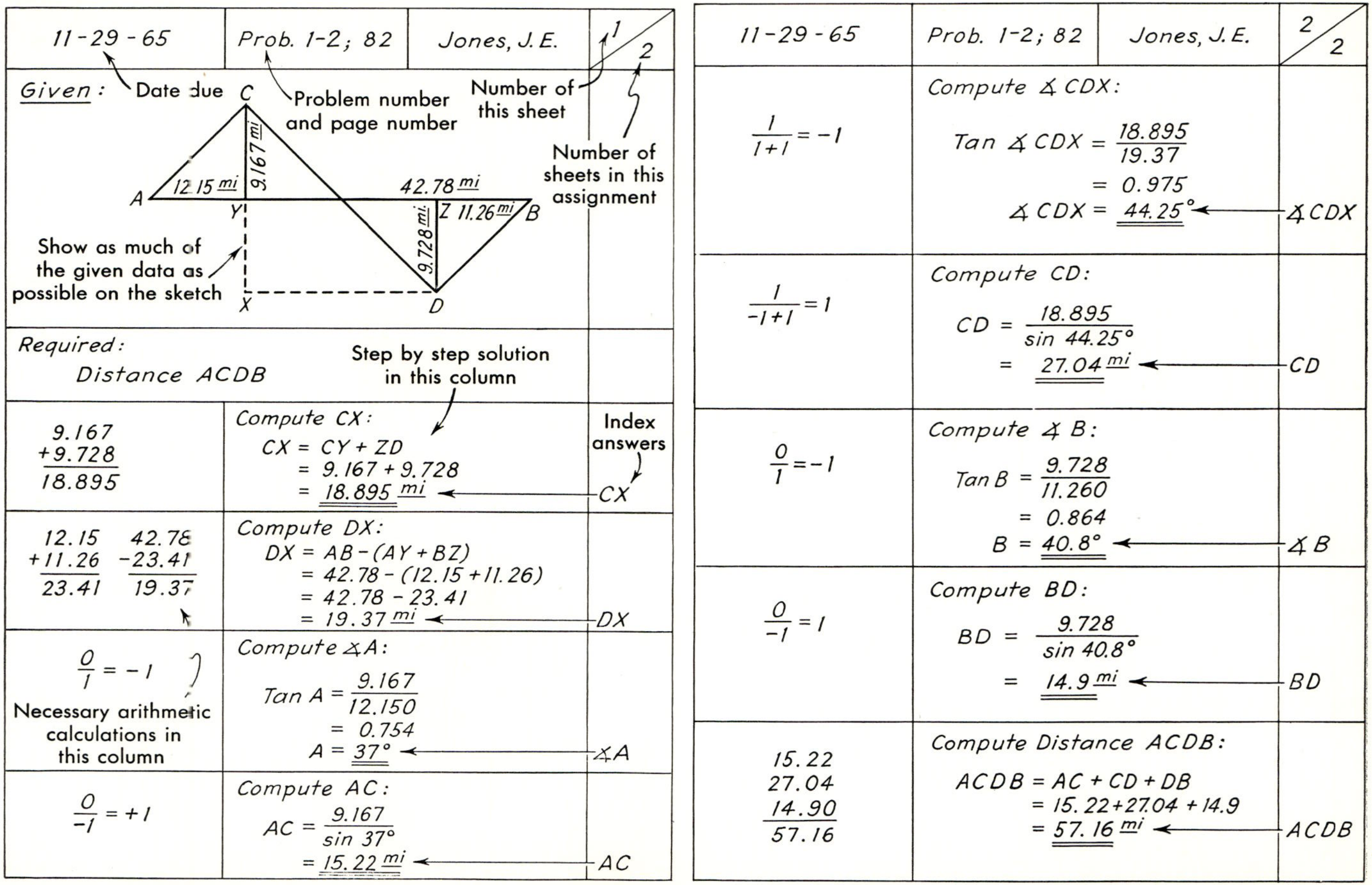

11-29-65	Prob. 1-2; 82	Jones, J.E.	1 / 2

Given: ← Date due — Problem number and page number — Number of this sheet

Number of sheets in this assignment

Sketch with triangle: A — 12.15 mi — C, C — 9.167 mi — Y, A — 42.78 mi — B, B — 11.26 mi — Z, Z — 9.728 mi — D

Show as much of the given data as possible on the sketch

Required: Distance ACDB

Step by step solution in this column

Compute CX: ← Index answers
$CX = CY + ZD$
$= 9.167 + 9.728$
$= \underline{18.895 \ mi}$ → CX

Compute DX:
$DX = AB - (AY + BZ)$
$= 42.78 - (12.15 + 11.26)$
$= 42.78 - 23.41$
$= \underline{19.37 \ mi}$ → DX

Compute ∡A:
$\text{Tan } A = \dfrac{9.167}{12.150}$
$= 0.754$
$A = \underline{37°}$ → ∡A

Compute AC:
$AC = \dfrac{9.167}{\sin 37°}$
$= \underline{15.22 \ mi}$ → AC

Necessary arithmetic calculations in this column:

9.167
+9.728
─────
18.895

12.15   42.78
+11.26 −23.41
─────   ─────
23.41   19.37

$\dfrac{0}{1} = -1$

$\dfrac{0}{-1} = +1$

11-29-65	Prob. 1-2; 82	Jones, J.E.	2 / 2

Compute ∡CDX:
$\text{Tan } ∡CDX = \dfrac{18.895}{19.37}$
$= 0.975$
$∡CDX = \underline{44.25°}$ → ∡CDX

Compute CD:
$CD = \dfrac{18.895}{\sin 44.25°}$
$= \underline{27.04 \ mi}$ → CD

Compute ∡B:
$\text{Tan } B = \dfrac{9.728}{11.260}$
$= 0.864$
$B = \underline{40.8°}$ → ∡B

Compute BD:
$BD = \dfrac{9.728}{\sin 40.8°}$
$= \underline{14.9 \ mi}$ → BD

Compute Distance ACDB:
$ACDB = AC + CD + DB$
$= 15.22 + 27.04 + 14.9$
$= \underline{57.16 \ mi}$ → ACDB

$\dfrac{1}{1+1} = -1$

$\dfrac{1}{-1+1} = 1$

$\dfrac{0}{1} = -1$

$\dfrac{0}{-1} = 1$

15.22
27.04
14.90
─────
57.16

Fig. 6-6. Model problem sheet, Style D. This style employs a sheet with heading and margin lines preprinted. Notice that all calculations are shown on the solution sheet.

85

chapter seven

Scientific Presentation of Data

Courtesy North American Aviation, Inc.

Data from engineering tests may be recorded on magnetic tape or on charts. These data, after recording, must be reduced and evaluated by the engineer so that they may be analyzed. Here an engineer is reviewing the results of tests which have been recorded on strip charts.

chapter seven

Scientific Presentation of Data

SIGNIFICANT FIGURES

A significant figure in a number may be defined as a figure which may be considered reliable as a result of measurements or of mathematical computations. In making measurements, it is customary to read and record all figures from the graduations on the measuring device and to include one estimated figure which is a fractional part of the smallest graduation. These figures are considered to be significant figures. For example, if we examine the sketch of the thermometer in Fig. 7-1, we see that the mercury column, represented in the sketch by a vertical line, lies between 71° and 72°. Since the smallest graduation is 1°, we should record 71° and include an estimated 0.5°. The reading would then be recorded as 71.5° and would contain three significant figures.

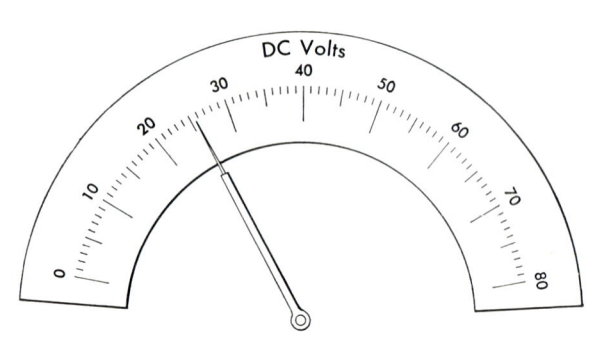

Fig. 7-1   Fig. 7-2

As another example, suppose it is necessary to record the voltmeter reading shown in Fig. 7-2. The needle obviously rests between the graduations of 20 and 30 volts. A closer inspection shows that its location can be more closely determined as being between 25 and 26 volts. However, this is the extent of the aid which we can get from the individual graduations. Any further refinement must be accomplished by eye.*

By eye, we can further divide the small space between 25 and 26 volts into ten smaller, equal parts. If we do so, then the needle may be estimated to

---

* In most cases, estimation by eye (beyond the precision obtainable from the graduations) is acceptable. It should be recognized that this final subdivision (by eye) will give doubtful results.

Scientific Presentation of Data

lie at the position 25.6 volts. In this case the digits 2 and 5 are well designated by the meter graduations, and the digit 6 is doubtful, since we may have erred in our estimation by eye. The designated digits, together with one doubtful digit, are said to be "significant figures." In reading values previously recorded, assume that only one doubtful digit has been recorded. This will usually be the last digit retained in any recorded measurement.

FALSE ACCURACY

In analysis of engineering problems one must prevent false accuracy from appearing in the calculations. False accuracy occurs when data are manipulated without regard to their degree of precision. For example, it may be desirable to find the sum of three lengths, each having been measured with a different type of instrument. These lengths might have been recorded in tabular form (rows and columns) as:

	Columns a b c d e f g	
First Measurement: Row A	1 5 7.3 9	±0.02 ft
Second Measurement: Row B	1 8.0 2 5	±0.001 ft
Third Measurement: Row C	8 5 3.	±2 ft
	1 0 2 8.4 1 5	(By regular addition)

Although the sum of the columns would be 1028.415, it would not be proper to use this value in other calculations. Since the last measurement (Row C) could vary from 851 to 855 (maximum variation in Column d), it would be trivial to include the decimal numbers in Rows A and B in the sum. The final answer should be expressed as 1028 ± 2, or merely 1028. In this case the last digit (8) is of doubtful accuracy.

In the tabulation of data (readings from meters, dials, gauges, verniers, scales, etc.) it is essential that only one doubtful digit be retained for any measurement. In the preceding example, the doubtful digits are 9 (Row A), 5 (Row B), and 3 (Row C). The example also shows that when numbers are added, the sum should not be written to more digits than the digit under the first column which has a doubtful number.

SCIENTIFIC NOTATION

The decimal point has nothing to do with how many significant figures there are in a number, and therefore it is impossible to tell the number of significant figures if written as 176,000., 96000., or 1000. This doubt can be removed by the following procedure:

1. Move the decimal point to the left or right until a number between 1 and 10 remains. The number resulting from this process should contain *only* significant figures.

2. This remaining number must be multiplied by the quantity $(10)^{\text{number of decimal moves}}$. If the decimal is moved to the left, the power of 10 is positive. If the decimal moves to the right, the power of 10 is negative.

Example: Express the number 1756000 to five significant figures:

$1\ 7\ 5\ 6\ 0\ 0\ 0.$ (Move the decimal point to the left to get a number between 1 and 10.)

Answer: $(1.7560)(10)^6$ (The power of 10 is the number of decimal moves.)

NOTE: Only the five significant figures remain to be multiplied by the power of 10.

Example: Express the number 0.016900 to three significant figures:

$0\ .\ 0\ 1\ 6\ 9$ (Move the decimal point to the right to get a number between 1 and 10.)

Answer $(1.69)(10)^{-2}$ (The power of 10 is the number of decimal moves and is negative in sign.)

NOTE: The three significant figures remain to be multiplied by the power of 10.

Examples of Significant Figures:

385.1	4 significant figures
38.51	4 significant figures
0.03851	4 significant figures
3.851×10^7	4 significant figures
7.04×10^{-4}	3 significant figures
25.5	3 significant figures
0.051	2 significant figures
0.00005	1 significant figure
27,855	5 significant figures
8.91×10^4	3 significant figures
2200	May have 2, 3, or 4 significant figures depending on the accuracy of the measurement that obtained the number. Where such doubt may exist, it is better to write the number as 2.2×10^3 to show 2 significant figures; or as 2.20×10^3 to show 3 significant figures.
55	2 significant figures
55.0	3 significant figures. The zero is significant in this case, since it is not otherwise needed to show proper location of the decimal point.

Scientific Presentation of Data 91

In engineering computations it is necessary to use standard computed constants, such as π (3.14159265 . . .) and ϵ (2.71828 . . .). It is feasible to simplify these values to fewer significant figures, since most calculations will be done on the slide rule where five, six, and seven significant figures are impossible to read. Usually three or four significant figures are sufficient, but this may vary somewhat with the nature of the problem. Since we do not need a large number of significant figures, let us examine some rules concerning "rounding off" the excess figures which need not be used in a given calculation.

RETENTION OF SIGNIFICANT FIGURES

1. In recording measured data, only one doubtful digit is retained, and it is considered to be a significant figure.
2. In dropping figures which are not significant, the last figure retained should be increased by 1 if the first figure dropped is 5 or greater.
3. In addition and subtraction, do not carry the result beyond the first column which contains a doubtful figure.
4. In multiplication and division, carry the result to the same number of significant figures that there are in the quantity entering into the calculation which has the least number of significant figures.

Problems

Determine the proper value of X for each problem.

7-1. $0.785 = 7.85(10^x)$
7-2. $0.005066 = 5.066(10^x)$
7-3. $6.45 = 64.5(10^x)$
7-4. $10.764 = 10764(10^x)$
7-5. $1973 = 0.01973(10^x)$
7-6. $0.3937 = 3937000(10^x)$
7-7. $30.48 = 0.03048(10^x)$
7-8. $2.54 = 254(10^x)$
7-9. $1000 = 10(10^x)$
7-10. $0.001 = 1(10^x)$
7-11. $44.2 = 0.442(10^x)$
7-12. $0.737 = 73.7(10^x)$
7-13. $1.093 = 10930(10^x)$
7-14. $4961 = 0.4961(10^x)$
7-15. $1.02 = 0.000102(10^x)$
7-16. $0.0914(10^{-3}) = 9.14(10^x)$
7-17. $745.6(10^4) = 7{,}456{,}000(10^x)$
7-18. $7.78(10^0) = 778(10^x)$
7-19. $14{,}800{,}000(10^{-2}) = 14.8(10^x)$
7-20. $23{,}700{,}000(10^6) = 23.7(10^x)$

Problems

ADDITION OF LABORATORY DATA

Add and then express the answer to the proper number of significant figures.

Engineering: Elementary Problem Analysis

7-21. 18016.
      54980.
         529.
       4406.
      30110.
        540.

7-22. 350.12
      316.70
      110.05
       76.96
       51.17
        8.55

7-23. 7.302
      1.005
      8.188
      4.000
      0.979
      2.673

7-24. 0.3377
      0.6905
      0.2205
      0.7254
      0.9697
      0.8863

7-25. 8.8907
      0.6565
      0.0330
      3.7219
      2.3676
      4.0084

7-26. 0.00657
      0.00430
      0.00201
      0.04583
      0.00297
      0.01644

7-27. 11.565
       4.900
     226.55
      52.824
      17.668
     108.77

7-28. 858.7
     404.3
      54.4
      19.8
       8.77
       2.04

7-29. 1.39395
       8.7755
     10.6050
     49.588
     88.870
    108.887

7-30. 6282.6
     545.81
     407.55
     334.75
      98.88
      28.77
       1.059

7-31. 8.808
     11.955
     35.357
     67.332
    105.65
    575.75

7-32. 0.005754
      0.006434
      0.014466
      0.085405
      0.191876
      0.97574

7-33. 7757.1
      54.540
      11.5
       1.0375
     378.64
    4372.1

7-34. 16.59
       0.0531
      11.72
     285.5
      44.41
       0.0748

7-35. 0.32
    6171.
     255.5
      80.60
     115.55
    3707.

7-36. 17.306
       1.6535
       0.07653
     653.22
      29.969
       0.02202

7-37. 61.309
       1.9792
       0.005531
     122.88
      52.88
      37.075

7-38. 1.0585
     18.08
    675.5
      0.0880
    111.0
    828.

Scientific Presentation of Data

SUBTRACTION OF LABORATORY DATA

Subtract and then express the answer to the proper number of significant figures.

7-39. 6508.
       3377.
	7-45. 7.114
	      10.075
		7-51. 766.07
		      −516.16

7-40. 8.104
       7.881
	7-46. 10276.
	      61552.
		7-52. 0.8280
		      −0.022

7-41. 0.04642
       0.01497
	7-47. 18.72
	      366.01
		7-53. −933.0
		       73.12

7-42. 731.16
       183.28
	7-48. 0.0166
	       0.1515
		7-54. −158.1
		         0.0663

7-43. 6623.2
        974.4
	7-49. 3.686
	      711.001
		7-55. −610.01
		      −355.65

7-44. 0.09755
       0.0188
	7-50. 12.8767
	       42.601
		7-56. −1.9767
		      −113.52

MULTIPLICATION OF LABORATORY DATA

Multiply and then express the answer to the proper number of significant figures.

7-57. 5166.
        238.
	7-63. 14.7400
	       0.7868
		7-69. 1975064.
		         17.6585

7-58. 32105.
          5.26
	7-64. 47.738
	       0.068
		7-70. 1.40069
		      5072.1

7-59. 535.58
         0.2769
	7-65. 15907.
	       0.00469
		7-71. 3510.3595
		        74.229

7-60. 84.676
      30869.
	7-66. −9754
	       0.05478
		7-72. 4.759627
		     −172.659

7-61. 1.03575
      54682.
	7-67. 7.5487
	      −542.16
		7-73. 0.00538395
		     −127403784.

7-62. 0.0548
       0.00376
	7-68. −0.0959
	      −11.6507
		7-74. −796.84207
		       −12.649385

DIVISION OF LABORATORY DATA

Divide and then express the answer to the proper number of significant figures:

7-75. $\dfrac{3928.}{5636.}$ 7-81. $\dfrac{73.65}{127.1}$ 7-87. $\dfrac{669.109}{7.83033}$

7-76. $\dfrac{216.75}{53.83}$ 7-82. $\dfrac{4.91}{1598.}$ 7-88. $\dfrac{0.85352}{172.6040}$

7-77. $\dfrac{7.549}{3.069}$ 7-83. $\dfrac{0.2816}{5383.}$ 7-89. $\dfrac{159.95}{0.003502}$

7-78. $\dfrac{539.77}{1.6303}$ 7-84. $\dfrac{-0.005295}{1728.}$ 7-90. $\dfrac{-2005.5}{0.01109}$

7-79. $\dfrac{0.5322}{0.343}$ 7-85. $\dfrac{0.07737}{-0.1293}$ 7-91. $\dfrac{0.0053022}{-0.00039975}$

7-80. $\dfrac{8831.}{128.75}$ 7-86. $\dfrac{-0.3343}{-52.1}$ 7-92. $\dfrac{-12.54953}{-0.08580}$

CALCULATION OF ERROR

The word "error" is used in engineering work to express the uncertainty in a measured quantity. When used with a measurement, it shows the probable reliability of the quantity involved. *Error*, as used here, does not mean the same as the word "mistake," and care should be exercised to call operations or results which are mathematically incorrect as mistakes and not as errors.

We can express the amount or number of objects by counting, as by counting the number of half-inch bolts in a carton. Such a process is not subject to what we define as error, although the results obtained by counting may contain mistakes. If we count the number of bolts in a container, we should always obtain exactly the same total count. However, if we weigh one bolt, then weigh a carton containing several hundred bolts, and then calculate the number of bolts from the weights, we would not likely get the same result as was achieved by counting, due simply to errors involved in weighing and calculating.

Since the reliability of engineering data is of extreme importance, familiarity with methods of computing probable error is essential. As the student has more opportunity to collect his own data, the need for means of expressing the reliability or uncertainty involved in measured quantities will become even more apparent. While a detailed study of theory of errors is beyond the scope of this book, a general discussion of some of the basic computations of errors is desirable.

Scientific Presentation of Data

Measurement and Error

Experimentation in the laboratory is necessary to verify the engineer's design analysis and to predict results in processes of manufacture. For certain tests the laboratory technician will attempt to secure data to prove the analytical results as predicted by the engineer. At other times emphasis will be directed to routine testing of items for acceptance. In any case, the results obtained in the laboratory will only approximate the true values, and the data tabulated will not be exact. Rather, every measurement taken and every gauge reading or scale deflection noted will reflect the accuracy with which the individual measuring instruments were designed and manufactured—as well as the human errors which may have appeared in the readings.

For example, it is convenient and many times expedient to estimate distances by eye when under other circumstances an unknown distance could be more accurately measured by using a surveyor's tape or perhaps a graduated scale. In a similar manner we may lift a given object and, from experience, estimate its weight. A more accurate procedure would be to weigh it on some type of balance. In general, the more precise the measuring device, the more accurate the measurement obtained.

As we know from practical experience, length, weight, time, etc., can be measured to various degrees of precision, depending upon the accuracy which has been designed into the measuring instrument being used. The engineer must therefore have some method whereby he can evaluate the degree of accuracy which has been obtained in any given measurement. Where a numerical error of plus or minus ($\pm$) 1 in. would not ordinarily make too much difference in a measured distance of 100 miles, the same numerical error (of 1 in.) would cause considerable concern if it occurred in a measured distance of 2 in. For this reason the engineer will frequently express the maximum error present in a measurement as "per cent error" instead of "numerical error."

By "per cent error" is meant how many parts out of each 100 parts that a number is in error. For example, if a yardstick is too long by 0.02 yd, the numerical error is 0.02 yd, the relative error is 0.02 yd in 1.00 yd, and the "per cent error" is therefore 2 per cent. In other words:

$$\text{per cent error} = \frac{(\text{numerical error})(100 \text{ per cent})}{(\text{measured value})}$$

$$\text{per cent error} = \frac{(1.02 - 1.00)(100 \text{ per cent})}{(1.00)} = 2 \text{ per cent}$$

In any measured quantity, the true value is never known. The measured value is usually expressed to the number of digits corresponding to the precision of measurement followed by a number showing the maximum probable error of the measurement. For example, if we measure the length of a desk to be 5.712 feet and we have estimated the last digit, 2, because of our inability to read our measuring device closely, we would need to know what the probable variation in this last digit could be. Assuming that we can estimate to the nearest 0.001 ft, we could show this measurement with its error as

$$5.712 \pm 0.001 \text{ ft}$$

In order to compute the per cent error of our measurement, we proceed as follows:

$$\text{per cent error} = \frac{\text{numerical error} \times 100 \text{ per cent}}{\text{measured value}}$$

$$\text{per cent error} = \frac{0.001 \times 100 \text{ per cent}}{5.712}$$

$$= 0.02 \text{ per cent}$$

The error in measurement could be less than 0.02 per cent, but this shows the maximum probable error in the measurement.

As another example, a measurement can be shown as a number, and a per cent error as

$$7.64 \text{ lb} \pm 0.2 \text{ per cent}$$

To express this measurement as a number and a numerical error, the procedure is as follows:

$$\text{numerical error} = (\text{measured value}) \frac{(\text{per cent error})}{100 \text{ per cent}}$$

$$\text{numerical error} = (7.64) \frac{(0.2 \text{ per cent})}{100 \text{ per cent}}$$

$$= 0.02 \text{ lb}$$

Expressing the measurement as a number,

$$7.64 \pm 0.02 \text{ lb}$$

Problems

(Note that the proper number of significant figures may not be given in the reading.)

Compute the Per Cent Error:

7-93. Reading of 9.306 ± 0.003
7-94. Reading of 19165 ± 2.
7-95. Reading of 756.3 ± 0.7
7-96. Reading of 2.596 ± 0.006
7-97. Reading of 13.750 ± 0.009

Scientific Presentation of Data 97

7-98. Reading of 0.0036 ± 0.0006
7-99. Reading of 0.7515 ± 0.02
7-100. Reading of $12,835 \pm 20$
7-101. Reading of 382.5 ± 5
7-102. Reading of 0.03 ± 0.03

Compute the Numerical Error:

7-103. Reading of 35.219 ± 0.03 per cent
7-104. Reading of 651.79 ± 0.01 per cent
7-105. Reading of 11.391 ± 0.05 per cent
7-106. Reading of 0.00365 ± 2 per cent
7-107. Reading of 0.03917 ± 0.6 per cent
7-108. Reading of 152 ± 4.0 per cent
7-109. Reading of 0.0575 ± 10 per cent
7-110. Reading of $7.65(10^7) \pm 7$ per cent
7-111. Reading of $3.080(10^{-4}) \pm 2.5$ per cent
7-112. Reading of $32.5(10^{-2}) \pm 30$ per cent

7-113. A surveyor measures a property line and records it as being 3207.7 ft long. The distance is probably correct to the nearest 0.3 ft. What is the per cent error in the distance?

7-114. The thickness of a spur gear is specified as 0.875 in. with an allowable variation of 0.3 per cent. Several gears that have been received in an inspection room are gauged, and the thickness measurements are as follows: 0.877, 0.881, 0.874, 0.871, 0.880. Which ones should be rejected as not meeting dimensional specifications?

7-115. A rectangular aluminum pattern is laid out using a steel scale which is thought to be exactly 3 ft long. The pattern was laid out to be 7.42 ft by 1.88 ft, but it was subsequently found that the scale was incorrect and was actually 3.02 ft long. What were the actual pattern dimensions and by what per cent were they in error?

*7-116. A resident of a city feels that his bill for water is considerably too high, probably due to a defective water meter. He proposes to check the meter on a do-it-yourself basis by using a gallon milk bottle to measure a volume of water. He believes that the volume of the bottle is substantially correct and that the error of filling should not exceed plus or minus two tablespoons full.

a. What would be the probable maximum error in gallons per 1000 gal of water using this measurement?
b. Using the milk bottle, he draws ten full bottles of water and observes that the meter indicates a usage of 1.345 ft^3 of water. If the average rate for water is \$1.05 per 1000 ft^3, by how much could his water bill be too high?

chapter eight

Graphs and Curve Plotting

Courtesy Oldsmobile Division, General Motors Corporation

Graphs are an important method of displaying data for rapid visualization of the variations of one quantity with respect to another. In this picture engineers are discussing a curve of measured valve positions in an automobile engine as compared with theoretical curves of cam contours to determine appropriate changes that may be necessary in the manufacture of the cams.

chapter eight

Graphs and Curve Plotting

PREPARATION OF GRAPHS

Graphs are a valuable aid in presenting many types of information where it is important that facts be grasped readily. They aid in the analysis of engineering data and facilitate the presentation of statistical information. Graphs generally may be classified as those used for technical purposes and those used for general presentation of information. To be of greatest value, graphs should be prepared in accord with the best current practice.

A graphical display of information may take any of several forms, depending upon the type of information to be presented and the use to be made of the information. For rapid dissemination of information, pictographs are convenient. Where more exact representation is desired, bar graphs or circle graphs may be employed. Most engineering data are displayed graphically, using line graphs. Such information is usually more exact and offers opportunity to interpolate values, extrapolate values, and to draw conclusions as to the behavior of the variable quantities involved. Examples of several types of graphs are shown in Figs. 8-1 to 8-7.

Since line graphs offer the best opportunity to present engineering data, the discussion here will be concerned chiefly with the preparation and use of line graphs. The general form of the graph sheet illustrated by Fig. 8-6 is the form used by the majority of engineering schools and is the style widely used in industry.

NOTES ON THE PREPARATION OF GRAPHS

1. Graphs usually are prepared in pencil on printed co-ordinate graph paper. Carbon paper backing should be used where sharpness of reproduction is a factor. For more permanent work or for display purposes, India ink should be used.

2. Arrange the data in tabular form for convenience in plotting, and determine the type of scales which will most logically portray the functional relationship between the variables.

3. Graphs are usually designated by naming ordinate values first, then abscissa quantities. It is customary to plot the dependent variable along the ordinate and the independent variable along the abscissa.

4. Make a trial computation to select the scale on each axis.

$$\text{Scale} = \frac{\text{range in the variable}}{\text{scale length available}}$$

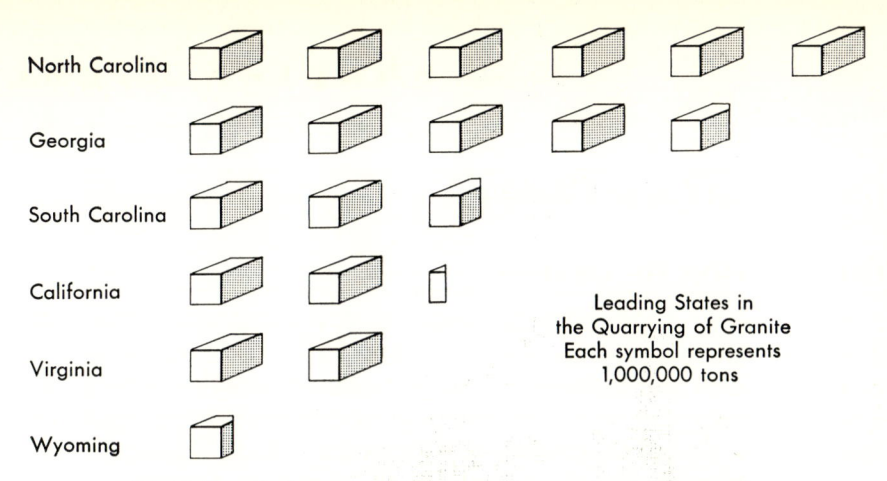

Fig. 8-1. A pictograph (data comparative in nature).

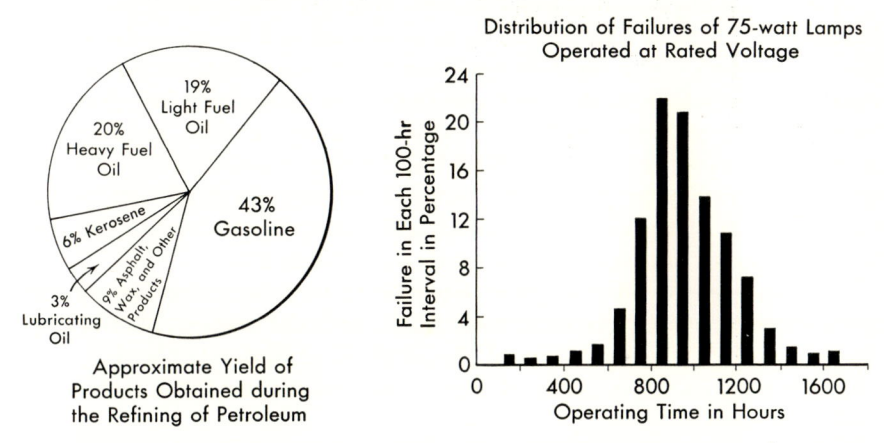

Fig. 8-2. A circle graph (data expressed as parts of a whole).

Fig. 8-3. A vertical bar graph (a family of individual sets of data).

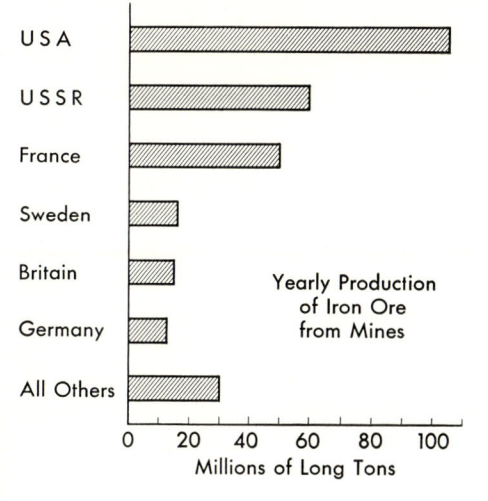

Fig. 8-4. A horizontal bar graph (numerical data).

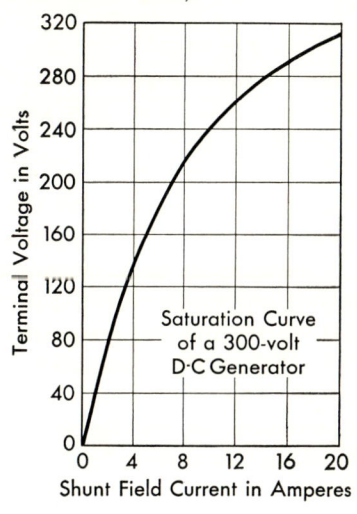

Fig. 8-5. A line graph used for display purposes.

101

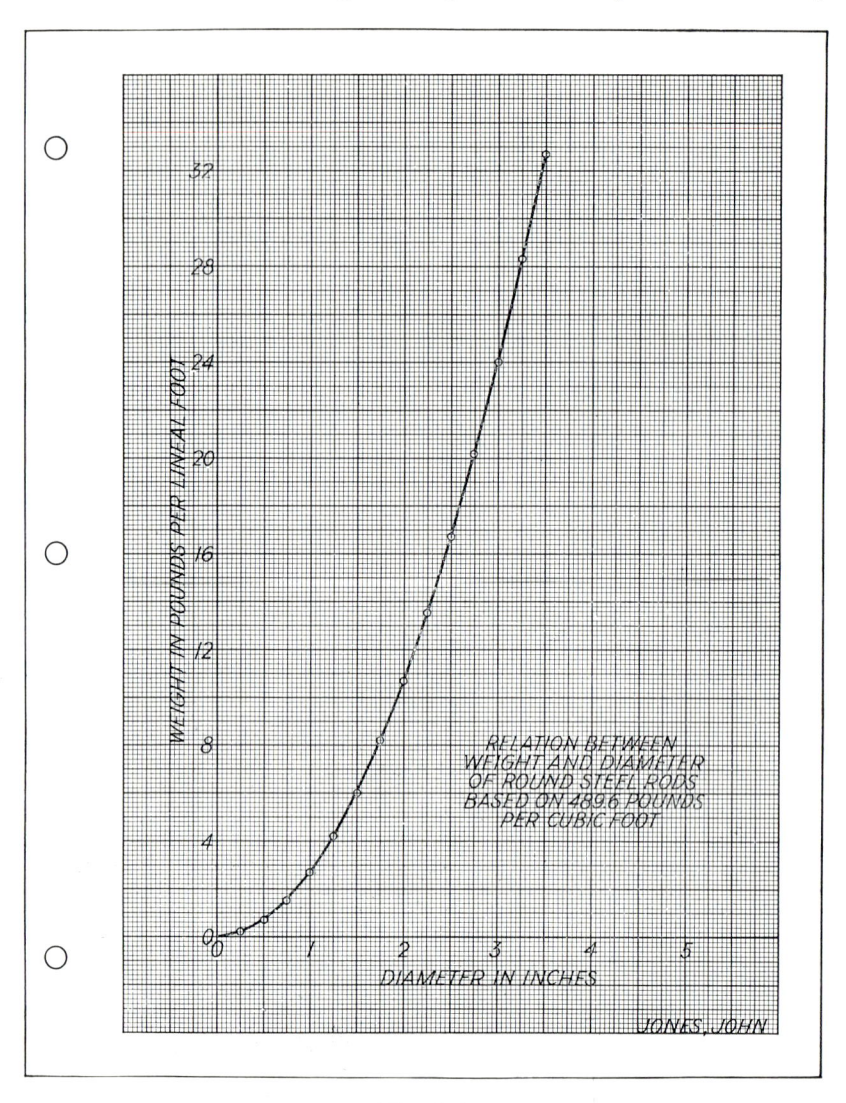

Fig. 8-6

5. The scale must be suitable for the paper used. For graph paper having twenty divisions per inch, scale divisions of 1, 2, 5, 10, or a multiple of these numbers are desirable for ease of plotting and reading. Do not use a scale that will require awkward fractions in the smallest calibration on the paper. The scale should be consistent with the precision of the data. If the numbers are very large or very small, they may be written as a number times ten to a power; for example $(3.22)(10)^{-5}$, or $(7.50)(10)^{6}$.

Graphs and Curve Plotting

6. It is desirable to show zero as the beginning of the ordinate and abscissa quantities unless this would compress the curve unnecessarily. The origin is usually placed in the lower left corner except in cases where both positive and negative values of a function are to be plotted. In such cases the origin should be located so all desired values can be shown.

7. Printed rectangular co-ordinate paper is not normally available with sufficient margins to accommodate the axes and the description of the quantities plotted. Therefore the axes should be drawn in far enough from the edge of the paper to allow for lettering. The sheet may be turned so that the abscissa is along either the short or long side of the paper. If the graph is prepared for a report, the holes in the paper should be either to the left or at the top of the sheet.

8. Lettering is usually three squares, or approximately 3/20 in. high. Either vertical or slant lettering may be used.

9. The ordinate and abscissa variables together with their respective units of measure should be labeled. For example: WEIGHT IN POUNDS

10. The plotted points are fine, tiny dots in pencil. After the points are located, draw a circle, not more than 1/16 in. in diameter, around each point. Where multiple curves are plotted on one sheet, the points for each curve may be identified by using distinctive identification symbols such as squares, triangles, diamonds, or other simple geometric figures. Distinctive line work such as solid line, dashed line, long dash-short dash, etc., may also be used to aid identification.

11. Graphs may be drawn for theoretical relationships, empirical relationships, or measured relationships. Curves of theoretical relationships will not normally have point designations. Empirical relationships should form smooth curves or straight lines, depending upon the form of the mathematical expression used. Datum points in measured relationships, not supported by mathematical theory or empirical relationships, should be connected by straight lines drawn from point to point. Otherwise the data obtained from measured relationships will be drawn to average the plotted points. For this reason curves showing measured data do not necessarily go from center to center of the points.

12. Much experimentally determined data when plotted will show a dispersion of the points about an average position due to the many variable factors entering into the measurement. For this condition draw a smooth curve or a straight line, as the data indicate, which as nearly as possible will average the plotted points. A light pencil freehand line will aid in locating the average, but the final line should be a mechanically drawn line. The example of Fig. 8-7 is taken from an actual test to show the dispersion that may occur.

13. In drawing the final curve do not draw the line through the symbols which enclose the plotted points, but stop at the perimeter.

104   *Engineering: Elementary Problem Analysis*

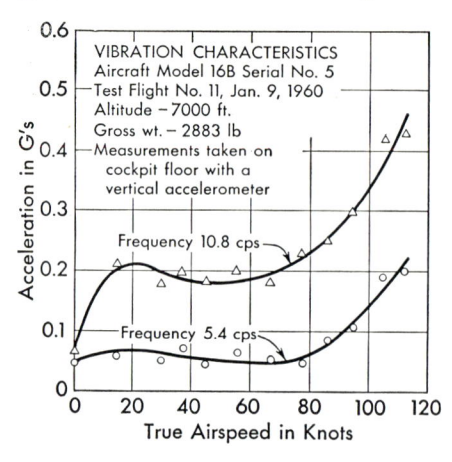

Fig. 8-7. An example of a graph displaying data which were subject to considerable variation. Obviously the curves can be only approximately located. Such curves are sometimes referred to as "paintbrush" curves.

Courtesy General Electric Company

Fig. 8-8. Graphs can be drawn mechanically by specialized curve plotting machines such as this recording photoelectric spectrophotometer which plots curves representing color values onto a strip chart.

14. The title of the graph should include the names of the plotted quantities and should include other descriptive information such as sizes, weights, names of equipment, date that the data were obtained, where data were obtained, serial numbers of apparatus, name of manufacturer of apparatus, and any other information which would help describe the graph.

Graphs and Curve Plotting

15. The title should be placed on the sheet where it will not interfere with the curve. The title section of display graphs is usually placed across the top of the sheet. Simple graphs which comprise parts of reports frequently have the title in either the lower right quadrant or the upper left quadrant.

16. The name of the person preparing the graph and the date the graph is plotted should be placed in the lower right hand corner of the sheet.

Problems on Graphs

8-1. Plot a graph showing the relation of weight to diameter for round steel rods. Plot values for every quarter-inch to and including 3 1/2 in. in diameter. (See model Fig. 8-6, p. 102.)

WEIGHT OF ROUND STEEL RODS
POUNDS PER LINEAL FOOT
(*Based on* 489.6 lb/ft^3)

SIZE IN.	WEIGHT LB/FT	SIZE IN.	WEIGHT LB/FT
¼	0.167	2	10.66
½	0.668	2¼	13.50
¾	1.50	2½	16.64
1	2.68	2¾	20.20
1¼	4.17	3	24.00
1½	6.00	3¼	28.30
1¾	8.18	3½	32.70

8-2. Plot a graph showing the relation of normal barometric pressure of air to altitude. Plot values up to and including 15,000 ft.

ALTITUDE, FEET ABOVE SEA LEVEL	NORMAL BAROMETRIC PRESSURE, INCHES OF MERCURY	ALTITUDE, FEET ABOVE SEA LEVEL	NORMAL BAROMETRIC PRESSURE, INCHES OF MERCURY
0	29.95	5000	24.9
500	29.39	6000	24.0
1000	28.86	7000	23.1
1500	28.34	8000	22.2
2000	27.82	9000	21.4
2500	27.32	10000	20.6
3000	26.82	15000	16.9
4000	25.84		

8-3. Plot a graph showing the relation between horsepower transmitted by cold drawn steel shafting and diameter for a speed of 72 rpm based on the formula:

$$\text{hp} = \frac{D^3 R}{50}$$

where hp = horsepower
 D = diameter of shaft in inches
 R = revolutions per minute of shaft

Calculate and plot values for every inch diameter up to and including 8 in.

8-4. Plot a graph for the following experimental data showing the relation between the period in seconds and the mass of a vibrating spiral spring.

PERIOD IN SECONDS	MASS IN GRAMS	PERIOD IN SECONDS	MASS IN GRAMS
0.246	10	0.650	70
0.348	20	0.740	90
0.430	30	0.810	110
0.495	40	0.900	130
0.570	50	0.950	150

8-5. Using data in Problem 8-4, plot a graph between period squared and mass on a vibrating spring.

8-6. Plot a graph of the variation of the boiling point of water with pressure.

BOILING POINT, DEGREES CENTIGRADE	PRESSURE IN CM OF MERCURY	BOILING POINT, DEGREES CENTIGRADE	PRESSURE IN CM OF MERCURY
33	3.8	98	72.9
44	5.3	102	85.8
63	17.2	105	93.7
79	34.0	107	102.2
87	48.1	110	113.5
94	69.1		

8-7. (a) Plot a graph showing the variation of the following measured values of sliding force with the normal force for a wood block on a horizontal wood surface.

SLIDING FORCE IN GRAMS	NORMAL FORCE IN GRAMS
100	359
130	462
155	555
185	659
210	765
240	859

(b) Determine the slope of the line plotted and compare with the average value of the coefficient of sliding friction obtained from individual readings of normal force and sliding force.

Graphs and Curve Plotting

Slope = tan θ (where θ is the angle that the line makes with the abscissa axis)

$$\tan \theta = \frac{y_2 - y_1}{x_2 - x_1}$$

8-8. Plot the variation of pressure with volume, using data as obtained from a Boyle's law apparatus.

PRESSURE IN CM OF MERCURY	VOLUME IN CM^3	PRESSURE IN CM OF MERCURY	VOLUME IN CM^3
50.3	23.2	76.8	15.1
52.5	22.4	79.7	14.7
54.5	21.5	82.7	14.1
56.9	20.9	84.2	13.6
59.4	19.6	87.9	13.2
63.0	18.5	90.6	12.8
65.3	17.8	93.5	12.5
67.2	17.3	95.7	12.3
72.6	16.1	101.9	11.4
74.5	15.6		

8-9. Using data in Problem 8-8, plot a graph of the relation between the pressure and the reciprocal of the volume.

8-10. Plot the relation between magnetic flux density in kilolines per square centimeter (*B*) and magnetizing force in gilberts per centimeter (*H*) for a specimen of tool steel. This graph will form what is customarily called a *B-H* curve.

B KILOLINES PER CM^2	H GILBERTS PER CM	B KILOLINES PER CM^2	H GILBERTS PER CM
9.00	27.1	14.66	189.7
11.80	54.2	14.86	216.8
13.02	81.3	14.98	243.9
13.75	108.4	15.23	271.0
14.09	135.5	15.35	298.1
14.22	162.6	15.57	325.2

8-11. The formula for converting temperatures in degrees Fahrenheit to the equivalent reading in degrees centigrade is:

$$C° = \tfrac{5}{9}(F° - 32°)$$

Plot a graph so that by taking any given Fahrenheit reading between 0° and 220° and using the graph, the corresponding centigrade reading can be determined.

8-12. Plot a graph showing the relation between drill speed and size of drill for carbon steel drills in brass.

DIAMETER OF DRILL IN INCHES	DRILL SPEED IN RPM	DIAMETER OF DRILL IN INCHES	DRILL SPEED IN RPM
1/16	6112	5/8	612
1/8	3056	11/16	555
3/16	2036	3/4	508
1/4	1528	13/16	474
5/16	1222	7/8	438
3/8	1018	15/16	407
7/16	874	1	382
1/2	764	1 1/16	359
9/16	679	1 1/8	340

8-13. Plot a graph showing the variation of temperature with electric current through a heating coil, using the following data which were taken in the laboratory.

CURRENT IN AMPERES	TEMPERATURE CHANGE IN DEGREES CENTIGRADE
0.0	0.0
0.46	0.5
1.05	1.2
1.50	2.0
2.06	5.1
2.20	7.7
2.35	8.8

8-14. The following data were taken in the laboratory for a 16-cp, carbon-filament electric light bulb. Plot a resistance-voltage curve.

VOLTAGE IN VOLTS	RESISTANCE IN OHMS	VOLTAGE IN VOLTS	RESISTANCE IN OHMS
10	169.5	70	114.5
20	140.0	80	113.2
30	129.0	90	112.5
40	121.5	100	111.8
50	117.0	110	111.2
60	113.2		

8-15. The following data were taken in the laboratory for a 60-watt, gas-filled, tungsten-filament light bulb. Plot a resistance-voltage curve.

VOLTAGE IN VOLTS	RESISTANCE IN OHMS	VOLTAGE IN VOLTS	RESISTANCE IN OHMS
10	47.5	70	160.2
20	77.5	80	170.0
30	100.3	90	178.3
40	119.0	100	189.0
50	132.6	110	200.1
60	144.2		

Graphs and Curve Plotting

8-16. The equation which expresses the variations of electric current with time in an inductive circuit is

$$i = I_0 \epsilon^{(-Rt)/L}$$

where i is the current in amperes.

I_0 is the original steady-state value of current and is a constant.
ϵ is the base of the natural system of logarithms and is approximately 2.7183.
R is the resistance in ohms in the circuit and is constant.
t is the time in seconds measured as the current i varies.
L is the inductance in henries and is a constant.

Let
$$I_0 = 0.16 \text{ amp}$$
$$R = 1.2 \text{ ohms}$$
$$L = 0.5 \text{ henry}$$

Calculate and plot values of i as t varies from 0 to 0.5 sec.

8-17. Plot the variations of efficiency with load for a 1/4-hp, 110-volt, direct-current electric motor, using the following data taken in the laboratory.

LOAD OUTPUT IN HORSEPOWER	EFFICIENCY IN PER CENT
0	0
0.019	24.0
0.050	42.0
0.084	44.9
0.135	50.7
0.175	56.5
0.195	58.0
0.248	59.1
0.306	58.0
0.326	56.2

PLOTTING ON SEMI-LOGARITHMIC GRAPH PAPER

The preceding discussion has concerned the graphing of data on rectangular coordinate paper. There are cases where the variation of the data is such that it may be desirable to compress the larger values of a variable. To do this, semi-logarithmic graph paper may be used. Semi-log paper, as it is usually called, is graph paper which has one co-ordinate ruled in equal increments and the other co-ordinate ruled in increments which are logarithmically expressed. When plotting on this type of paper, it may be turned so that either the horizontal co-ordinate or the vertical co-ordinate will have the logarithmic divisions. Semi-log paper is available in either one-cycle, two-cycle, three-cycle, four-cycle, or five-cycle ruling.

A semi-log grid is especially useful in the derivation of relationships where it is difficult to analyze the rate of change or trend as depicted on rectangular co-ordinate paper. Data that will plot as a curve on rectangular co-ordinate paper may plot as a straight line on semi-log paper. In many instances this is desirable because the trends are more easily detected. Where straight lines do not occur on a semi-log grid, the rate of change is varying.

The same rules apply for plotting on semi-log paper as were given for rectangular co-ordinate paper, except that the numbering of the logarithmic

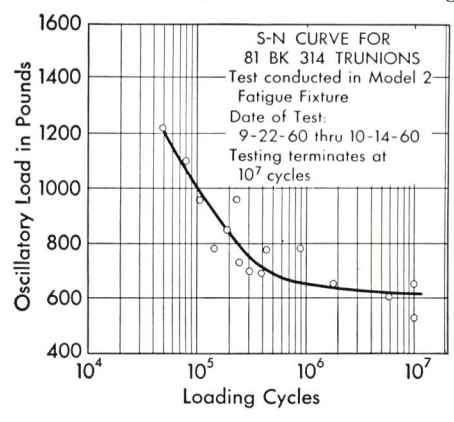

Fig. 8-9

divisions cannot begin with zero. Each cycle on the paper represents a multiple of ten in value, and the graduations may begin with any power of ten. When reading from a logarithmic graph, interpolations should be made logarithmically rather than arithmetically. An example of data plotted on semi-log paper is shown in Fig. 8-9.

PLOTTING ON LOG-LOG GRAPH PAPER

Log-log graph paper, as its name indicates, has both co-ordinate divisions expressed as logarithmic functions. This subdivision of the sheet serves to compress the larger values of the plotted data. In addition, data that plotted as a curve on rectangular co-ordinate paper may plot as a straight line on log-log paper. For example, the graphs of algebraic equations representing multiplication, division, powers, and roots may be straight lines on log-log paper.

As an example, the plot of the algebraic expression

$$X = Y^2$$

on rectangular co-ordinate paper is a parabola. However, if its values are plotted on log-log paper, it is equivalent to taking the logarithm of the expression.

$$\log X = 2(\log Y)$$

Fig. 8-10

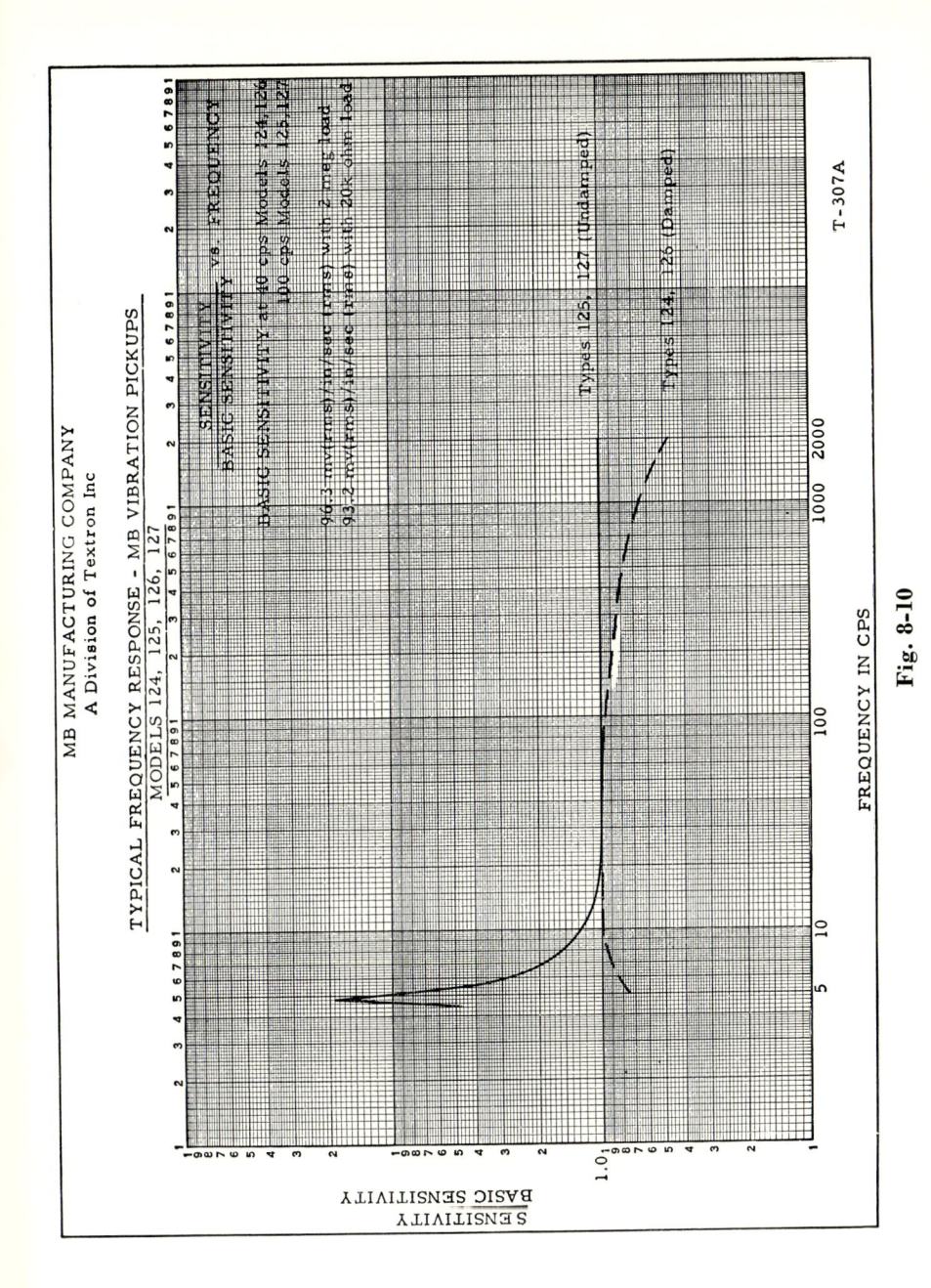

This expression has the form of a linear equation having a slope of 2. Thus, a relationship of variable quantities that may be expressed as $X = Y^2$ when plotted on log-log paper will be a straight line with a slope of 2.

Log-log paper may be secured in 8 1/2 by 11-in. or larger sheets which have one or more cycles for each co-ordinate direction. The axis lines are drawn on the sheet in a manner similar to the procedure described for plotting on rectangular co-ordinate paper. However, the beginning values for the axes will never be zero but will always be a power of ten.

An example of data plotted on log-log paper is shown in Fig. 8-10.

PLOTTING ON POLAR GRAPH PAPER

Polar graphs are sometimes used where a variable quantity is to be examined with respect to various angular positions. The same general principles of plotting apply as were outlined for rectangular plots except that the outer border is marked off in degrees for the independent variable, and either the horizontal or vertical radial line is marked off for the dependent variable.

Polar graphs frequently are used to display the light output of luminous sources, the response of microphone pickups, and the behavior of rotating objects at various angular positions. An example of a graph plotted on polar co-ordinate paper is shown in Fig. 8-11.

DETERMINING EMPIRICAL EQUATIONS FROM CURVES

Experimentally determined data when plotted usually will approximate a straight line or a simple curve. By plotting experimentally determined data, it is frequently possible to obtain a mathematical equation which closely expresses the relations of the variables.

Many equations encountered in engineering work have the form

$$y - k = m(x - h)^n$$

where n may have either positive or negative values. If the exponent n is 1, the equation reduces to the familiar straight-line slope-intercept form. If the value of n is positive, the equation is a parabolic type, but if the value of n is negative, the equation is a hyperbolic type. This expression affords a means of securing empirical equations from experimental data.

If experimental data are to be plotted and an empirical equation is to be determined, it is advisable first to plot the test data on rectangular co-ordinate paper in order to gain some idea of the shape of the graph. If the locus approximates a straight line, the general equation $y = mx + b$ may be assumed. The Y-intercept b and the slope m may be measured by taking a straight line drawn so as to average the plotted points.

Graphs and Curve Plotting

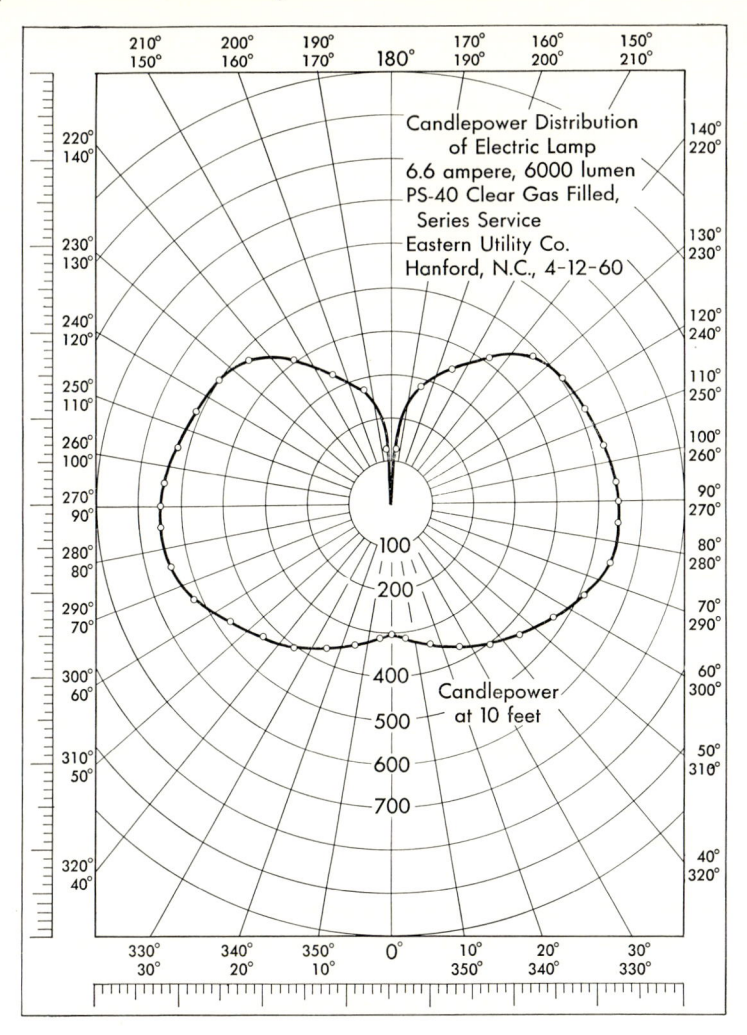

Fig. 8-11

Figure 8-12 is a plot of data taken in the laboratory for a test involving the magnitude of frictional forces.

A straight line is drawn to average the plotted points, and the slope of the line is found by taking any two points along the line and determining the X-component and the Y-component between the two points according to the plotted scales. In this example the slope is approximately 65/500, or 0.13. If the line is projected to the Y-axis, corresponding to a value of $x = 0$, the Y-intercept is seen to correspond approximately to 14 lb. An approximate equation of these data would be $y = 0.13x + 14$.

114   *Engineering: Elementary Problem Analysis*

If a plot of experimental data on rectangular co-ordinate paper should appear to be approximately parabolic in shape, an empirical equation may be obtained by plotting the datum points on log-log paper. The slope of the line determines the exponent of the independent variable, and the Y-intercept, when $x = 1$, defines the coefficient of the independent variable.

For example, a plot of data taken in the laboratory is shown in Fig. 8-13.

A straight line is drawn to average the plotted points. Using a linear scale, measure the X-component and Y-component values for two points on the plotted line. The slope of the graph in Fig. 8-13 is 2.2/2.0, or 1.1, and

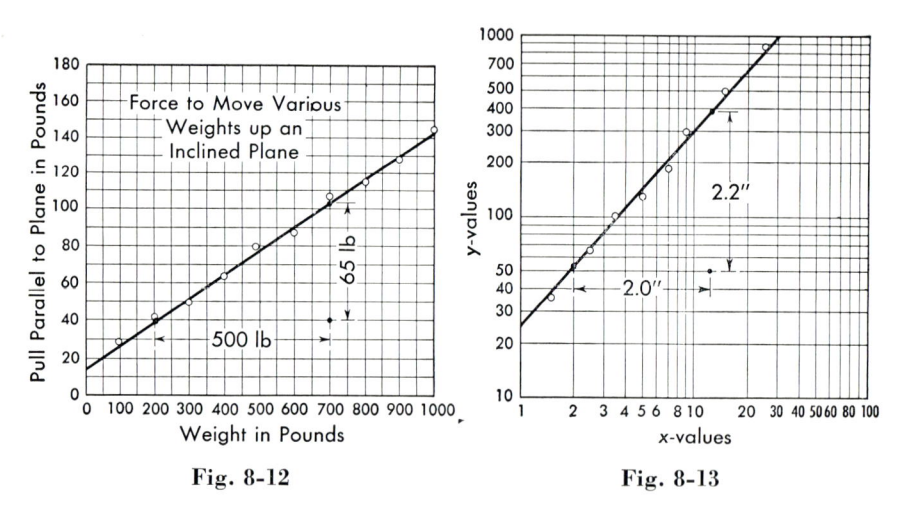

Fig. 8-12

Fig. 8-13

the Y-intercept is 23.3. Substituting these values in the basic equation of a parabola gives $y = 23.3(x^{1.1})$ for the approximate equation.

In case the plotted points on log-log paper curve upward as x increases, the expression may approximate the form $y = ax^n + k$. To straighten the curve, try subtracting a constant from the y-values. By trial and error a value of k may be found which will cause the plot to follow a straight line. If this is done, the approximate equation may be determined.

If log-log paper is not available, it is still possible to use rectangular co-ordinate paper to plot a curve as a straight line. If the data indicate the equation may be of the form $y = ax^n$, we can take the logarithm of the equation and plot logarithmic values for the datum points. For example, if we express $y = ax^n$ in logarithmic form, it will be $\log y = \log a + n \log x$. Let $v = \log y$; $C = \log a$; and $u = \log x$. The straight line equation will then be

$$v = nu + C$$

Plot the logarithm of the data values on rectangular co-ordinate paper. Measure the slope and the Y-intercept. Assume that the slope is measured to be 1.8, using the scales of the plot, and the Y-intercept is 0.755. The

Graphs and Curve Plotting

straight line equation is

$$v = 1.8u + 0.755$$
or
$$\log y = 1.8 \log x + 0.755$$
Since
$$C = \log a = 0.755$$
then
$$a = 5.69$$

The equation then is
$$y = 5.69(x^{1.8})$$

There are other methods of determining empirical equations, such as the method of least squares, but a complete discussion of such techniques is beyond the scope of this book. Also, data that plot into curves following harmonic laws or exponential laws are not discussed here.

NOMOGRAPHS

Nomographs are a pictorial method of solving problems which involve equations of various types. Nomographs consist of scales graduated so that

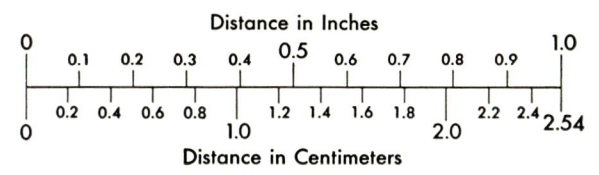

Fig. 8-14

distances are proportional to the variables involved. A simple example would be a single line having graduations corresponding to inches on one side and graduations corresponding to centimeters on the other (see Fig. 8-14).

The layout of nomographs is beyond the scope of this book, but since the solution to problems involving repeated readings of process or laboratory data may be obtained readily by use of nomographs, a brief discussion of the types and uses of the charts is presented.

Figure 8-14 is an example of a *functional chart*. Charts of this type are frequently used when two variables are related by a constant coefficient.

An *alignment chart* is another example of a nomograph. A simple form consists of three parallel lines graduated so that a straight line passing through points on two of the graduated lines will intersect the third graduated line at a point that will satisfy the relations between the variables (see Fig. 8-15).

Example: Given an alignment chart for the equation $x + y = z$. Solve for the value of z when $x = 4$ and $y = 2$.

Solution: Lay out a straight line connecting the point on the x-scale corresponding to 4 and the point on the y-scale corresponding to 2. The intersection of this line with the z-scale at 6 is a solution to this problem.

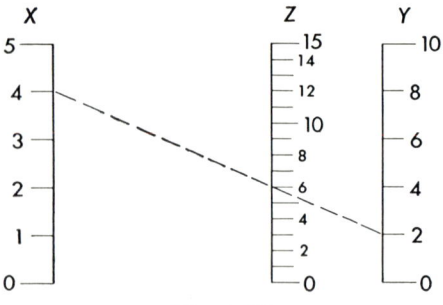

Fig. 8-15

Repeating this procedure with other values will enable one to locate the position of the z-scale with regard to the x- and y-scales.

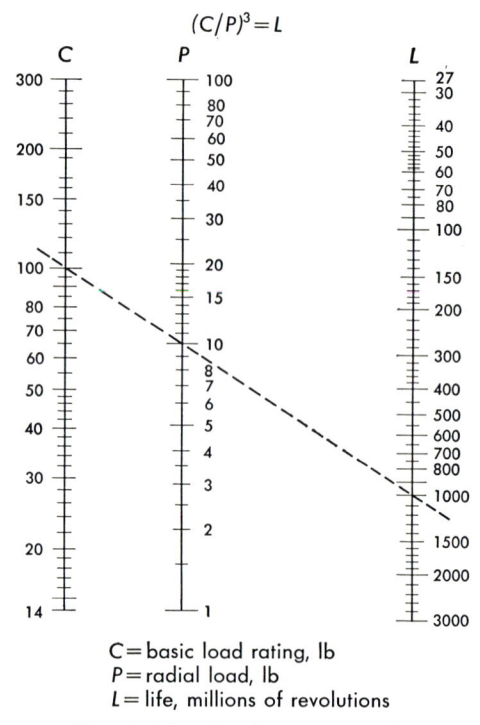

$$(C/P)^3 = L$$

C = basic load rating, lb
P = radial load, lb
L = life, millions of revolutions

Fig. 8-16. Load nomograph.

Another form of alignment chart that is of considerable use is the Z-chart, so named because the center graduated line runs diagonally. It may be set up to provide a solution to equations of the form $x = (y)(z)$. Other alignment charts may provide solutions to problems having three or four variable quantities by employing multiple interior graduated lines.

Alignment charts are all used in the same manner; that is, a straight line

Graphs and Curve Plotting

connects two points on the graduated lines and intersects another graduated line, thereby providing a solution to a given problem.

As an example, the nomograph given in Fig. 8-16 permits an evaluation of factors concerned with the life of a ball bearing. The straight line drawn across the chart shows that for a basic load rating of 100 lb and a radial load of 10 lb, the expected service life of the ball bearing should be 1000 million revolutions.

Problems

8-18. Plot the values given in Problem 8-1, page 105, on semi-log paper.
8-19. Plot the values given in Problem 8-4, page 106, on semi-log paper.
8-20. Plot the values given in Problem 8-8, page 107, on semi-log paper.
8-21. Plot the values given in Problem 8-16, page 109, on semi-log paper.
8-22. Plot the values given in Problem 8-1, page 105, on log-log paper.
8-23. Plot the values given in Problem 8-3, page 105, on log-log paper.
8-24. Plot the values given in Problem 8-8, page 107, on log-log paper.

Determine the slope of the line and give the approximate form of the equation shown by the plot.

8-25. The following data were taken from an acoustical and electrical calibration curve for a Type 1126 microphone. The test was run with an incident sound level of 85 db perpendicular to the face of the microphone.

FREQUENCY IN CPS	RELATIVE RESPONSE IN DB
20	-40
50	-29
100	-19
400	-5
1,000	$+1$
2,000	$+1$
3,000	0
6,000	-4
10,000	-11

Plot a graph on semi-log paper showing the decibel response with frequency.

8-26. The electrical frequency response of a Type X501 microphone is given below.

FREQUENCY IN CPS	RELATIVE RESPONSE IN DB
20	−40
40	−33
80	−22
100	−18
200	−11
400	−5
600	−2
1,000	+1
2,000	+2
4,000	−1
6,000	−4
10,000	−10

Plot a graph on semi-log paper showing the decibel response with frequency.

8-27. The variation of sensitivity of a Model 932 vibration sensing unit with frequency is given below. The basic sensitivity is taken as 96.3 mv (rms) with a 2-megohm load

FREQUENCY IN CPS	RATIO OF SENSITIVITY AT VARIOUS FREQUENCIES TO BASIC SENSITIVITY
4.0	4.6
4.8	19.0
5.0	11.0
6.0	2.7
7.0	1.9
8.0	1.6
10	1.3
20	1.05
40	1.00
80	0.98
100	0.97
300	0.85
600	0.76
1000	0.66
2000	0.46

Plot sensitivity against frequency on three-cycle log-log paper.

Graphs and Curve Plotting

8-28. According to recommendations of the Thrust Bearing Engineers Committee, bearing loads for bearings lubricated with oil having a viscosity range of 115 to 165 Saybolt sec at 100°F should fall between values given in tables below.

SPEED IN RPS	BEARING LOAD IN LB
10	400
100	170
1,000	74
10,000	32
40,000	20
10	1,700
100	650
1,000	275
10,000	123
40,000	70

Plot graphs of bearing loads against speeds on log-log paper to show the range of acceptable operating speeds.

8-29. A series of test specimens of a crank arm, part No. 466-1, were tested for the number of cycles needed to produce fatigue failure at various loadings. The results of the tests are tabulated below.

SPECIMEN NUMBER	OSCILLATORY LOAD IN LB	OPERATING CYCLES TO PRODUCE FAILURE
1	960	1.1×10^5
2	960	2.2×10^5
3	850	1.5×10^5
4	850	2.4×10^5
5	800	4.2×10^5
6	800	6.0×10^5
7	700	2.4×10^5
8	700	3.1×10^5
9	700	5.1×10^5
10	650	1.8×10^6
11	650	2.6×10^6
12	600	7.7×10^6
13	550	1.0×10^7

Plot a graph of load against operating cycles (*S-N* curve) on semi-log paper for the above tests.

8-30. A test on an acorn-type street lighting unit shows the mean vertical candlepower distribution to be as given in the table below.

MID-ZONE ANGLE DEGREES	CANDLEPOWER AT 10 FT	MID-ZONE ANGLE DEGREES	CANDLEPOWER AT 10 FT
180	0	85	156
175	0	75	1110
165	0	65	1050
155	1.5	55	710
145	3.5	45	575
135	5.5	35	500
125	8.5	25	520
115	13.5	15	470
105	22.0	5	370
95	40.0	0	370

Plot the above data on polar co-ordinate paper. (While data for only half the plot are given, the other half of the plot may be made from symmetry of the light pattern.)

8-31. The candlepower distribution of a 400-watt, Type J-H1 fluorescent lamp used for street light service was measured with a photometer, and the following data were obtained:

MID-ZONE ANGLE DEGREES	CANDLEPOWER AT 10 FT	MID-ZONE ANGLE DEGREES	CANDLEPOWER AT 10 FT
180	0	75	7700
165	0	72	8600
145	0	65	7100
135	3	55	5300
125	20	45	4300
115	100	35	3500
105	700	25	2700
95	1200	15	2300
85	3000	5	2100
		0	2000

Plot the above data on polar co-ordinate paper. (While data for only half the plot are given, the other half of the plot may be made from symmetry of the light pattern.)

Graphs and Curve Plotting

8-32. A Weather Bureau report gives the following data on the temperature over a 24-hr period for October 12.

MIDNIGHT	47°	2 PM	73°
2 AM	46°	4 PM	75°
4 AM	44°	6 PM	63°
6 AM	43°	8 PM	58°
8 AM	49°	10 PM	57°
10 AM	55°	MIDNIGHT	57°
NOON	68°		

Plot the above data on polar co-ordinate paper.

8-33. From data determined by the student, draw a circle chart (pie graph) to show one of the following.

    a. Consumption of sulfur by various industries in the United States.
    b. Budget allocation of the tax dollar in your state.
    c. Chemical composition of bituminous coal.
    d. Production of aluminum ingots by various countries.

8-34. Make a bar chart showing the number of men students registered in your school for each of the past ten years.

8-35. Plot the following data and determine an empirical equation for the plotted points:

X:	100	200	300	400	500	600	700	800	900
Y:	0.25	0.38	0.53	0.66	0.79	0.90	1.06	1.17	1.30

8-36. Determine the empirical equation, using the following data which were taken in the laboratory for a test involving accelerated motion:

t:	5	10	20	40	60	80	100
s:	0.93	5.6	32	175	490	989	17,600

8-37. Laboratory data taken on an adjustable time-delay relay show the following values:

Dial index settings D:	2	4	6	8	10
Seconds delay time T:	0.124	0.084	0.063	0.026	0.014

Find an empirical equation to express the data.

8-38. The following data were recorded during a laboratory test of a system of gears. Find an empirical equation to express the data.

| Applied force F: | 11.0 | 13.0 | 21.5 | 26.0 | 34.0 | 39.0 | 41.0 | 49.0 | 50.5 |
| Weight lifted W: | 135 | 180 | 210 | 345 | 275 | 310 | 340 | 370 | 400 |

8-39. Data taken on a laboratory test involving pressure-volume relations of a gas are as follows:

| P: | 14.6 | 17.5 | 20.9 | 25.0 | 29.0 | 33.6 | 39.0 | 45.5 |
| V: | 26.4 | 22.3 | 19.1 | 16.3 | 14.1 | 12.2 | 10.5 | 9.2 |

Determine an empirical equation for the data.

8-40. Determine an empirical equation to express data given in Problem 8-2, page 105.

8-41. Determine an empirical equation that will express data given in Problem 8-4, page 106.

8-42. Plot a graph on rectangular co-ordinate paper of $N = (1.296)^x$ for values of x from -9.0 to $+9.0$ in 0.5 increments.

8-43. Plot a graph on rectangular co-ordinate paper of the equation $N = (0.813)^x$ for values of x from -9.0 to $+9.0$ in 0.5 increments.

8-44. Using the nomograph of Fig. 8-16, what will be the allowable radial load on a ball bearing if the basic load rating is 22 lb and the expected life of the bearing is to be $1.4(10)^8$ revolutions?

8-45. Construct a functional scale about 6 in. long that will relate temperatures in degrees Fahrenheit and degrees centigrade for the range of $-40°C$ to $100°C$.

8-46. Construct a functional scale about 10 in. long that will show the relation between the diameter and circumference of a circle for values of diameter from 2 to 9 in.

chapter nine

Mathematical Tools Useful in Problem Solving

Courtesy of Atomics International, a Division of North American Aviation, Inc.

Algebra is the basis for all forms of higher mathematics. Its principles must be mastered before one can proceed to the analysis of practical problems which involve such advanced mathematical techniques as shown here.

chapter nine

Mathematical Tools Useful in Problem Solving

A large part of the work of an engineer is of a mathematical nature, which means that a thorough knowledge of the uses and applications of mathematics is a necessary tool for the engineer. Since students begin college engineering courses with a variety of backgrounds in high school mathematics, it is advisable that a review of high school mathematics be given to refresh and fill in gaps in the student's mathematical knowledge.

The transition from high school to college is quite a jump for many students—both in the type of work to be performed and in the effort to be expended. Unfortunately some high schools do not offer a vigorous mathematical curriculum, and the student, while he may be pleased at the time he is in high school, finds when he gets to college that he lacks skill in mathematical manipulations.

It is the intention of the authors in presenting this section to offer representative types of problems for the student to solve so that he may check himself on his high school mathematics. It is not intended as a comprehensive course or as an intensive review. The student is advised to notice the sections in which he is having the greatest difficulty and arrange for extra practice to improve his proficiency. Above all the student is cautioned not to allow himself to rush through these problems and hope he will not encounter them again, for it is upon the principles established by high school mathematics that the greater part of higher mathematics is based.

A—ALGEBRA

FACTOR

9-1. $b^2 + 4b + 4$
9-2. $x^2 - a^2$
9-3. $36c^2f^2 - 25w^2$
9-4. $cx + x + c^2x$
9-5. $b^2 - \dfrac{1}{9}$
9-6. $a - 3ab - 5a^2$
9-7. $-x^3 - x^2$
9-8. $49Z^2X^2 - 126a^2b^2$
9-9. $2cy - y + b^2y$
9-10. $-ax + 3cx - x^2$
9-11. $6m^2 + 5m + 1$
9-12. $15w^2 + 22w + 8$
9-13. $5h^2 - 9h - 2$
9-14. $R^2 + 3R + 2$
9-15. $2N^2 - 5N + 3$

REMOVE THE PARENTHESES

9-16. $-(7 + 3w)$
9-17. $-(304c)$
9-18. $7(1 + 2k)$
9-19. $-2(3 - 6b)$
9-20. $-3(-2 - 4m)$
9-21. $0.8d(4d + 6)$

Mathematical Tools Useful in Problem Solving

9-22. $2x - (4x - 1)$
9-23. $-(b - 3) - [2b - (b - 2)]$
9-24. $-[2r + (3 - 4r)]$
9-25. $-[3B - (5 - 6B)]$
9-26. $-(-9 - 3b) - (2b - 3)$

9-27. $150 + 1.27x + 0.12 + x$
9-28. $0.89 - (9 + 6) - 2.96$
9-29. $d - (9 - 5d) - 2 + 3$
9-30. $4 + (-6) - 2 + 3$
9-31. $0.61(-3c + 0.31)$

SIMPLIFY

9-32. $\dfrac{4a^2 - ab}{a}$

9-33. $\dfrac{180h - 16}{4}$

9-34. $\dfrac{(16c^2 - 4cb)}{(4c - b)}$

9-35. $\dfrac{18d + 4e}{-2}$

9-36. $\dfrac{15.6h + 3.9h^2 b}{h}$

SOLVE FOR THE VALUE OF x

9-37. $3x = 5$
9-38. $2x = 18$
9-39. $\dfrac{x}{2} = 7$
9-40. $\dfrac{x}{3} = 7$
9-41. $\dfrac{3}{x} = 7$
9-42. $3 = \dfrac{7}{x}$
9-43. $3 = 7x$
9-44. $3x + 3 = 5$
9-45. $3.1x - 5.2 = 100$
9-46. $0.008 + 0.011 = 5.5x$

9-47. $18x + 6x = 5 + x$
9-48. $12 + \dfrac{x}{2} = 17$
9-49. $\dfrac{x}{3} + \dfrac{x}{7} = 55$
9-50. $x + \dfrac{x}{10} = 10 + x$
9-51. $\dfrac{1}{x} = 20$
9-52. $37x + x = 22$
9-53. $5x + 3 = 2x$
9-54. $2x - x = 1$
9-55. $4x + 12 = 0$
9-56. $12.2 = x + 3.5x$

SOLVE FOR a AND b

9-57. $3a + 4b = 21$

9-58. $\dfrac{2}{a} + \dfrac{1}{b} = \dfrac{1}{6}$

$\dfrac{2}{a} - \dfrac{3}{b} = \dfrac{4}{5}$

9-59. $5b + 3a = \dfrac{1}{2}$

$2a - b = \dfrac{1}{4}$

9-60. $6a + 6b = 6$

$5b - 2a = 1\dfrac{1}{2}$

9-61. $32 - 3b = -8$
9-62. $6a - 7b = 26$

$16b - 8a = -8$

9-63. $7b + 3a = 26$

$a - b = 42$

9-64. $18b - 16a = 13$

$b - a = -16$

Laws of Exponents

The following laws of exponents hold, providing a is a positive number and m and n are real numbers:

I. $(a^m)(a^n) = a^{m+n}$ **Examples:** a. $(2^3)(2)^4 = (2)^{4+3} = (2)^7 = 128$
b. $(x^5)(x)^{-3} = (x)^{5+(-3)} = x^2$

II. $\dfrac{a^m}{a^n} = a^{m-n}$ **Examples:** a. $\dfrac{(3)^6}{(3)^2} = (3)^{6-2} = (3)^4 = 81$
b. $\dfrac{y^9}{y^5} = (y)^{9-5} = (y)^4$

III. $(a^m)^n = (a)^{mn}$ **Examples:** a. $(4^2)^3 = (4)^{3 \times 2} = (4)^6 = 4096$
b. $(x^3)^8 = (x)^{3 \times 8} = x^{24}$

IV. $a^{-n} = \dfrac{1}{a^n}$ **Examples:** a. $(3)^{-2} = \dfrac{1}{(3)^2} = \dfrac{1}{9}$
b. $(x)^{-5} = \dfrac{1}{(x)^5}$

V. $a^0 = 1$ **Examples:** a. $(5)^0 = 1$
b. $(y)^0 = 1$

VI. $(abc)^n = a^n b^n c^n$ **Examples:** a. $(xyz)^3 = x^3 y^3 z^3$
b. $[(2)(3)(4)]^2 = (2)^2(3)^2(4)^2 = 576$

VII. $\left(\dfrac{a}{b}\right)^n = \dfrac{a^n}{b^n}$ **Examples:** a. $\left(\dfrac{2}{3}\right)^3 = \dfrac{(2)^3}{(3)^3} = \dfrac{8}{27}$
b. $\left(\dfrac{3}{5}\right)^2 = \dfrac{(3)^2}{(5)^2} = \dfrac{9}{25}$

VIII. $\sqrt[n]{a} = a^{\frac{1}{n}}$ **Example:** $\sqrt[3]{27} = (27)^{\frac{1}{3}} = 3$

IX. $\sqrt[n]{a^m} = a^{\frac{m}{n}}$ **Example:** $\sqrt[3]{a^5} = a^{\frac{5}{3}}$

Exponent Problems

Some of these problems may be simplified merely by removing parentheses and collecting terms. Others are simple exponent problems and should be solved by using the laws of exponents as given in previous instructions.

SOLVE

9-65. $a^9 a^3$
9-66. $x^4 x^5$
9-67. $z^5 z^6$
9-68. $(b^2)^4$
9-69. $(bc)^4$
9-70. $(x^3)^2$
9-71. $(cx)^7$

9-72. $(y^4)^3$
9-73. $(ef)^3$
9-74. $aa^3 a^4$
9-75. $(x^3 x^2)$
9-76. $y^4 y y^3$
9-77. $(b^2 c^m)$
9-78. $(a^3 b)^2$

9-79. $(xm^x)^4$
9-80. $\dfrac{x^5}{x^3}$
9-81. $\dfrac{x^7}{x^9}$
9-82. $\dfrac{b^3}{b^6}$

Mathematical Tools Useful in Problem Solving

9-83. $\left(\dfrac{5}{6}\right)^0$

9-84. $\left(\dfrac{5}{e}\right)^3$

9-85. $\left(\dfrac{y}{2}\right)^5$

9-86. $\left(\dfrac{e^5}{e^2}\right)^3$

9-87. $(3a)^4$

9-88. $(5x)^2$

9-89. $\dfrac{a^3}{a^8}$

9-90. $\dfrac{x^9}{x}$

9-91. $(-a6^3)^5$

9-92. $\left(\dfrac{x^3}{3}\right)^3$

9-93. $(-3h^3)^3$

9-94. $(-5a^2)^3$

9-95. $(-7a^3)^5$

9-96. $(-3bc^3)^4$

9-97. $(-2b)^5$

9-98. $(2x^n y^c)^m$

9-99. $a^r a^s a^n$

9-100. $(x^3 y^2)^k$

9-101. $3x^3(xy^k)^4$

9-102. $(c^k)^0$

9-103. $\dfrac{4ab^3}{6ab}$

9-104. $sn^x(s^3 n^y)$

9-105. $-ax^4(-3a^4 x)$

9-106. $2c^3 d(3c^s d^2)^3$

9-107. $3x^3(4x^4 y)^2$

9-108. $-9x^3 y^4 (3yx^{-4})^3$

9-109. $-3a^2 b^2 c^2 (-3a^{-3} b^3 c^2)^3$

9-110. $a^n b^n (-4b^{3n} a^{2n})^3$

9-111. $c^n x^m (x^{n-m} c^{m-n})$

9-112. $a^p a^{3p} a^{4p}$

9-113. $\dfrac{50 a^5 d^3}{-15 a^8 d}$

9-114. $\dfrac{-30 a^4 b^5}{6 a^2 b^9}$

Complex numbers

A form of algebra which is frequently used in solving problems involving vectors* is called *complex number algebra*. This notation permits an analysis of problems where quantities may be represented by vectors and affords a method of solving problems where roots of equations of second degree or higher are involved.

Before a discussion of complex quantities is made, some of the principles of imaginary numbers should be reviewed.

Imaginary Numbers

While a complete discussion of imaginary numbers is beyond the scope of this book, we may review some of the principles involved in an analysis

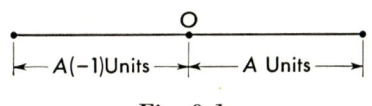

Fig. 9-1

of problems such as $X^2 + 1 = 0$. If a solution to this problem is possible, there must be some number whose square is -1. Let us call this number i, so that $i^2 = -1$ by definition. In order to obtain a physical representation of the number i, we may use a graphical approach.

Let us show graphically a distance A by drawing a line A units long to

---

* For a discussion of vectors see Chapter 13.

the right of a beginning point O (Fig. 9-1). To plot $-A$, we draw a line to the left of O, which is A units long. The line just drawn is a graphical plot of the expression $(A)(-1)$. This means that we may represent graphically a real number, which has been multiplied by -1, as a line which has been rotated through 180°, or through two right angles. If we let the quantity i^2 be equal to -1, then the graphical picture of $-A$ may be written as $i^2 A$.

When we multiply A by i, it will be equivalent graphically to rotating A through one right angle. From Fig. 9-2 it can be seen that a graphical picture of successive positions of A, as it is revolved through 90° steps,

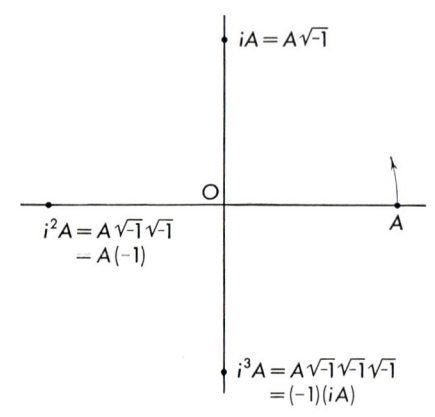

Fig. 9-2

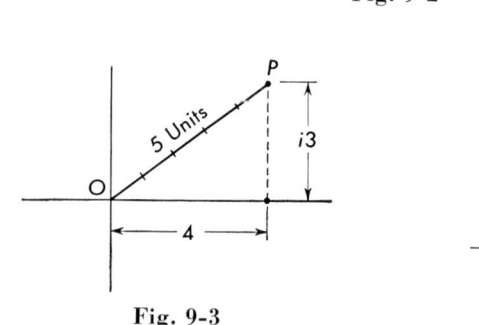

Fig. 9-3

Fig. 9-4

involves repeated multiplication by i, or $\sqrt{-1}$. The abscissa values of A are called *real values*, since they lie along the axis called the *axis of reals*. Ordinate values of A are called *imaginary values*, since they lie along the axis of imaginaries.

A complex number is a number which consists of a real part and an imaginary part. For example, the expression $4 + i3$ can be shown graphically in Fig. 9-3 to describe the location of the point P in the first quadrant. It also will describe the vector OP which is five units long and makes an angle of arc tan (3/4) with the axis of reals.

Mathematical Tools Useful in Problem Solving 129

Complex numbers may be added, subtracted, multiplied, or divided. To add complex numbers, add their respective real and imaginary parts.

Example: Add $3 + i2$ and $1 + i5$. Referring to Fig. 9-4, let OA represent $3 + i2$ and OB represent $1 + i5$. The vector sum is OC.

$$OC = 4 + i7$$

In a similar manner we can subtract complex numbers.

Example: $\qquad (2 + i2) - (3 - i4)$

Following algebraic rules, change the sign of the subtrahend and add.

$$\begin{array}{r} 2 + i2 \\ -3 + i4 \\ \hline -1 + i6 \quad \text{(remainder)} \end{array}$$

Multiplication of complex numbers is performed in accordance with algebraic rules which apply to real numbers.

Example: $(3 + i2)(4 - i)$

$$\begin{array}{r} 3 + i2 \\ 4 - i1 \\ \hline 12 + i8 \\ -i3 - i^2 2 \\ \hline 12 + i5 - i^2 2 \end{array}$$

Since $i^2 = -1$, we can write the product as $14 + i5$.

At this point the student should prove that:

$$(X_1 + iY_1)(X_2 + iY_2) = (X_1 X_2 - Y_1 Y_2) + i(X_1 Y_2 + X_2 Y_1)$$

Division of complex numbers can be performed by first simplifying the expression by multiplying both the divisor and the dividend by the divisor with the sign of the imaginary part of the number changed.

Example: $\qquad \dfrac{5 + i3}{1 - i4}$

Multiply both the numerator and the denominator by $1 + i4$ to make the denominator a real number.

$$\dfrac{(5 + i3)(1 + i4)}{(1 - i4)(1 + i4)} = \dfrac{(5 - 12) + i(3 + 20)}{(1)^2 + (4)^2}$$

$$= -7/17 + i23/17 \quad \text{(quotient)}$$

Complex numbers can be written in polar form. Referring to Fig. 9-5, the location of point P may be given either by $X + iY$ or by the length of a line OP which makes an angle θ with the axis of reals. For example, let the position of P be described by the complex number $X + iY$. It can be written in polar form by using simple trigonometric transformations. Let

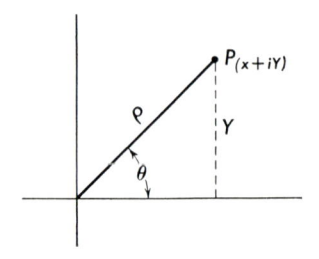

Fig. 9-5

the distance OP be represented by ρ, called the *modulus*, or *absolute value*; then

$$X = \rho \cos \theta$$
and
$$Y = \rho \sin \theta$$
Then
$$X + iY = \rho \cos \theta + i\rho \sin \theta$$
$$= \rho(\cos \theta + i \sin \theta)$$

where $\rho = \sqrt{X^2 + Y^2}$ and $\theta = \arctan Y/X$.

Using numerical values, assume the complex number $3 + i4$ describes the location of point P.

$$\rho = \sqrt{3^2 + 4^2} = 5$$
$$\theta = \arctan 4/3$$
$$= \arctan 1.33 = 53.1°$$

In polar form $3 + i4 = 5(\cos 53.1° + i \sin 53.1°)$.

Multiplication and Division of Complex Numbers in Polar Form

Multiplication and division of complex numbers can be accomplished readily if the numbers are in polar form. The following rules apply:

Multiplication: If two complex numbers are expressed in polar form, their product is equal to the product of their absolute values, and the angle of the product is equal to the sum of the angles.

Example: $[7(\cos 23° + i \sin 23°)][4(\cos 51° + i \sin 51°)]$
$$= (4)(7)[\cos (23° + 51°) + i \sin (23° + 51°)]$$
$$= 28(\cos 74° + i \sin 74°)$$

Division: If two complex numbers are expressed in polar form, their quotient

Mathematical Tools Useful in Problem Solving

is equal to the quotient of their absolute values, and the angle of the quotient is equal to the difference of the angles.

Example: $\dfrac{15(\cos 35° + i \sin 35°)}{3(\cos 21° + i \sin 21°)}$

$= {}^{15}\!/_{3}[\cos (35°{-}21°) + i \sin (35°{-}21°)]$
$= 5(\cos 14° + i \sin 14°)$

In some engineering work the symbol j is used to represent $\sqrt{-1}$, rather than the symbol i. For example, in electrical problems involving complex notation, the symbol j is always used to represent the imaginary number, since the letter i is universally used in electrical notation to represent electric current.

Problems

ADD

9-115. $(2 + i3) + (6 + i3)$
9-116. $(1 + i) + (4 + i5)$
9-117. $(1.5 + i0.3) + (0.5 - i2.1)$
9-118. $(-3.1 - i1.1) + (0.0 + i5.7)$
9-119. $(7.11 + i0.0) + (0.86 - i123.3)$

SUBTRACT

9-120. $(3 + i3) - (2 + i2)$
9-121. $(4 + i1) - (3 - i7)$
9-122. $(4.2 - i3.0) - (-12.0 + i3.8)$
9-123. $(-0.05 - i13.4) - (16.80 - i7.9)$
9-124. $(0.0 - i158.0) - (44.0 - i1.5)$

MULTIPLY

9-125. $(2 + i3)(3 + i1)$
9-126. $(1 + i)(3 + i\sqrt{3})$
9-127. $(4.5 - i1.02)(0.5 - i0.30)$
9-128. $(0.02 + i11.1)(-7.1 - i55.8)$
9-129. $(-8.8 + i0.0)(-2.7 - i31.4)$

DIVIDE

9-130. $\dfrac{3 + i11}{2 + i3}$

9-131. $\dfrac{-31 - i97}{5 - i3}$

9-132. $\dfrac{11.7 - i5.8}{3.5 + i1.2}$

9-133. $\dfrac{0.47 + i37.5}{5.5 - i0.7}$

9-134. $\dfrac{0.0 - i3.2}{7.5 - i0.0}$

132 Engineering: Elementary Problem Analysis

***9-135.** Prove that

$$[\rho_1(\cos\theta_1 + i\sin\theta_1)][\rho_2(\cos\theta_2 + i\sin\theta_2)]$$
$$= \rho_1\rho_2[\cos(\theta_1 + \theta_2) + i\sin(\theta_1 + \theta_2)]$$

***9-136.** Prove that

$$\frac{\rho_1(\cos\theta_1 + i\sin\theta_1)}{\rho_2(\cos\theta_2 + i\sin\theta_2)} = \frac{\rho_1}{\rho_2}[\cos(\theta_1 - \theta_2) + i\sin(\theta_1 - \theta_2)]$$

***9-137.** Solve: $(3 + j4)^3 = ?$ (HINT: Convert to polar form.)
***9-138.** Solve: $(2 + 5i)^{\frac{1}{3}} = ?$ (HINT: Use De Moivre's theorem.)

B—LOGARITHMS

In some cases students may have missed a study of logarithms. It is necessary, however, that all engineers be proficient in the use of this mathematical tool. Since logarithms are the basis for the construction of the slide rule, it is desirable that an intensive review of logarithms precede the study of the slide rule.

What Is a Logarithm?

A logarithm is an exponent, and the laws of exponents apply to logarithms as well as to exponents. To be more concise, the logarithm of any number to a given base is equal to the power to which the base must be raised to give the number. The base must be a positive number different from unity and zero.

The process of expressing exponential equations in logarithmic form can be shown as follows:

$$(5)^3 = 125 \qquad \log_5 125 = 3$$

Equation A — Equation B

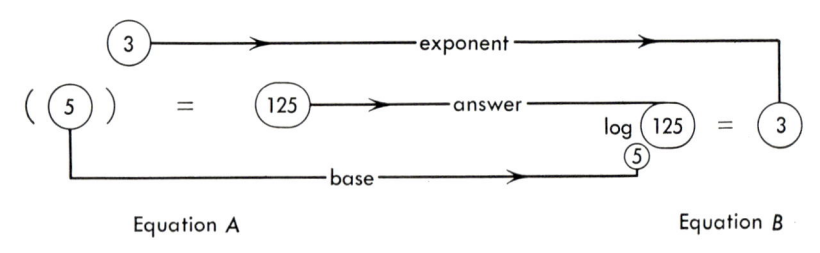

Fig. 9-6

In Eq. A we have an exponential equation, and when we rewrite this equation in logarithmic form in Eq. B, we note that the logarithm algebraically equals the exponent. This shows that our previous definition (that a logarithm is an exponent) is correct.

Mathematical Tools Useful in Problem Solving

In rewriting the exponential equation in the form of a logarithmic equation, note where each part of the equation was replaced.

Examples: $(2)^3 = 8$ or $\log_2 8 = 3$
$(a)^3 = b$ or $\log_a b = 3$
$(d)^x = 6$ or $\log_d 6 = x$

The base most commonly used is 10, and logarithms to this base are known as *common* or *Briggs* logarithms. Another base often used is the *natural* or *Napierian*, designated by the letter ϵ and having a value of 2.71828—. All logarithm tables used in this course are computed to the base 10. Since 10 is the common base, in practice the number 10 is usually omitted; that is, $\log_{10} 52$ is written $\log 52$. Logarithms to the base ϵ are sometimes written as $\ln$ rather than as $\log_\epsilon$. Before proceeding with the study of logarithms, the student should be certain that he understands the method of interchanging logarithmic and exponential forms.

PROBLEMS: CHANGE TO THE LOGARITHMIC FORM

9-139. $(7)^a = cx$
9-140. $(a)^b = c$
9-141. $(2)^5 = 32$
9-142. $(6)^b = a$
9-143. $(b)^x = C$
9-144. $(B)^A = 10$
9-145. $(R)^{25} = 6.3$
9-146. $N = (5)^2$

9-147. $N = (30)^{-4}$
9-148. $N = (6)^{\frac{1}{4}}$
9-149. $(10)^N = 862$
9-150. $(1)^{10} = N$
9-151. $(R)^{0.2} = 15$
9-152. $(10)^{-5} = S$
9-153. $N = (10)^{0.78}$
9-154. $64 = (2)^6$

9-155. $(x)^{bc} = \dfrac{N}{3}$
9-156. $(MS)^{ac} = 106$
9-157. $A = \dfrac{c}{(10)^2}$
9-158. $(RM)^3 = c$

PROBLEMS: CHANGE TO THE EXPONENTIAL FORM

9-159. $\log_3 N = 3$
9-160. $\log_5 N = 2$
9-161. $\log_8 N = 2$
9-162. $\log_6 N = 3$
9-163. $\log_A C = X$
9-164. $\log_{25} B = 3$
9-165. $\log_9 A = \dfrac{1}{3}$
9-166. $\log N = 3$
9-167. $\log N = 1$
9-168. $\log N = 0$
9-169. $\log_S 343 = 3$
9-170. $\log_{64} A = \dfrac{1}{2}$

9-171. $\log_D 144 = 2$
9-172. $\log_N 0.0225 = 2$
9-173. $\log_9 N = 1$
9-174. $\log_7 N = 3$
9-175. $\log_4 N = \dfrac{1}{2}$
9-176. $\log_W 32 = 5$
9-177. $\log_Z 2 = \dfrac{1}{4}$
9-178. $\log_{27} P = \dfrac{1}{3}$

Since 10 is the common base used for logarithmic work, let us examine the resulting equations when 10 is raised to various powers.

$$(10)^0 = 1 \quad \text{or} \quad \log_{10} 1 = 0.0000$$
$$(10)^1 = 10 \quad \text{or} \quad \log_{10} 10 = 1.0000$$
$$(10)^2 = 100 \quad \text{or} \quad \log_{10} 100 = 2.0000$$
$$(10)^3 = 1000 \quad \text{or} \quad \log_{10} 1000 = 3.0000$$
$$(10)^4 = 10000 \quad \text{or} \quad \log_{10} 10000 = 4.0000$$

By studying the preceding table, we can see that $\log 1 = 0$ and $\log 10 = 1$; hence the logarithm of a number between 1 and 10 would lie between the values 0.0000 and 1.0000.

Example:

$$\log 5 = 0.6990 \quad \text{or} \quad (10)^{0.6990} = 5$$
$$\log 8 = 0.9031 \quad \text{or} \quad (10)^{0.9031} = 8$$
$$\log 8.75 = 0.9420 \quad \text{or} \quad (10)^{0.9420} = 8.75$$

This same reasoning can be found from the inspection of the logarithms of numbers between 10 and 100. These logarithms would lie between 1.0000 and 2.0000.

Example: $\quad \log 17.5 = 1.2430 \quad$ or $\quad (10)^{1.2430} = 17.5$

A logarithm is always composed of two parts; a decimal part or *mantissa* which is usually positive, and a whole number which is either positive, negative, or zero. This whole number is called the *characteristic*. In the above example ($\log 17.5 = 1.2430$), the characteristic is 1.0000, while the mantissa is 0.2430.

Examples:

	(characteristic)	plus	(mantissa)	= logarithm
$\log 19.75 = 1.2956$ or	1.0000	+	0.2956	= 1.2956
$\log 1975. = 3.2956$ or	3.0000	+	0.2956	= 3.2956
$\log 19750. = 4.2956$ or	4.0000	+	0.2956	= 4.2956

It is evident from the above examples that the characteristic changes as the decimal point moves, while the mantissa is affected only by the sequence of digits that form the number.

Let us examine other exponential equations involving the use of negative exponents.

$$(10)^0 = 1 \quad \text{or} \quad \log 1 = 0.0000$$
$$(10)^{-1} = \tfrac{1}{10} = 0.1 \quad \text{or} \quad \log 0.1 = -1.0000$$
$$(10)^{-2} = \tfrac{1}{100} = 0.01 \quad \text{or} \quad \log 0.01 = -2.0000$$
$$(10)^{-3} = \tfrac{1}{1000} = 0.001 \quad \text{or} \quad \log 0.001 = -3.0000$$
$$(10)^{-4} = \tfrac{1}{10000} = 0.0001 \quad \text{or} \quad \log 0.0001 = -4.0000$$

A brief study of this table will show that the logarithms of numbers less

Mathematical Tools Useful in Problem Solving

than 1 will have negative characteristics. The mantissas, however, are still dependent on the sequence of digits in the numbers.

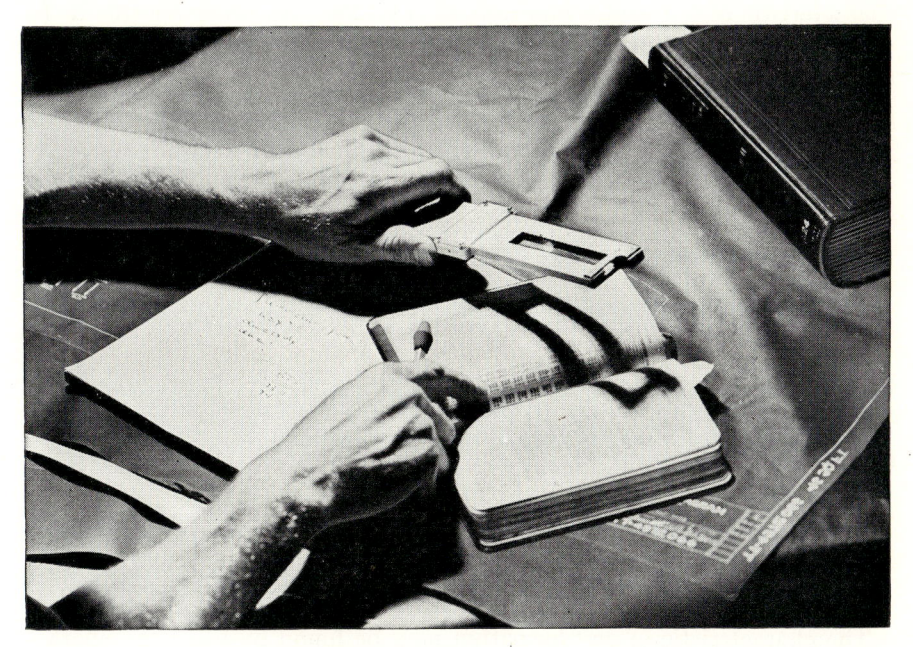

Fig. 9-7. Logarithm tables and slide rules are useful tools to engineers, and a knowledge of the use of logarithms is necessary in order to perform many engineering calculations.

Rules for Characteristics

NUMBER	CHARACTERISTIC
1 or greater	The characteristic is positive and is one less than the number of digits to the left of the decimal point.
Less than 1	The characteristic is negative in sign and one greater than the number of ciphers (zeros) between the decimal point and the left-hand digit.

The mantissa is usually positive, while the characteristic may be positive, negative, or zero. The logarithm (or sum of the mantissa and characteristic) can be written easily if the characteristic is zero or positive, but some trouble may be encountered when the characteristic is negative.

Example:

	characteristic	plus	mantissa	equals	logarithm
log 13.2 =	+1	+	+0.1206	=	1.1206
log 1.32 =	0	+	+0.1206	=	0.1206
log 0.132 =	−1	+	+0.1206	=	−0.8794

Since it is desirable to keep the characteristic separated from the mantissa, the above expression, log 0.132, would of necessity be written with a characteristic of -1 and a mantissa of $+0.1206$. In order for this to be written without confusion, we must add 10 to the characteristic and subtract 10 from the logarithm.

Example:

	characteristic	plus	mantissa	
log 0.132 =	-1	+	$+0.1206$	
	10			-10
	$+9$	+	$+0.1206$	-10
		(or, 9.1206 $-$ 10)		

We see that the characteristic and mantissa are now both positive, and it is in this form that all logarithms with negative characteristics should be expressed.

Other Examples:

	characteristic	plus	mantissa	equals	logarithm
log 0.00365 =	-3	+	$+0.5623$	=	7.5623 $-$ 10
log 0.791 =	-1	+	$+0.8982$	=	9.8982 $-$ 10
log 0.000169 =	-4	+	$+0.2279$	=	6.2279 $-$ 10

The characteristic of any logarithm may be found by using the characteristic rules, but the mantissa (to the base 10) must be found by referring to common logarithm tables. To obtain the mantissa from tables, follow these steps:

1. Find the first two digits of the number and locate them in the *number* column.
2. Follow horizontally across the page to the column headed with a single, bold digit. This is the third digit of the number.
3. The value on the horizontal line and in this column is the mantissa (decimal part) of the logarithm.

Example: Find the mantissa of the number 156 (see Fig. 9-8).

Hence, the mantissa is 0.1931.

Remember that the mantissa is always read from tables, and the characteristic is determined from the characteristic rules.

Number	0	1	2	3	4	5	⑥	7	8	9
13										
14										
⑮							1931			
16										
17										

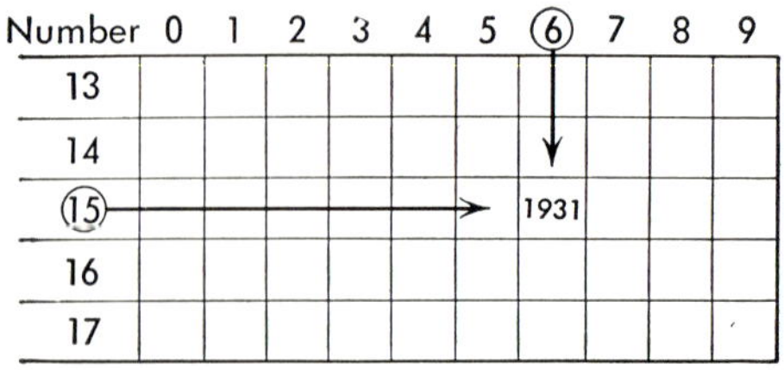

Fig. 9-8

Mathematical Tools Useful in Problem Solving

Interpolation

It is frequently necessary to evaluate the mantissas of numbers which lie between those given in the tables. For example, the mantissa of 896. (see page 379) is 0.9523, and the mantissa of 897 (see page 379) is 0.9528. Although the mantissa of 896.4 cannot be located in the three-place log tables, its value may be calculated as follows: Let 0.xxxx = the mantissa of 896.4. Then

$$1.0 \begin{bmatrix} \text{Number} \\ 897.0 \\ 896.4 \\ 896.0 \end{bmatrix} 0.4 \quad 0.0005 \begin{bmatrix} \text{Mantissa} \\ 0.9528 \\ 0.\text{xxxx} \\ 0.9523 \end{bmatrix} Y$$

Set up the ratio:

$$\frac{0.4}{1.0} = \frac{Y}{0.0005}$$

$$Y = \frac{(0.4)(0.0005)}{1.0}$$

$$= 0.0002$$

The value Y is the distance that the mantissa 0.xxxx lies above the mantissa 0.9523. Thus, the mantissa of 896.4 is

$$\begin{array}{r} 0.9523 \\ +0.0002 \\ \hline \end{array}$$

Mantissa 0.xxxx = 0.9525

Anti-logarithms

Often we know the logarithm of a number and wish to find the number. This process is known as finding the anti-logarithm, and the procedure followed is in reverse order to that of finding the logarithm of a number.

Example: Find the anti-logarithm of 1.3010.

Steps

1. Hunt in the common logarithm tables until the given mantissa of 0.3010 is found.
2. Moving horizontally to the left, read the digits *20* in the number column on the same line.
3. Reading vertically, annex the single digit *0* at the head of the column in which the mantissa is found.
4. Point off the decimal place for a characteristic of +1. Thus the anti-logarithm of

$$1.3010 = (2.00)(10)^1$$

Engineering: Elementary Problem Analysis

Problems

Solve for the logarithm, using the tables on pages 378 to 379. Interpolate where necessary.

9-179. 560.	9-204. 299.4
9-180. 125,900.	9-205. $(9.87)(10)^2$
9-181. 0.00337	9-206. $(5.09)(10)^9$
9-182. 0.2366	9-207. $(1.11)(10)^{-6}$
9-183. 0.775	9-208. $(0.99)(10)^4$
9-184. 0.0001	9-209. $(44.8)(10)^3$
9-185. 1515.	9-210. $(1.09)(10)^5$
9-186. 43.39	9-211. $(188.)(10)$
9-187. 4.939	9-212. $(0.044)(10)^7$
9-188. 1.114	9-213. $(11.93)(10)^{-1}$
9-189. 222.8	9-214. $(233.8)(10)^{-8}$
9-190. 435.2	9-215. $(3.007)(10)^{-17}$
9-191. 1122.	9-216. $(98.54)(10)^{26}$
9-192. 6.009	9-217. $(678.3)(10)^{45}$
9-193. 25.11	9-218. $(72.09)(10)^{33}$
9-194. 0.0006	9-219. $(133.3)(10)^{-65}$
9-195. 13.99	9-220. $(55.38)(10)^{-10}$
9-196. 45.87	9-221. $(2.003)(10)^{-4}$
9-197. 666.2	9-222. $(1148.)(10)^{89}$
9-198. 0.02778	9-223. $(2050.)(10)^{-20}$
9-199. 73.90	9-224. $(1191.)(10)^{107}$
9-200. 0.9004	9-225. $(0.0003)(10)^{-99}$
9-201. 21.12	9-226. $(0.0000005988)(10)^{-8}$
9-202. 0.0907	9-227. $(0.00001866)(10)$
9-203. 11.55	9-228. $(23,970,000.)(10)^{-17}$

Problems

Solve for the anti-logarithms, using the tables on pages 378 to 379. Interpolate where necessary.

9-229. 1.4800	9-237. 1.4330	9-245. 6.4409 − 10
9-230. 0.9991	9-238. 8.0043	9-246. 5.5551 − 5
9-231. 0.9191	9-239. 0.8567	9-247. 8.8808 − 18
9-232. 7.5289	9-240. 7.7709	9-248. 1.3118 − 17
9-233. 3.0294	9-241. 3.3222	9-249. 5.8887 − 10
9-234. 9.5011	9-242. 19.0719	9-250. 4.7513 − 10
9-235. 4.8048	9-243. 0.9170	9-251. 7.2553 − 19
9-236. 0.0934	9-244. 2.8657 − 1	9-252. 2.0414 − 4

Mathematical Tools Useful in Problem Solving

9-253. 3.3304 − 9
9-254. 9.9460 − 10
9-255. 3.0600
9-256. 5.8895
9-257. 6.9993
9-258. 14.4850
9-259. 0.4335
9-260. 0.8360 − 10
9-261. 4.1066 − 7

9-262. 1.0060
9-263. 7.7777 − 10
9-264. 0.2156 − 4
9-265. 8.4803 − 26
9-266. 17.5430 − 43
9-267. 87.0870 − 41
9-268. 0.1100 − 77
9-269. 77.8400 − 100
9-270. 48.1322 − 100

9-271. 11.2000
9-272. 1.4255 − 82
9-273. 0.6508 − 21
9-274. 3.8770 − 100
9-275. 45.0660 − 87
9-276. 0.0020 − 7
9-277. 22.5100 − 81
9-278. 5.1291 − 4

Laws of Logarithms

Since a logarithm is an exponent, all the laws of exponents should be reviewed. Let us examine a few of these laws.

EXPONENTIAL LAW I : $(a)^m(a)^n = a^{m+n}$ (see page 126)

We can put the above equation in statement form, since we know that logarithms are exponents and therefore follow the laws of exponents.

LAW I

The logarithm of a product equals the sum of the logarithms of the factors.

Example:
$$(5)(7) = ?$$
$$\log_{10} 5 + \log_{10} 7 = \log_{10} \text{ans.}$$
$$0.6990 + 0.8451 = \log \text{ans.}$$
$$1.5441 = \log \text{ans.}$$
$$\text{Answer} = (3.50)(10)^1$$

This is true because
$$5 = (10)^{0.6990}$$
$$7 = (10)^{0.8451}$$
$$\text{product} = (10)^{0.6990}(10)^{0.8451}$$
$$\text{product} = (10)^{0.6990+0.8451}$$
$$\text{product} = (10)^{1.5441}$$
$$\text{product} = (3.50)(10)^1$$

EXPONENTIAL LAW II : $\dfrac{a^m}{a^n} = a^{m-n}$ (see page 126)

Putting the above equation in statement form, we obtain the following law.

LAW II

The logarithm of a quotient equals the logarithm of the dividend minus the logarithm of the divisor.

Example:

$$5/4 = ?$$
$$\log 5 - \log 4 = \log \text{ans.}$$
$$0.6990 - 0.6021 = \log \text{ans.}$$
$$0.0969 = \log \text{ans.}$$
$$\text{Answer} = 1.25$$

LAW III

The logarithm of the x power of a number equals x times the logarithm of the number.

Example:

$$(5)^3 = ?$$
$$3(\log 5) = \log \text{ans.}$$
$$3(0.6990) = \log \text{ans.}$$
$$2.0970 = \log \text{ans.}$$
$$\text{Answer} = (1.25)(10)^2$$

LAW IV

The logarithm of the x root of a number equals the logarithm of the number divided by x.

Example:

$$\sqrt[3]{3375.} = ?$$
$$\frac{\log 3375.}{3} = \log \text{ans.}$$
$$\frac{3.5282}{3} = \log \text{ans.}$$
$$1.1761 = \log \text{ans.}$$
$$\text{Answer} = (1.50)(10)^1$$

NOTE: Law IV is actually a special case of Law III.

In some instances a combination of Law III and Law IV may be used.

Example:

$$(0.916)^{\frac{3}{4.15}} = ?$$
$$\frac{(\log 0.916)(3)}{4.15} = \log \text{ans.}$$
$$\frac{(9.9619 - 10)(3)}{4.15} = \log \text{ans.}$$

Perform multiplication first:

$$\frac{29.8857 - 30}{4.15} = \log \text{ans.}$$

To divide by 4.15, it is necessary that the negative number be divisible an even number of times. Therefore the characteristic (which is -1) is written as $414.0000 - 415$. There are several values which could be chosen, such as $4149.0000 - 4150$, which would satisfy the condition that

Mathematical Tools Useful in Problem Solving 141

the characteristic be -1. Rewriting and dividing,

$$\frac{414.8857 - 415}{4.15} = \log \text{ans.}$$

$$99.9725 - 100 = \log \text{ans.}$$

$$\text{Answer} = (9.39)(10)^{-1}$$

The Cologarithm

Many times it is helpful to use the cologarithm of a number rather than the logarithm. The cologarithm of a number is the logarithm of the reciprocal of the number. The cologarithm is also the difference between the logarithm and the logarithm of unity.

Example:
$$\text{colog } 5 = \tfrac{1}{5}$$
$$= \log 1 - \log 5$$
$$= 0.0000 - 0.6990$$
$$= -0.6990$$

Since log 5 equals 0.6990, we see that the colog $x = -\log x$. Therefore:

1. The logarithm of the quotient of two numbers equals the logarithm of the dividend plus the cologarithm of the divisor.
2. The logarithm of the product of two numbers equals the logarithm of one number minus the cologarithm of the other number.

Problems

Solve, using logarithms. Interpolate where necessary.

9-279. (23.8)(11.9)
9-280. (11,080.)(0.0911)
9-281. (290.)(38.7)
9-282. (11.05)(0.9933)
9-283. (77.3)(0.145)(17.55)
9-284. (0.359)(0.567)(0.000661)
9-285. (56,040.)(65,140.)(22.1)
9-286. (0.04177)(33,890.)(0.928)
9-287. (55.01)(133.4)(11,950.)
9-288. $(41.44 \times 10^3)(0.9912 \times 10^{-9})$
9-289. $(12.99)(1.445 \times 10)$
9-290. (54,770.)(21,660.)(0.445)
9-291. $(1.339 \times 10^{-23})(11.56 \times 10^{67})$
9-292. (0.0005991)(0.02341)(17.93)
9-293. $(880.3 \times 10^{-5})(35.77)(66.45)$
9-294. $\dfrac{43.9}{11.8}$
9-295. $\dfrac{190,300.}{77,190.}$
9-296. $\dfrac{0.7629}{21.77}$
9-297. $\dfrac{91.06}{366.8}$
9-298. $\dfrac{64,990.}{0.1108}$
9-299. $\dfrac{603,400.}{3,973.}$

Engineering: Elementary Problem Analysis

9-300. $\dfrac{(8.56)(18.46)}{(1,045.)}$

9-301. $\dfrac{(5.661)(66.88)}{(79,050.)(22.99)}$

9-302. $\dfrac{(44.02)(89,090.)}{(344.7)(66.01)}$

9-303. $\dfrac{(15,580.)(11.03)}{(87.77)(14,040.)}$

9-304. $\dfrac{(44.76)(56,844.)}{(1.005)(88.4)}$

9-305. $(21.6)^{3.5}$

9-306. $(11.55)^7$

9-307. $(104.2)^{5.7}$

9-308. $(39,050.)^{0.4}$

9-309. $(5.077)^{2.5}$

9-310. $(0.4494)^{55.9}$

9-311. $(3.018)^{6.22}$

9-312. $(0.09437)^{0.225}$

9-313. $(21.39)^{9.77}$

9-314. $(10.78)^{0.00498}$

9-315. $(889.4)^{0.4116}$

9-316. $(6,901.)^{8.55}$

9-317. $(11,190.)^{44.6}$

9-318. $(35.88)(45.94)^{1.066}$

9-319. $\sqrt[4]{(1.339)(10)^5}$

9-320. $\sqrt{(761)(10)^{-3}}$

9-321. $\sqrt{(4439)(10)^{-9}}$

9-322. $\sqrt[3]{0.0031651}$

9-323. $\sqrt[2.1]{66.63}$

9-324. $\sqrt[6.6]{2.316}$

9-325. $\sqrt[6.6]{0.3163}$

9-326. $\sqrt[9.1]{1,165,400}$

9-327. $\sqrt[2.2]{0.6166}$

9-328. $(236)^{\frac{1}{0.3315}}$

9-329. $(1655)^{\frac{1}{6.05}}$

9-330. $(7676)^{\frac{1}{906}}$

9-331. $(765.5)^{0.331}$

9-332. $(1.3916)^{\frac{1}{5.22}}$

9-333. $(0.7712)^{\frac{1}{6.21}}$

9-334. $(0.6114)^{\frac{1}{7.67}}$

9-335. $(883)^{\frac{6}{6.23}}$

9-336. $(0.0316)^{\frac{0.2}{0.331}}$

9-337. $(6.791)^{\frac{3}{55.6}}$

9-338. $(89.06)^{\frac{1}{0.261}}$

9-339. $(23.55)^{\frac{1}{0.916}}$

9-340. $(1.1106)^{\frac{9}{5.23}}$

9-341. $(838)^{\frac{3}{1.88}}$

9-342. $(1692)^{\frac{0.1}{3.57}}$

9-343. $(0.09166)^{0.7651}$

9-344. $(8.103)^{17.66}$

9-345. $(66.23)^{1.36}(0.3165)^{0.9166}$

9-346. $(79.16)^{2.35}(0.6175)^{1.75}$

9-347. $(23.16)^{0.356}(1.657)^{23.9}$

9-348. $(66,175)^{0.33}(1.913)^{10.03}$

9-349. $(76.66)^{12.33}(0.206)^{12.33}$

9-350. $(55.55)^{1.33}(0.00316)^{7.55}$

9-351. $(1.336)^{7.03}(5.261)^{9.23}$

9-352. $\dfrac{(66.17)(0.3316)(0.3991)}{(1.5537)}$

9-353. $\dfrac{(79.661)(55.331)(0.6753)}{(1.039)(6617)(0.05)}$

9-354. $\dfrac{(71.66)(10)^5(16.31)(10)^8}{(16.33)(10)^3(15.22)(10)^9}$

9-355. $\dfrac{(23.22)(66.0)(10)(8)}{\sqrt{67.32}\,(0.3317)}$

9-356. $\dfrac{(46.66)(0.33165)(0.6617)^{0.31}}{\sqrt{32.22}\,(0.913)^{1.26}}$

9-357. $\dfrac{(6.755)(0.6615)(3155)}{(0.1033)^{0.1033}\sqrt[7]{5.216}}$

9-358. $\dfrac{\dfrac{1}{64.1}\sqrt[3]{31,800}}{(9.030)\sqrt{3.60/429}}$

Mathematical Tools Useful in Problem Solving

9-359. $\dfrac{(0.04110)(\sqrt{245})}{(0.005041)(7.13)^3}$

9-360. $\dfrac{\sqrt{8.67}}{(3.14)(109.7)}$

9-361. $\dfrac{(431.6)(0.065)(0.0009811)}{(34.12)(0.0629)}$

9-362. $\dfrac{\sqrt{0.817}\ \sqrt[3]{4.929}}{(1.795)(9.03)}$

9-363. $\dfrac{(19{,}800)^{0.55}(1007)^{0.7}}{(16.2)^2(0.00488)^{1.6}}$

9-364. $\dfrac{(0.000000397)^{0.5}(6.06)^{2.3}}{(2.41)}$

9-365. $\dfrac{1}{(1/3.88)(2.04)^{3.4}}(181.6)^{1.41}$

9-366. $\dfrac{(7.22 \times 10^{-3})(0.3051)^{0.41}}{\sqrt[3]{0.811}\ (5.35 \times 10^4)}$

9-367. $\dfrac{(367{,}000)\sqrt{75{,}000}}{(1755)(5888)(3.14)^2}$

9-368. $\dfrac{(8.91)^3(19.6)^3(0.000733)^2(40.06)^{21}}{(0.337)(21.3)\sqrt[3]{0.03117}}$

9-369. $\dfrac{(44.93)^{6.7}(0.007113)^{-0.88}}{\sqrt{0.009144}\ (3.336)^{0.88}}$

9-370. $\dfrac{\sqrt[3]{566.9}\ (0.4459)^2(61.11)^3}{(71.39)\sqrt{8.002}\ (0.00008811)}$

9-371. $\dfrac{\sqrt{0.8119}\ (7.044)^{5.99}(21.11)^{0.88}}{(68.44)(38.88)\sqrt[3.1]{0.443}}$

9-372. $\dfrac{(66.91)^{5.88}(4.099)^5(41{,}960.)^4}{(8.013)(44.43)^{5.98}}$

9-373. $\dfrac{(11{,}860.)^{-5.12}(22.05)^{3.77}}{\sqrt[0.7]{0.4699}\ (77.71)^{15.44}}$

9-374. $\dfrac{(0.056)^{2.32}(0.1166)^{0.0217}}{\sqrt[0.83]{0.4577}\ (39.44)^6}$

9-375. $\dfrac{(14.41)^4(61.93)^6(0.8911)^{2.9}}{(8.335)(0.1066)\sqrt[3]{0.5122}}$

9-376. $\dfrac{(11.090.)^{-0.55}(35.88)^{-6.7}(14.11)^{-0.6}}{(1.388)^{-7}(0.4499)^{-91}(81.07)^{-6.6}}$

9-377. $\dfrac{(0.6199)^{9.7}(36.99)^{5.3}(0.1105)^{-5.7}}{(0.7719)^9(345.7)^8(81.02)^{-44}}$

9-378. $\dfrac{(0.8805)^{-6.92}(43.77)^{-0.1145}(17.45)^{0.356}}{(21.21)^7(0.698)^{45}(0.177)^{0.771}(0.0934)^{-1487}}$

Natural Logarithms

When certain derivations of engineering formulas are made, a term may appear which contains a natural logarithm. For example, the magnetic field intensity near a current-carrying conductor varies with distance from the conductor according to a logarithmic pattern. In advanced texts it may be shown that a natural logarithm function, when plotted, gives an exponential curve whose slope at any point is equal to the ordinate at that point.

In solving problems involving natural logarithms, tables of natural logarithms may be used if they are available, or the natural logarithm, frequently abbreviated as "ln," may be converted to a logarithm to the base 10. To perform this latter operation, an algebraic transformation called *change of logarithmic base* is used. This transformation can be performed as follows:

$$\text{Natural logarithm} = (\text{common log})(\log_\epsilon 10)$$

Since $\log_\epsilon 10 = 2.3026$, we may write:

$$\text{Natural logarithm} = (\text{common log})(2.3026)$$

If natural logarithms are computed, it must be remembered that the mantissa is not independent of the location of the decimal point. Therefore the same sequence of significant figures does not have the same mantissa, as is the case with common logarithms.

Example: Find the natural logarithm of 245.

$$\log_{10} 245 = 2.3892$$
$$\ln 245 = (2.3892)(2.3026)$$
$$= 5.5014$$

Example: Find the natural logarithm of 2.45

$$\log_{10} 2.45 = 0.3892$$
$$\ln 2.45 = (0.3892)(2.3026)$$
$$= 0.8961$$

The natural logarithm of a number less than 1 is a negative number.

Example: Find the natural logarithm of 0.245

$$\log_{10} 0.245 = 9.3892 - 10$$

Since the logarithm has a negative characteristic, we can solve by first finding the colog and then multiplying by $\log_\epsilon 10$

$$\text{colog}_{10} 0.245 = -0.6108$$
$$\ln 0.245 = (-0.6108)(2.3026)$$
$$= -1.4046$$

Mathematical Tools Useful in Problem Solving

Problems

Solve for the natural logarithms of the following numbers:

9-379. 1.309	9-396. 0.001036	9-413. $(1562)(10)^3$
9-380. 0.369	9-397. 0.0000555	9-414. $(36.17)(10)^{-4}$
9-381. 0.9016	9-398. 7.660	9-415. $(1.667)(10)^{-8}$
9-382. 17560000	9-399. 0.0001661	9-416. $(2.316)(10)^{-3}$
9-383. 79600	9-400. 0.992	9-417. $(6.171)(10)^{-2}$
9-384. 0.756	9-401. 156000	9-418. $(2.316)(10)^{-1}$
9-385. 1.791	9-402. 1.096	9-419. 1.992
9-386. 5700	9-403. 1.0020	9-420. 6.075
9-387. 2000	9-404. 3.650	9-421. 50.33
9-388. 1503	9-405. 1773	9-422. $(16.3)(10)^{-7}$
9-389. 26.3	9-406. 98220	9-423. $(0.316)(10)^{-4}$
9-390. 10050	9-407. 503.100	9-424. $(0.003119)(10)^3$
9-391. 7.32	9-408. 17.992	9-425. $(75.32)(10)^5$
9-392. 0.617	9-409. 56.92	9-426. $(391.6)(10)^6$
9-393. 0.9160	9-410. 0.3316	9-427. $(1.0399)(10)^7$
9-394. 0.000677	9-411. 0.15276	9-428. $(60.33)(10)^{-8}$
9-395. 0.00271	9-412. $(15.6)(10)^{-3}$	

C—TRIGONOMETRY

As a mathematical tool for the engineer, trigonometry is next to arithmetic and algebra in importance. Principles of trigonometry are commonly applied in the analysis of problems involving the sides and angles of right triangles and oblique triangles and in computations of areas of triangles.

The engineer finds that, in addition to uses purely in problem solving that involves triangles, the relationships developed in trigonometry have by derivations been carried into many other calculations not directly involving triangles. For example, trigonometric functions are used in electrical theory to aid in describing the time relations of voltage to current.

Since the engineer will have frequent need for a knowledge of trigonometry, it should be familiar enough in its basic forms to be adapted to many different problems. The discussion in this book will be made from the standpoint of a review of basic principles rather than as a complete text of trigonometry. In some instances a student will be taking a formal course in trigonometry at the same time he is pursuing the course in engineering problems analysis. In other cases this study has already been completed, and therefore the problems in this book will be designed to illustrate some of the practical uses of the mathematics called "trig."

Fig. 9-9. Surveying, one of the oldest sciences of measurement, is still used extensively today.

Right Triangles

Since by far the greatest proportion of calculations involving trigonometry will make use of right triangle relations, it is necessary that they be memorized in all their forms. The triangle has three sides and three angles. In the right triangle one angle is 90° and the sides are named in their relations to the angles. In Fig. 9-10 the angle at A is the one under consideration, and the sides with respect to this angle are: AB, the side adjacent to the angle; CB, the side opposite the angle; and AC, the hypotenuse which is always opposite the right angle. If the relations are memorized as ratios of side opposite, side adjacent, and hypotenuse, the triangle can be in any position in any situation and still the relations can be easily applied. If the

Mathematical Tools Useful in Problem Solving 147

angle at C were the angle considered, AB would be the side opposite; CB, the side adjacent; and AC, the hypotenuse. Frequently Greek letters such as θ (theta), α (alpha), and β (beta) are used to represent the angle.

It may be shown by measurements and by formal derivations that for a given size of angle at A or C, the ratio of the lengths of the sides to each other

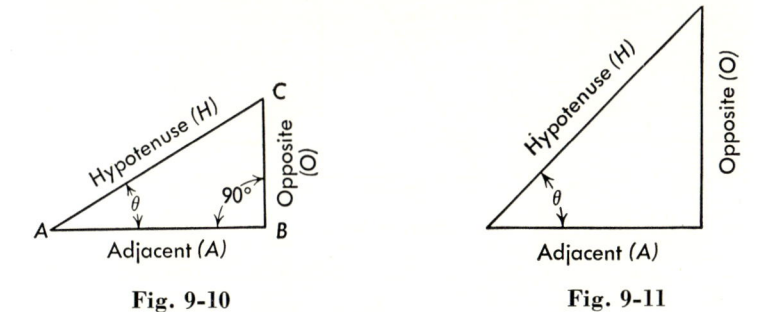

Fig. 9-10

Fig. 9-11

in a right triangle is always a constant, regardless of the numerical value of the lengths. These ratios have been given names as follows:

$$\frac{\text{Opposite side}}{\text{Hypotenuse}} = \sin\theta$$

$$\frac{\text{Adjacent side}}{\text{Hypotenuse}} = \cos\theta$$

$$\frac{\text{Opposite side}}{\text{Adjacent side}} = \tan\theta$$

$$\frac{\text{Adjacent side}}{\text{Opposite side}} = \cot\theta$$

$$\frac{\text{Hypotenuse}}{\text{Adjacent side}} = \sec\theta$$

$$\frac{\text{Hypotenuse}}{\text{Opposite side}} = \csc\theta$$

These six relations should be memorized because they are so frequently needed that the engineer should be able to use them without reference to texts. The relations are usually abbreviated (Fig. 9-11) as follows:

$$\sin\theta = \frac{O}{H} \qquad \tan\theta = \frac{O}{A}$$

$$\cos\theta = \frac{A}{H} \qquad \cot\theta = \frac{A}{O}$$

$$\sec\theta = \frac{H}{A}$$

$$\csc\theta = \frac{H}{O}$$

The use of the relations is simple, as may be shown by a sample problem.

148   *Engineering: Elementary Problem Analysis*

Example: One side of a right triangle is 32 ft and the angle opposite this side is 30°. How long is the hypotenuse?

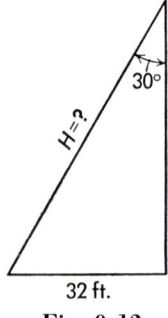

Fig. 9-12

Analysis: The sine, cosine, and tangent functions will ordinarily be sufficient for any problem solution, since the cotangent, secant, and cosecant functions are reciprocal relations of the first three. With this in mind, find in a table of sines, or determine on a slide rule, the numerical value of the sine 30°. The value is 0.5 and has no units because it is the ratio of two lengths.

Substituting:

$$\sin \theta = \frac{O}{H}$$

$$0.5 = \frac{32 \text{ ft}}{H}$$

$$H = \frac{32 \text{ ft}}{0.5} = 64 \text{ ft}$$

This shows that for a right triangle having a 30° angle, the side opposite the 30° angle is half the length of the hypotenuse. Using the sine of 60° the side opposite the 60° angle will be 0.866 times as long as the hypotenuse. Similar values will apply for the other relations.

It is helpful to remember the variation of values of the sine, cosine, and tangent terms as the angles are varied.

	0°	30°	45°	60°	90°
Sine	0	0.5	0.707	0.866	1.00
Cosine	1.00	0.866	0.707	0.5	0
Tangent	0	0.577	1.00	1.73	∞

Notice that the sine of an angle varies from zero to 1.00 as the angle varies from 0° to 90° and the cosine function varies from 1.00 to zero as the angle varies from 0° to 90°. The sine and cosine functions are never greater than

Mathematical Tools Useful in Problem Solving 149

1.00. The tangent of an angle is zero at 0° and has values less than 1.00 for angles less than 45°. For angles larger than 45°, the tangent function may have any value up to $+\infty$ at 90°.

There are two additional functions that are used in some solutions to problems in surveying. They are:

Versed sine of an angle = 1 − cosine of the angle
Coversed sine of an angle = 1 − sine of the angle

These are usually abbreviated to the form:

$$\text{Vers } \theta = 1 - \cos \theta$$
$$\text{Covers } \theta = 1 - \sin \theta$$

A more complete discussion of these functions may be found in texts on trigonometry and surveying.

Right Triangle Problems

9-429. The hypotenuse of a right triangle is 38 ft and one of the legs is 22 ft. Find the angle opposite the given leg.

9-430. The sides of a right triangle are 2.25 in. and 3.91 in. Find the angle opposite the shorter leg. Find the hypotenuse without using the Pythagorean theorem.

9-431. A right triangle has an angle of 56° and the side adjacent to this angle is 202 ft long. What will be the length of the hypotenuse? What will be the area of the triangle?

9-432. A right triangle has an angle of 21° and the hypotenuse is 35.4 ft. What are the lengths of the other two sides?

9-433. A right triangle has an angle of 46° and the side opposite this angle is 26.4 in. Find the length of the other leg. Find the length of the hypotenuse.

9-434. The three sides of a right triangle are 3 ft, 4 ft, and 5 ft. What are the angles of the triangle?

9-435. A ladder 12.2 ft long leans against a vertical wall. The foot of the ladder is 3.55 ft from the wall. How far up the wall will the ladder reach?

9-436. An inclined ramp rises 2.6 ft in 10 ft of horizontal distance. What angle does the ramp make with the horizontal?

9-437. A shed 10 ft wide is to be built with a sloping roof. The front wall will be 12.2 ft high and the rear wall 10.5 ft high. How long will the rafter need to be if a 1-ft overhang is allowed at the front and rear of the shed?

9-438. A triangular plot of ground is to be fenced. The angles are 41°, 49°, and 90°, and the longest side (hypotenuse) of the plot is 156.5 ft. How many rods of fence will be needed to enclose the plot of ground?

9-439. A telephone pole is to be secured with a guy wire attached to the pole at a point 18.5 ft above the ground and to an anchor at the ground

15.2 ft from the pole. Allowing 2 ft for tying, how long will the guy wire need to be?

9-440. The length of the shadow of a flagpole is measured to be 44 ft 3 in. long at the same time that the shadow of a yard stick is found to be 30 1/2 in. long. How tall is the flagpole?

9-441. To measure the width of a river, two points A and B are set up 100.5 ft apart on one bank of the river. Point C is located on the other bank of the river directly opposite point A. The angle between the line CA and CB is found to be 38°30′. What is the width of the river?

9-442. In a certain stairway the tread of a single step is 8 in. wide and the rise is 6 in. high. If 26 steps are required to go from one floor to another, what angle does the stairway make with the floor?

9-443. A hexagonal bolt head is 1.5 in. across flats (flat sides). What is its dimension across diagonal corners?

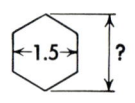

Fig. 9-13

9-444. A standard hexagonal nut for a 2 1/2 in. bolt is 4.476 in. from one corner to a diagonally opposite corner. What is its dimension between opposite flat sides?

9-445. A man climbs a spiral stairway in going from the first to the fourth floor of a building. The vertical distance is 45 ft and the stairway rises 8 ft per turn. If the man follows a spiral path having a radius of 3 ft, how far will he travel in the ascent?

9-446. A tract of land has dimensions as shown in Fig. 9-14. Find the area of the tract in acres.

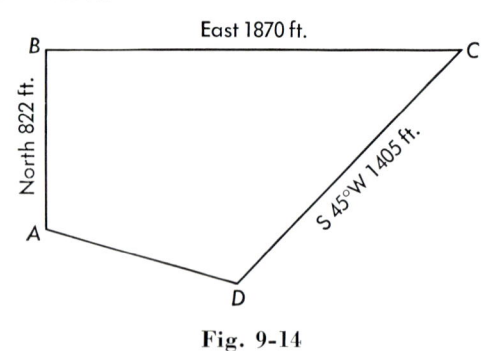

Fig. 9-14

9-447. Find the angle at C and the side BC in Fig. 9-15.

9-448. Find the sides EF and DF in Fig. 9-16.

9-449. Find the area of a triangular lot having the dimensions shown in Fig. 9-17.

Mathematical Tools Useful in Problem Solving

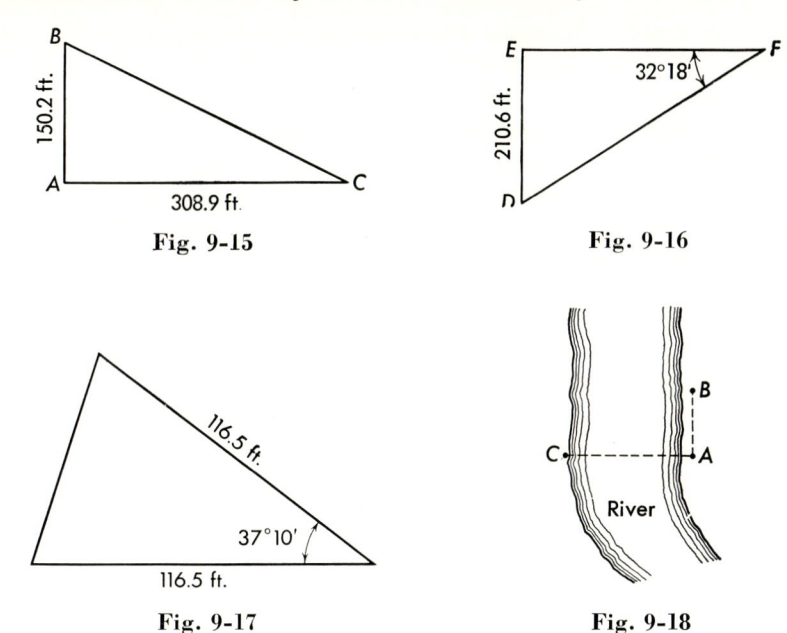

Fig. 9-15

Fig. 9-16

Fig. 9-17

Fig. 9-18

9-450. It is desired to find the width of a river at AC in Fig. 9-18. A line AB 103.7 ft long is laid off along the river bank perpendicular to AC. The angle ABC is measured and found to be 69°47'. How wide is the river at AC?

9-451. A wheelbarrow runway is to be constructed from the ground to the top of a building 22 ft high. The slope of the runway must not exceed 28 per cent. What length must the runway be?

9-452. An aircraft wall panel is in the shape of a right triangle, one angle of which is 65°. The hypotenuse is 20.2 ft long. What are the lengths of the other two sides of the triangle?

9-453. A ladder 14 ft long is leaning against a vertical wall. If the ladder makes an angle of 23°40' with the wall, how far from the wall is the foot of the ladder?

9-454. A guy wire for a telephone pole makes an angle of 56° with the ground and goes to the ground at a point 13.6 ft from the base of the pole. Allowing 6 ft for tying, how long is the guy wire?

9-455. A 4 in. thick concrete slab is to be formed in the shape of a right triangle. One angle of the triangle is 66°40', and the side adjacent this angle is 46 ft 8 in. long. What are the lengths of the hypotenuse and other side of the triangle?

9-456. A storage area in a factory is laid out in the shape of a right triangle. One angle is 57°20', and the side opposite this angle is 84.2 ft. What are the lengths of the hypotenuse and the other side of the triangle?

9-457. The wall of a building is to have a section in the shape of a right triangle painted as the background for a sign. One of the angles is 73°50', and the hypotenuse is 18.83 ft long. What will be the lengths of the other two sides and what will be the area to be painted?

9-458. A factory is to clear an area in the shape of a right triangle in one corner of a building to install a new testing machine, and the area is to be outlined on the floor with a painted stripe. One of the angles in the triangle is 21°20¹, and the hypotenuse is 103.3 ft long. What are the lengths of the other two sides, and what area will be enclosed by the stripe?

9-459. A sheet of No. 4130 steel, 0.250 in. thick, is cut in the shape of a right triangle with the hypotenuse 7.05 in. long. One of the angles is measured to be 38°45'. What will be the area of the triangular section that has been cut?

9-460. A pipe 18.4 ft long is leaning against a vertical wall and reaches to a point 11.8 ft above the base of the wall. What angle does the pipe make with the wall?

9-461. A guy wire is attached 2 ft below the top of a pole 25 ft high. The wire makes an angle of 58°18' with the ground. How long is the guy wire between the pole and the ground?

9-462. A wheelbarrow runway, 38 ft long, reaches from the ground to a point 8 ft above the ground on a building under construction. What is the slope of the runway expressed in percentage?

9-463. How tall is a tower that casts a shadow 142 ft long when the rays of the sun make an angle of 68.5° with the horizontal?

9-464. Find the area in acres of a tract of land in the shape of a right triangle, one angle being 55°30', and the shortest side being 1755 ft long.

9-465. A room is 12 ft wide, 16 ft long, and the ceiling is 10 ft from the floor. How long a piece of wire will be needed to reach from one corner at the floor to a diagonally opposite corner at the ceiling?

9-466. A field is in the shape of a right triangle. The longest side is 872 ft and one other side is 452 ft. How many rods of fence are needed to enclose the field?

9-467. An electric light pole is 32 ft high and has a guy wire fastened to it one-third of the distance from the top. The guy wire is fastened on a level with the bottom of the pole at a point 18 ft away from the foot of the pole. If 30 in. on each end of the wire are used for fastening, how long should the wire be?

9-468. Two fields have the dimensions shown on Fig. 9-19.

$$AD = 451 \text{ ft}$$
$$AB = 1075 \text{ ft}$$
$$BC = 318 \text{ ft}$$

Mathematical Tools Useful in Problem Solving

Angles DAB, ABC, and CED are right angles.
(a) How many rods of fence are necessary to enclose each field separately?
(b) How many acres are in each field?

9-469. A coal hoist track has a slope of 35 per cent. (a) What angle does the track make with the vertical? (b) What length of track will be needed to raise the coal a vertical distance of 88.5 ft?

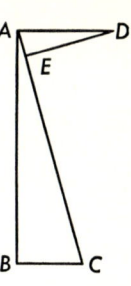

Fig. 9-19

General Triangle Solutions

In many cases the triangle under consideration is not a right triangle, and the simple sine, cosine, and tangent functions cannot be used directly. There are several derived expressions called *laws* which are useful in solving problems on oblique triangles. Since the type of solution to a particular problem will depend on the data given, a discussion of the laws will first be made in order to show what method may be applied.

SINE LAW

In any triangle the ratio of the length of a side to the sine of the angle opposite that side is the same as the ratio of any other side to the sine of the angle opposite it. In symbol form:

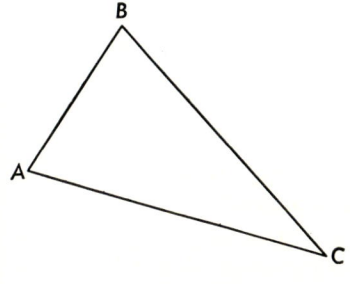

$$\frac{AB}{\sin \angle C} = \frac{BC}{\sin \angle A} = \frac{AC}{\sin \angle B}$$

Fig. 9-20

This expression is called the *sine law*. The student is cautioned not to confuse the meanings of sine functions and sine law.

Example: A triangle has angles of 37° and 68°, and the side included between them is 212 ft long. (a) What is the other angle? (b) What are the lengths of the other two sides?

Solution: As was shown in plane geometry, the sum of the interior angles of a triangle total 180°. The third angle, which we shall call $\angle C$, is therefore

$$\angle C = 180° - (\angle A + \angle B)$$
$$= 180° - (37° + 68°) = 180° - 105°$$
$$\angle C = 75°$$

In order to find the other two sides, use is made of the sine law. Let $AB = 212$ ft, $\angle A = 37°$, and $\angle B = 68°$. Then

$$\frac{AB}{\sin \angle C} = \frac{BC}{\sin \angle A}$$

$$BC = \frac{(AB)(\sin \angle A)}{\sin \angle C}$$

$$= \frac{(212 \text{ ft})(\sin 37°)}{\sin 75°}$$

$$= \frac{(212 \text{ ft})(0.602)}{0.966}$$

$$BC = 132 \text{ ft}$$

AC may be found in the same manner.

$$\frac{AC}{\sin \angle B} = \frac{AB}{\sin \angle C}$$

$$AC = \frac{AB \sin \angle B}{\sin \angle C}$$

$$= \frac{(212 \text{ ft})(\sin 68°)}{\sin 75°}$$

$$= \frac{(212 \text{ ft})(0.927)}{0.966}$$

$$AC = 203.5 \text{ ft}$$

In the event one of the angles of a triangle is larger than 90°, a simple way to obtain the value of the sine of the angle is to subtract the angle from 180° and obtain the sine of this angle to use in the sine law expression.

The sine law can also be used if two sides and an angle of a triangle are known, provided the angle is not the one included between the sides. However, as explained in trigonometry texts, the product of the sine of the angle and the side adjacent must be equal to or less than the side opposite the angle; otherwise no solution is possible.

As an alternate method, the general triangle can be made into right triangles by adding construction lines. Using the data of the example worked above, we may add construction lines (Fig. 9-21) in order to use right triangle solutions.

$$AB = 212 \text{ ft}$$
$$A = 37°$$
$$B = 68°$$

Find: AC, AB, $\angle C$.

The construction line BD is added so that BD is perpendicular to AC.

Mathematical Tools Useful in Problem Solving 155

This divides the triangle ABC into two right triangles, ABD and BDC. Angle C can be found by subtracting the sum of angles A and B from $180°$. In triangle ABD, side BD can be found by using the sine function; and in triangle BDC, since BD and $\angle C$ are known, the use of the sine function will

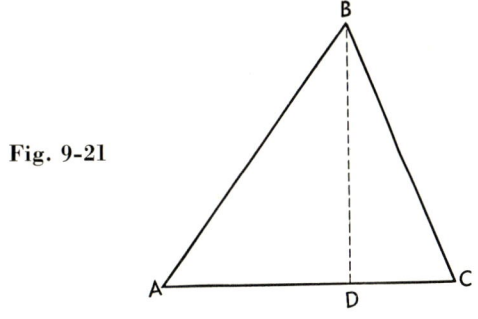

Fig. 9-21

give the length BC. In a similar manner, by using the cosine function, the lengths AD and DC can be found which, when added, will give the length AC. This method of using right triangle solutions is as exact as the sine law but usually will take more time than the sine law method.

Problems

9-470. Solve the following oblique triangles for the unknown sides and angles:

    a. $BC = 48.3$ ft; $\angle A = 43°45'$; $\angle B = 67°30'$
    b. $AC = 241$ ft; $\angle A = 31°10'$; $\angle B = 26°20'$
    c. $BC = 412$ ft; $\angle A = 68°0'$; $\angle B = 65°45'$
    d. $AC = 510$ ft; $\angle B = 44°20'$; $\angle C = 75°40'$
    e. $AB = 179.3$ ft; $\angle B = 22°10'$; $\angle C = 51°50'$
    f. $AB = 1698$ ft; $\angle A = 35°35'$; $\angle C = 122°30'$
    g. $BC = 94.6$ ft; $\angle A = 141°15'$; $\angle C = 17°20'$

9-471. A survey line will cross a small lake (Fig. 9-22). In order to obtain the distance across it, an offset line is run in two legs around the lake.

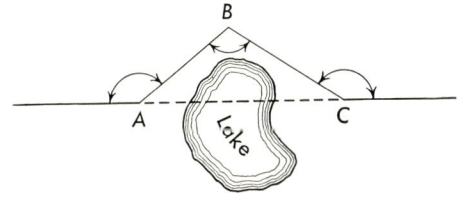

Fig. 9-22

The measurements are as follows: $\angle A = 142°20'$; $\angle B = 107°5'$; $AB = 2075$ ft. (a) How long will the leg BC be in order to locate the point

C on the original line? (b) How long is the computed distance *AC*? (c) What angle must be used at *C* in order to prolong the original line?

9-472. A triangular plot of ground is to be enclosed by a sidewalk. The plot is measured and two angles are found to be 38°30′ and 69°0′, and the side between the two angles is 26.2 ft. The sidewalk is to be 4 ft 6 in. wide and will completely surround the plot on the outside. How many square feet of sidewalk will be needed?

9-473. Solve the following oblique triangles (Fig. 9-23) for the unknown sides and angles:

a. $AC = 61.5$ ft; $BC = 132$ ft; $\angle A = 29°$
b. $AB = 109.7$ ft; $BC = 51.8$ ft; $\angle A = 13°30'$
c. $AB = 606$ ft; $BC = 388$ ft; $\angle A = 36°40'$
d. $AC = 801$ ft; $BC = 1005$ ft; $\angle B = 41°10'$
e. $BC = 492$ ft; $AB = 124$ ft; $\angle A = 36°42'$
f. $BC = 67.4$ ft; $AB = 50.8$ ft; $\angle A = 77°15'$
g. $BC = 838$ ft; $AC = 118.6$ ft; $\angle A = 79°40'$

COSINE LAW

In an oblique triangle, the square of any side is equal to the sum of the squares of the other two sides minus twice the product of the other two sides times the cosine of the included angle. In symbol form:

$$(AB)^2 = (AC)^2 + (BC)^2 - (2)(AC)(BC)(\cos \angle C)$$

This expression is called the *cosine law* and is useful in many problems, although it may not give an answer to the desired precision.

Example: In the triangle in Fig. 9-23, $AC = 35.5$ ft, $BC = 12.6$ ft, and $\angle C = 27°$. Find the side AB and angles A and B.

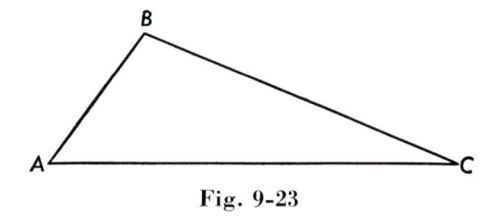

Fig. 9-23

Solution: Using the law of cosines:

$$(AB)^2 = (AC)^2 + (BC)^2 - (2)(AC)(BC)(\cos \angle C)$$
$$(AB)^2 = (35.5)^2 + (12.6)^2 - (2)(35.5)(12.6)(\cos 27°)$$
$$(AB)^2 = (1260) + (159) - (895)(0.891)$$
$$(AB)^2 = 621$$
$$AB = 24.95 \text{ ft}$$

Mathematical Tools Useful in Problem Solving

It may be seen that we are adding and subtracting terms which have only three significant figures and as a result the answer may not be so precise as we may desire.

After the side AB has been determined, the angles at A and B can be found by using the law of sines.

In the event that the angle used in the cosine law formula is larger than 90°, subtract the angle from 180° and determine the cosine of this angle. Remember, however, that the cosine of an angle between 90° and 180° is minus. If the angle used in the formula is larger than 90°, the last term will add to the squared terms.

The above problem may also be solved by using construction lines and making right triangles from the figure. To do this we construct the line BD perpendicular to AC. This will form two right triangles, ABD and

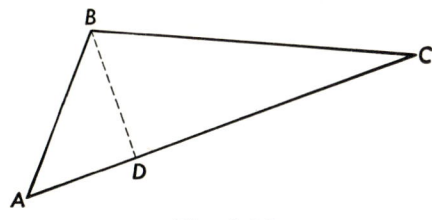

Fig. 9-24

BCD. In triangle BCD, side BD may be found by using BC and the sine of $\measuredangle C$. In a similar manner, by using the cosine of $\measuredangle C$, side DC may be found. From this we can determine side AD in triangle ABD.

$$AC = 35.5 \text{ ft}$$
$$BC = 12.6 \text{ ft}$$
$$\measuredangle C = 27°$$

Using the tangent function, the angle at A can be found, and AB can be determined by the use of the sine or cosine function or the Pythagorean theorem $(AB)^2 = (BD)^2 + (AD)^2$. The right triangle method, while it may take longer to solve, will in general give a more accurate answer.

Problems

9-474. Solve the following oblique triangles for the unknown sides and angles:

a. $BC = 138.7$ ft; $AC = 229.5$ ft; $\measuredangle C = 55°50'$
b. $BC = 426$ ft; $AC = 528$ ft; $\measuredangle C = 50°10'$
c. $AC = 1233$ ft; $AB = 2110$ ft; $\measuredangle A = 115°20'$
d. $BC = 12.11$ ft; $AB = 19.22$ ft; $\measuredangle B = 134°30'$
e. $BC = 691$ ft; $AC = 551$ ft; $\measuredangle C = 49°45'$
f. $AC = 781$ ft; $AB = 221$ ft; $\measuredangle A = 68°15'$
g. $AC = 2487$ ft; $AB = 5143$ ft; $\measuredangle A = 141°40'$

158 Engineering: Elementary Problem Analysis

9-475. Points A and B are located on opposite sides of a building and are located so that they can be seen from a point C. The distance CA is 256 ft and CB is 312 ft. The angle between lines CA and CB is 105°30′. How far apart are points A and B?

9-476. A piece of tin in the shape of a triangle has sides of 3.05 in. and 6.11 in., and the angle between these sides is 76°18′. (a) What are the other angles? (b) What is the area of the piece of tin?

THREE SIDES LAWS

There are a number of formulas derived in trigonometry that will give the angles of an oblique triangle when only three sides are known. The formulas differ considerably in ease of application and precision, especially if logarithms are used. Of all the formulas available, in general the half-angle

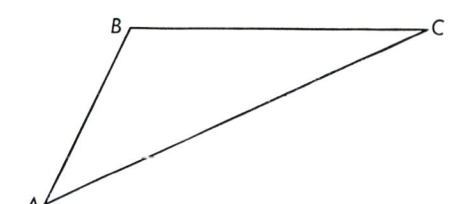

Fig. 9-25

(tangent) formula is better than the others. The formula (half-angle solution) is as follows:

$$\tan \tfrac{1}{2} A = \frac{r}{S - BC}$$

where

$$r = \sqrt{\frac{(S - AB)(S - AC)(S - BC)}{S}}$$

and

$S = \tfrac{1}{2}$ perimeter of triangle

Other formulas that may be used are:

Sine formula (half-angle solution) $\sin \tfrac{1}{2} A = \sqrt{\dfrac{(S - AC)(S - AB)}{(AC)(AB)}}$

Cosine formula (half-angle solution) $\cos \tfrac{1}{2} A = \sqrt{\dfrac{(S)(S - BC)}{(AC)(AB)}}$

Cosine formula (whole angle solution) $\cos A = \dfrac{(2S)(S - BC)}{(AB)(AC)} - 1$

In the last formula, the quantity $(2S)(S - BC)/(AB)(AC)$ will usually be between 1 and 2 and may be read to four figures on the slide rule. Subtracting the 1 in the equation will leave the cosine of the angle correct to three figures. The formula has the advantage that it requires fewer operations. Also it is convenient to use if the slide rule is employed in solving problems.

After finding one angle, the remaining angles may be found by successive

Mathematical Tools Useful in Problem Solving 159

applications of the law, being careful to use the proper side of the triangle in the formula. The sine law may also be used after one angle is found. In order to have a check on the solution, it is better to solve for all three angles rather than solve for two angles, and then subtract their sum from 180°. If each angle is computed separately, their sum should be within the allowable error range of 180°.

As an incidental item in the tangent formula, the constant r is equal to the length of the radius of a circle that may be inscribed in the triangle.

Methods of Solving Oblique Triangle Problems

In order to solve an oblique triangle problem, at least three of the six parts of the triangle must be known, and at least one of the known parts must be a side. In the suggested methods listed below, only the most effective methods are given.

1. Given: two sides and an angle opposite one of them:
   a. Law of sines
   b. Right triangles
2. Given: two angles and one side:
   a. Law of sines
   b. Right triangles.
3. Given: two sides and the included angle:
   a. Law of cosines (answer is usually not dependable to more than three significant figures).
   b. Right triangles.
4. Given: three sides only:
   a. Tangent formula (half-angle solution).
   b. Sine formula (half-angle solution). This formula is not very exact if the half-angle is near 90°.
   c. Cosine formula (half-angle solution). This formula is not very exact if the half-angle is about 6° or less.
   d. Cosine formula (whole angle solution).
   e. Law of cosines (answer is usually not dependable to more than three significant figures).

Methods for Finding Areas of Oblique Triangles

The area of an oblique triangle may be found by any of several methods. Some of the more common methods are given below:

1. Area = ($\frac{1}{2}$)(base)(altitude).
2. Area = $\sqrt{(S)(S - AB)(S - BC)(S - AC)}$, where $S = \frac{1}{2}$ perimeter of the triangle.
3. Area = $\frac{1}{2}$ (product of two sides)(sine of the included angle).

General Problems

9-477. In surveying, the determination of the distance AB is required. The given measurements are shown in Fig. 9-26. What is the distance AB?

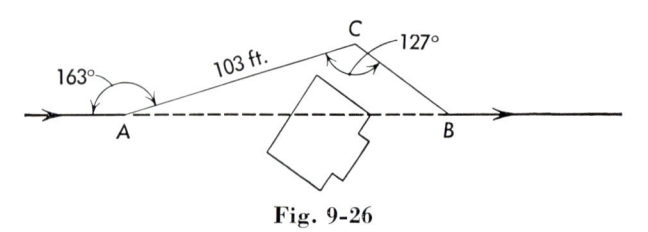

Fig. 9-26

9-478. In a survey, an obstacle in the line AB is encountered. To determine the distance AB, the measurements shown in Fig. 9-27 were made. What is the computed distance AB?

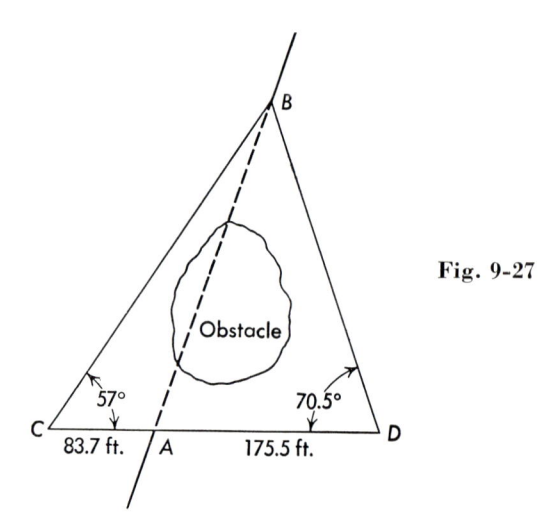

Fig. 9-27

9-479. A triangle has sides 288 ft and 391 ft long, and the angle between the sides is 122°. Find the length of the other side of the triangle.

9-480. What is the area of a triangular tract of land if two sides are 453 ft and 807 ft and the angle between them is 75°?

9-481. From a point 150 ft above a river level and some distance away at right angles to the stream, the angles of depression of the near and far sides in the same line are respectively 30°20′ and 22°45′. What is the width of the river and what is the air line distance from the observer to the far side of the river?

9-482. It is desired to measure the distance across a lake. A stake is set in the ground on each side of the lake 30 ft from the lake, and the distance

Mathematical Tools Useful in Problem Solving

to each stake is found to be 787 ft and 503 ft, respectively. The angle between the line of sight to each stake is found to be 112°. Determine the distance across the lake.

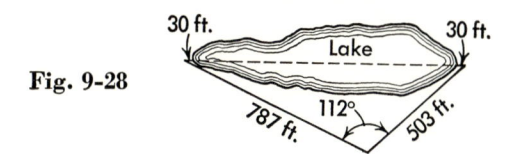

Fig. 9-28

9-483. A triangular tract of land is measured and found to have angles of 45°12′ and 63°50′, and the side between the angles is 902.3 ft. Find the other sides.

9-484. An airplane pilot wishes to fly from town A to town B 158 miles away. The course from A to B is 266° measured clockwise from true north. The airplane airspeed is 85 mph, and the wind is blowing 25 mph from 7° clockwise from true north. (a) How long will it take the plane to fly from A to B, not allowing for time to take off and land? (b) What will be the wind-correction angle, and what should the compass read in order to fly this course?

9-485. Corsicana is 242 miles north 31° east from San Antonio. Beaumont is 286 miles north 78° east from San Antonio. Compute the distance and direction from Beaumont to Corsicana.

9-486. A given tract of land is in the shape of a triangle. One side is 208.3 ft long, another side is 153.8 ft long, and the angle between these two sides is 122°. (a) What is the area of the tract of land? (b) What is the length of the third side?

9-487. An airplane pilot is flying 95 mph along a course of 26° (measured clockwise from true north), but a 20-mph wind from due west is blowing him off his course. What will be his ground speed? What will be his drift angle?

9-488. A piece of land is in the shape of a triangle. One side is 735 ft long, another side is 1035 ft long, and the angle between these sides is 112°. Find the length of the unknown side.

9-489. An airplane pilot wishes to fly from town A to town B, which would be on a line north 18° east (18° east of true north) from A to B. The airline distance is 237 miles from A to B. The wind is blowing from due east with a speed of 32 mph. Airplane speed is 85 mph. (a) What will be the plane speed relative to the ground if he flies along the line joining A and B? (b) What angle will the plane have to be headed to fly this true course? (c) How long will it take to fly from A to B, making no allowance for taking off and landing?

9-490. What is the area of a triangular tract of land if two sides are 453 ft and 807 ft and the angle between them is 128°?

9-491. Find the area of a sheet of galvanized iron having dimensions as shown in Fig. 9-29.

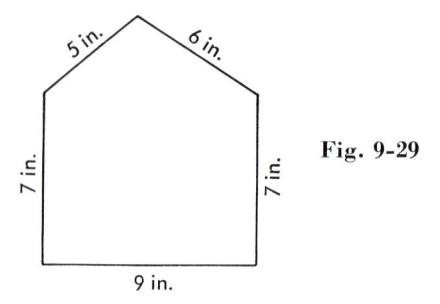

Fig. 9-29

D—THE SLIDE RULE

The study of the slide rule is a further study of logarithms. The slide rule is a graphic logarithmic table and owes its beginning to John Napier who in 1614 announced his discovery of logarithms. In 1620 Edmund Gunter conceived the idea of using logarithm scales constructed with antilogarithm markings for use in simple mathematical operations. William Oughtred, Sir Isaac Newton, Amedee Mannheim, and others further developed these logarithmic scales until today there are many types and shapes of rules available.

Essentially the slide rule in general use is a close adaption of Gunter's logarithmic scales, so arranged in convenient form that the logarithms may be mechanically added and subtracted.

Care of the Slide Rule

The slide rule is a precision instrument and should be afforded reasonable care in order to preserve its accuracy. Modern rules stand up well under normal usage, but dropping the rule or striking objects with it will likely impair its accuracy.

In use the rule may collect dirt under the glass of the indicator. Inserting a piece of paper under the glass and sliding the indicator across it will frequently dislodge the dirt without necessitating the removal of the indicator glass from the frame. If the glass has to be removed for cleaning, it should be realigned when replaced, using the techniques described below.

The rule should never be washed with abrasive materials, alcohol, or other solvents, since these will remove the markings on the rule. If the rule needs to be cleaned, it may be wiped carefully with a damp cloth, but the excessive use of water should be avoided because this will cause wooden rules to warp.

The metal-frame rules are not subject to warping due to moisture changes, but they must be protected against blows which would bend them or other-

Mathematical Tools Useful in Problem Solving 163

wise throw them out of alignment. A light layer of lubricant of the type specified by the manufacturer of the metal rule will increase the ease with which the working parts move. This is particularly important during the "breaking in" period of the new rule. The same precautions for wooden rules with regard to cleaning the markings on the face should be observed for metal rules.

Manipulation of the Rule

Some techniques in manipulation of the rule have been found to speed up the setting of the slide and indicator. Two of these suggested procedures are described in the following paragraphs.

1. Settings may usually be made more rapidly by use of two hands and holding of the rule so that the thumbs are on the bottom of the rule with the backs of the hands toward the operator.

2. In moving either the indicator or the slide, the settings are easier to make if the index fingers and thumbs of both hands are used to apply forces toward each other than if only one hand is used to apply force. For example, in setting the indicator, put the forefinger of each hand against the respective edges of the indicator and move it by a combined squeezing and rolling motion of the forefingers. The same general procedure is used in

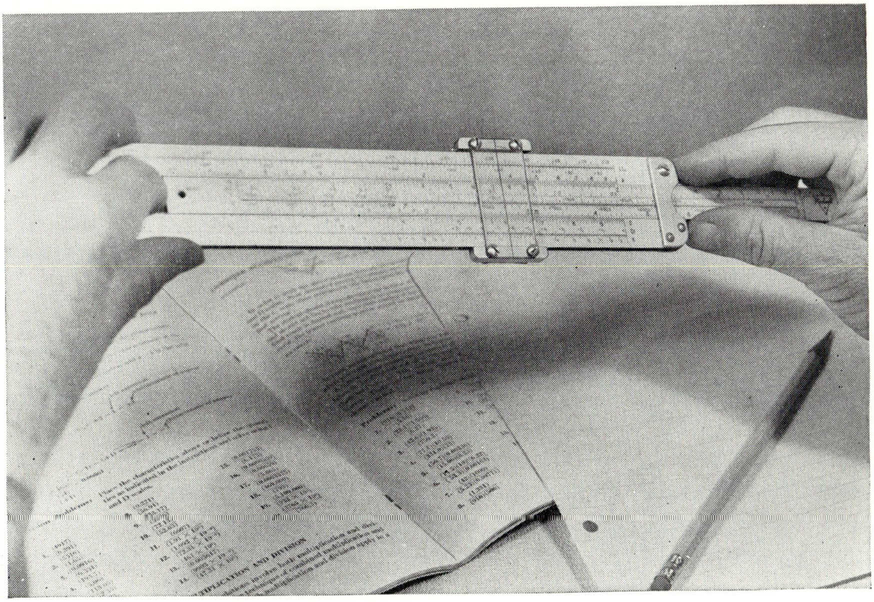

Fig. 9-30. In moving the slide, use fingers to exert forces toward each other. A rolling motion with the forefinger aids in setting the indexes. Avoid pinching the frame because this will make the slide bind.

setting the slide, where both hands exert forces toward each other. The student is cautioned in setting the slide not to squeeze the frame of the rule, since this will cause the slide to bind.

Adjusting the Rule

Regardless of the make, most rules have the same general form of adjustment. The method of adjustment is simple but should not be applied in a hurry. It is desirable to use a magnifying glass, if one is available, to aid in lining up the scales and hairline.

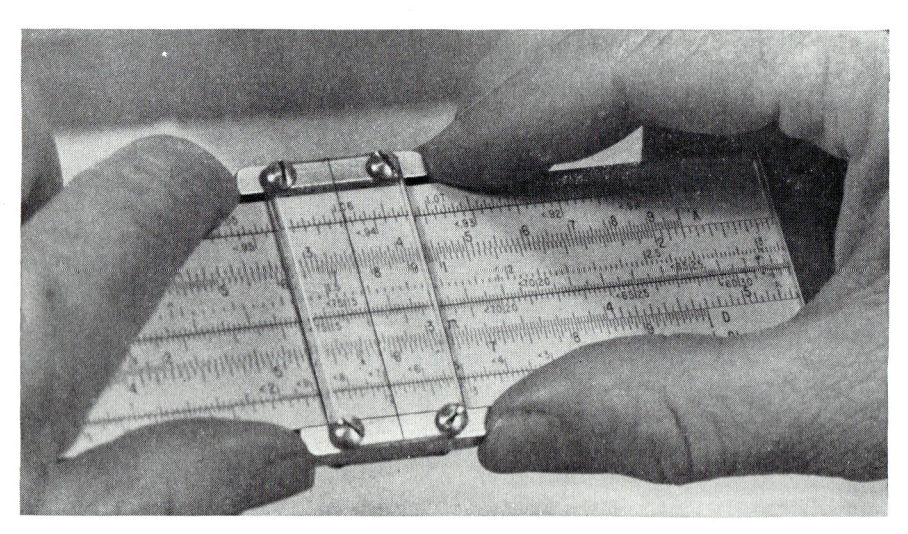

Fig. 9-31. **In setting the indicator, a rolling motion with the forefingers will permit rapid and precise locations to be made. Keeping the fingers of both hands in contact with the indicator, exert slight forces toward each other with both hands.**

To determine whether or not a rule needs adjustment, line up the indexes of the C and D scales. The indexes of the scales above and below the C and D scales should also be aligned. If they do not coincide, slightly loosen the screws which clamp the top bar of the frame and carefully move the frame to the right or left until the indexes are aligned. Tighten the screws slightly and move the slide to check for proper friction. If the alignment and friction are satisfactory, tighten the frame screws to complete that part of the adjustment.

Next, test the hairline for proper alignment by setting the hairline over the indexes of the C and D scales and checking to see that the hairline also coincides with the other indexes on this side of the rule. If it does not coincide with all the scale indexes, slightly loosen the screws which hold the glass frame to the indicator. Rotate the frame slowly until the hairline

Mathematical Tools Useful in Problem Solving 165

coincides with the indexes on this side of the rule. Tighten the screws holding this frame; then, while the hairline is aligned on the indexes of the C and D scales, turn the rule over and check for the alignment of the hairline with the indexes of the scales on the other side of the rule. If the hairline does not coincide with the indexes on this side of the rule, loosen the screws on the indicator and make the necessary adjustment as before.

Check the tightness of all screws when the adjustment is completed. The student is cautioned not to use excessive force in tightening any screws, as the threads may become stripped. With reasonable care, a slide rule will usually require very little adjustment over a considerable period of time.

Accuracy of the Rule

Most measurements made in scientific work contain from two to four significant figures; that is, digits which are considered to be reliable. Since the mathematical operations of multiplication, division, and processes involving roots and powers will not increase the number of significant figures when the answer is obtained, the slide rule maintains an accuracy of three or four significant figures. The reliability of the digits obtained from the rule depends upon the precision with which the operator makes his settings. It is generally assumed that with a 10-in. slide rule, the error of the answer will not exceed about a tenth of 1 per cent. This is one part in a thousand.

A common tendency is to use more than three or four significant digits in such numbers as π (3.14159265 · · ·) and ϵ (2.71828 · · ·). The slide rule automatically "rounds off" such numbers to three or four significant figures which prevents false accuracy (such as can occur in longhand operations) from occurring in the answer.

Rules of modern manufacture are designed so that results read from the graduations are as reliable as the naked eye can distinguish. The use of magnifying devices may make the settings easier to locate but usually do not have an appreciable effect on the accuracy of the result.

Instructions for Reading Scale Graduations

Before studying the scales of the slide rule, let us review the reading of scale graduations in general. First let us examine a common 12-in. ruler.

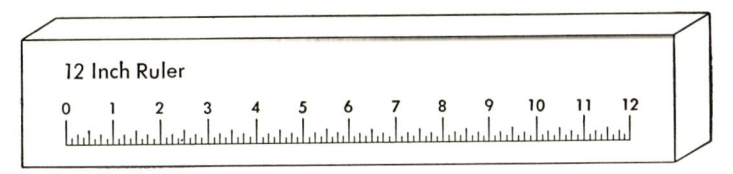

Fig. 9-32

Example:

We see that the total length of 1 ft has been divided into twelve equal parts and that each part is further divided into quarters, eighths, and sixteenths. This subdivision into eighths, sixteenths, etc., is necessary so that the workman need not estimate fractional parts of an inch.

Example: Measure the unknown lengths L_1 and L_2.

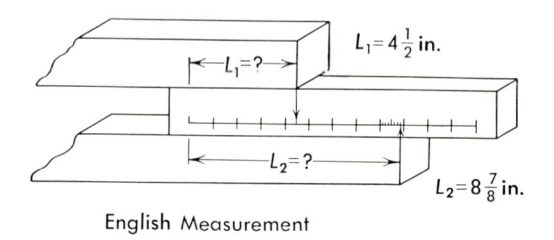

English Measurement

Fig. 9-33

The English system of measurement as shown in Fig. 9-33 is probably familiar to all students. The unit of length in the metric system which corresponds to the yard in the English system is called the *meter*. The meter is 39.37 in. in length. For convenience, the meter is divided into one hundred equal parts called *centimeters*, and each centimeter is divided into ten equal parts called *millimeters*. Since we can express units and fractional parts of units as tenths or hundredths of the length of a unit, this system of measurement is many times preferred for engineering work.

Example: Measure the unknown lengths L_1 and L_2.

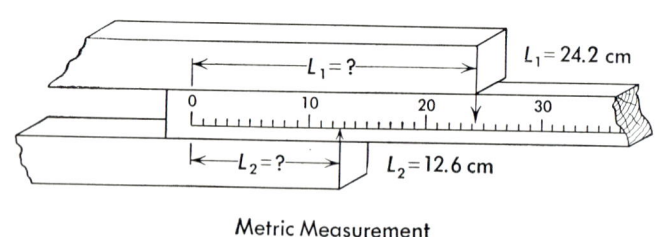

Metric Measurement

Fig. 9-34

Mathematical Tools Useful in Problem Solving

The scales of the slide rule are basically divided as in the metric system in that between each division there are ten subdivisions. However, the student will find that the main divisions are not equal distances apart. Sometimes the divisions will be subdivided by graduations, and at other times the student will need to estimate the subdivisions by eye. Let us examine the D scale of a slide rule.

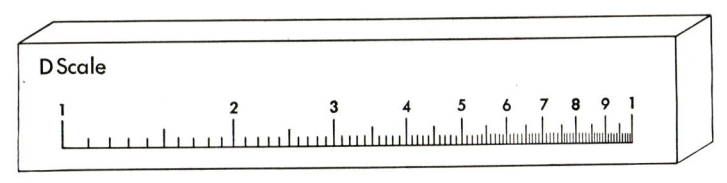

Fig. 9-35

Since the graduations are so close together, let us examine the rule in three portions: from left index to 2, from 2 to 4, and from 4 to right index.

Example: Left index to 2.

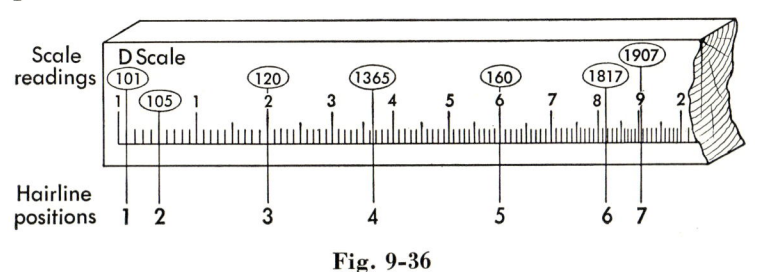

Fig. 9-36

The student should refer to his own rule for comparisons as he studies the diagrams in this chapter. In the above example we note that from the left index (read as one-zero-zero) to the digit 1 (read as one-one-zero), there are ten graduations. The first is read as *one-zero-one* (101), the second as *one-zero-two* (102), etc. Digit 2 is read as *one-two-zero* (120), digit 3 as *one-three-zero* (130), etc. If need be, the student can subdivide by eye the distance between each of the small, unnumbered graduations. Thus, if the hairline is moved to position 4 (see example above), the reading would be *one-three-six-five* or 1365. Position 6 might be read as 1817 and position 7 as 1907. The student is reminded that each small graduation on the rule has a value of 1.

168   *Engineering: Elementary Problem Analysis*

Example: 2 to 4.

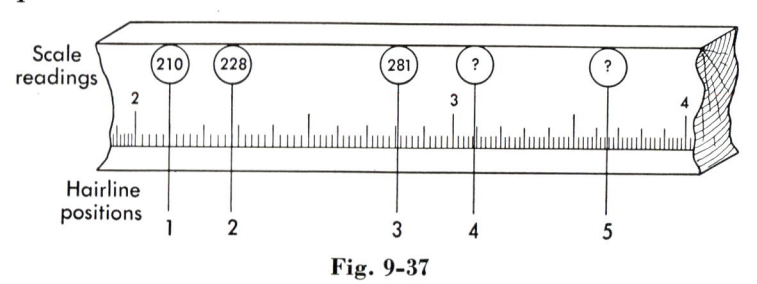

Fig. 9-37

Since the distance between 2 and 3 is not so long as the distance from the left index to 2, no numbers are placed over the graduations. However, we can use the same reasoning and subdivide as in the previous examples. Set the hairline in position 1 (see example) and read *two-one-zero*, or 210. We note that the distance between 200 and 210 has been divided into five divisions. Each subdivision would thus have a value of 2. Consequently, if the hairline is in position 2, a reading of 228 would be obtained. Remember that each of the smallest graduations is valued at 2 and not 1. What are the readings at 3, 4, and 5?*

Example: 4 to right index.

The distance between 4 and 5 is still shorter than the distance between 3 and 4, and it becomes increasingly more difficult to print such small subdivisions. For this reason there are ten main divisions between 4 and 5,

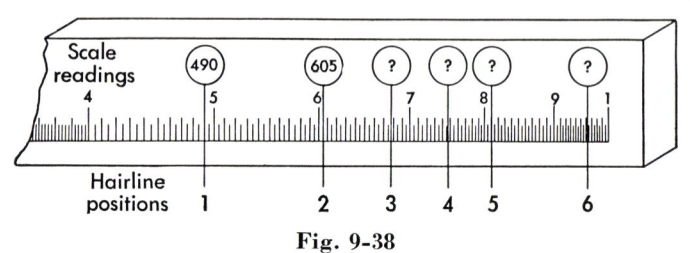

Fig. 9-38

each of which is subdivided into two parts. With this type of marking it is possible to read two figures and estimate the third or to get three significant figures on all readings. If the hairline is set as indicated in position 1, the reading would be *four-nine-zero* (490), and position 2 would give *six-zero-five* (605). What are the readings at hairline positions 3, 4, 5, and 6?†

If the student has followed the reasoning thus far, he should have little trouble in determining how to read an indicated value on any scale of the slide rule. Several of the following problems should be worked, and the student should thoroughly understand the principle of graduation subdivision before he attempts to delve further into the uses of the slide rule.

* Readings at 3, 4, and 5 are respectively 281, 309, and 365.
† Readings at 3, 4, 5, and 6 are respectively 678, 746, 810, and 963.

Problems on Scale Readings

9-492.

Read Answer on

SET HAIRLINE TO	ST SCALE	T SCALE	LL$_3$ SCALE	CI SCALE	K SCALE	DF SCALE	LL$_{01}$ SCALE	LL$_2$ SCALE	L SCALE
1. 210 on D									
2. 398 on D									
3. 1056 on D									
4. 1004 on D									
5. 866 on D									
6. 222 on D									
7. 1196 on D									
8. 439 on D									
9. 5775 on D									
10. 2325 on D									
11. 917 on D									
12. 323 on D									
13. 1077 on D									
14. 1854 on D									
15. 268 on D									
16. 833 on D									
17. 551 on D									
18. 667 on D									
19. 8125 on D									
20. 406 on D									
21. 918 on D									
22. 5775 on D									
23. 1466 on D									
24. 288 on D									
25. 466 on D									
26. 789 on D									
27. 1107 on D									
28. 396 on D									
29. 1999 on D									
30. 998 on D									

Construction of the Scales

Let us examine how the main scales (C and D) of the rule are constructed. As a basis for this examination, let us set up a scale of some length with a beginning graduation called a *left index* and an end graduation called a *right index*.

Example:

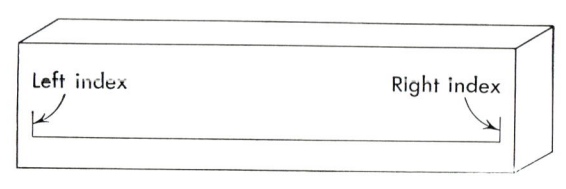

Fig. 9-39

Next let us subdivide this scale into ten equal divisions and then further subdivide each large division into ten smaller divisions. We call this the *L scale*.

Example:

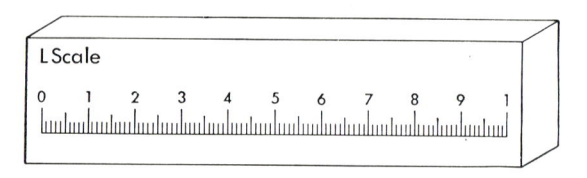

Fig. 9-40

Let us place a blank scale beneath this L scale so that the left index of the L scale will coincide with the left index of the blank scale. We shall call the blank scale the *D scale*.

Example:

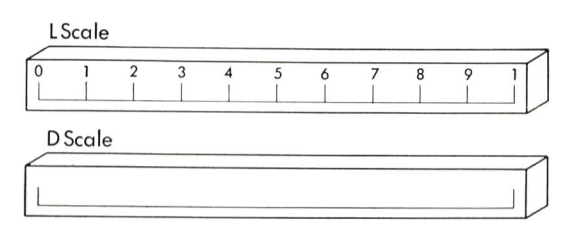

Fig. 9-41

Mathematical Tools Useful in Problem Solving

Now let us graduate the D scale in such a way that each division mark is directly beneath the mark on the L scale which represents the mantissa of the logarithm of the number. Before examining the scales closer, we should note that the mantissa of 2 is 0.3010, the mantissa of 3 is 0.4771, the mantissa of 4 is 0.6021, and the mantissa of 5 is 0.6990, etc.

If the student will examine his rule, he will find a C or D scale and an L scale. The C and D scales are identical, so use the D scale since it is printed on the body of the rule. Several problems should be worked, determining the logarithms of numbers by using the slide rule.

Example:

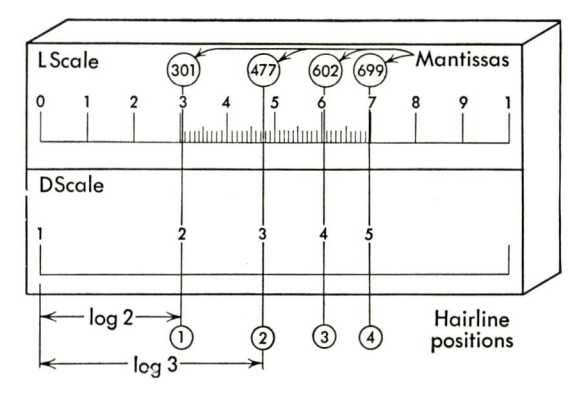

Fig. 9-42

Remember to:
1. Set the number on the D scale.
2. Read the mantissa of the number on the L scale.
3. Supply the characteristic, using the *characteristic rules* given in the discussion on logarithms.

Example: What is the logarithm of 55.8?

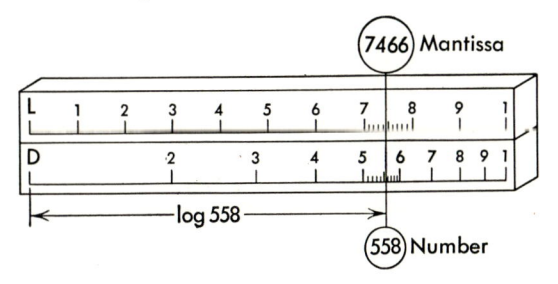

Fig. 9-43

172   *Engineering: Elementary Problem Analysis*

From slide rule: Mantissa of 55.8 = 0.7466

From characteristic rules:

                Characteristic of 55.8 = 1.0000
Therefore   log of 55.8 = 1.7466

From the preceding example we can see that the D scale is so constructed that each number lies below the mantissa of its logarithm. Also we note that the distance from the left index of the D scale to any number on the D scale represents (in length) the mantissa of the number. Since the characteristic of a logarithm is governed merely by the location of the decimal point, we may neglect it for the time being.

Example: D Scale.

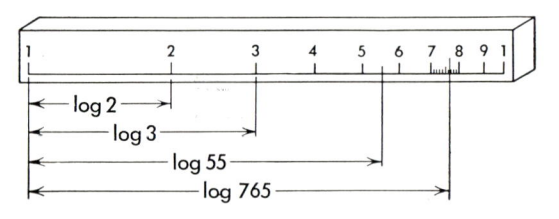

Fig. 9-44

Problems

Use the slide rule and find the logarithms.

9-493. 894.
9-494. 1.845
9-495. 0.438
9-496. 81.5
9-497. 604.
9-498. 7.41
9-499. 11.91
9-500. 215.
9-501. 993,000.
9-502. 5.91×10^7

9-503. 9.06×10^{-4}
9-504. 66.9×10^8
9-505. 155.8×10^2
9-506. 23.66×10^{-4}
9-507. 0.06641×10^8
9-508. 9.33×10^{-2}
9-509. 29.88×10^{-1}
9-510. 0.552×10^6
9-511. 33.67×10^{-9}
9-512. 4.40×10^3

9-513. 98,700
9-514. 40.3×10^{-9}
9-515. 21.8×10^9
9-516. 1.057×10^{-3}
9-517. $719. \times 10^5$
9-518. 49.2×10^7
9-519. 0.00885×10^1
9-520. 0.0305×10^3
9-521. 0.000551×10^{-12}
9-522. 13.35×10^{-6}

Multiplication

As shown in Fig. 9-42 the C and D scales are divided logarithmically with all graduations being marked with their corresponding antilogarithms. These scales can be used for multiplication by adding a given logarithmic length on one of the scales to another logarithmic length which may be found on the other scale.

Mathematical Tools Useful in Problem Solving

Example: $(2)(3) = 6$.

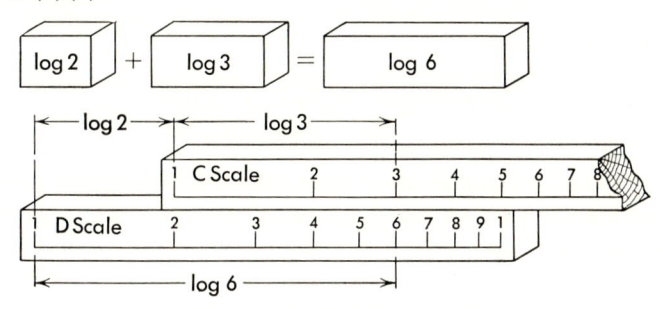

Fig. 9-45

Procedure:

1. Set the left index of the C scale above the digit 2 on the D scale.
2. Move the hairline to the right until it is directly over 3 on the C scale.
3. Read the answer (6) directly under the hairline on the D scale.

In some cases when the logarithm of one number is added to the logarithm of another number, the multiplier extends out into space, and it is impossible to move the indicator to the product (Fig. 9-46).

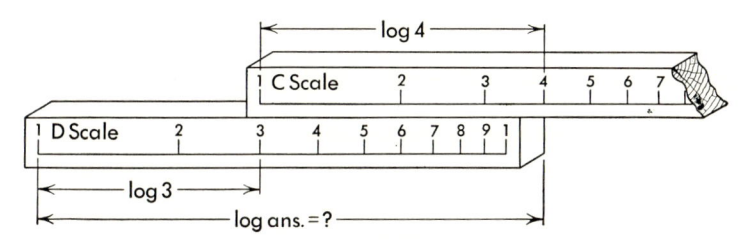

Fig. 9-46

Example: $(3)(4) = ?$

In this case it is necessary to relocate the right index of the C scale above the figure 3 on the D scale and move the hairline to 4 on the C scale.

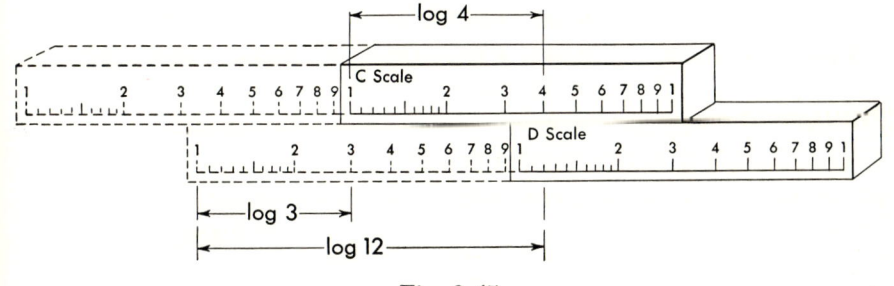

Fig. 9-47

Example: $(3)(4) = 12$

Procedure:

1. Set the right index of the C scale above the digit 3 on the D scale.
2. Move the hairline to the left until it is directly over 4 on the C scale.
3. Read answer (12) directly under the hairline on the D scale.

The location of the decimal point in multiplication problems is ascertained either by inspection or by applying one of the several methods explained in the following paragraphs.

Methods of Determining Decimal Point Location

Several methods which may be used are given below. While these methods are by no means all-inclusive of ways to determine decimal point location, they will be suitable for instruction of students, particularly those having an elementary mathematical background.

INSPECTION METHOD

This is the simplest method and consists of determining the decimal point location by observing the location of the decimal point in the numbers involved in a slide rule operation and locating the decimal point in the answer by a quick estimation.

Example: $\dfrac{(28.1)}{(7.20)} = 390$ (decimal point to be determined)

A quick examination of the numbers involved shows that the answer will be somewhere near the number "4," so the answer evidently will be 3.90. This method will have its widest application where only one or two operations are involved and where the numbers lie between 1 and 100.

Example: $(1.22)(58.2) = 70.9$

In the above example, it is seen that the number 58.2 is multiplied by a number which is a little more than 1. Therefore the answer will be slightly greater than 58.2.

APPROXIMATE NUMBER METHOD

This method is an extension of the inspection method. It involves the same general procedures except that the numbers used in a problem are "rounded off" and written down, and an approximate answer is obtained which will show the decimal point location.

Example: $(37.6)(0.188)(5.71)(11.92) = 482$ (decimal point to be located)

Rewrite, using simple numbers near in value to the problem numbers.

$$[(40)(0.2)][(6)(10)] = (8)(60) = 480$$

Mathematical Tools Useful in Problem Solving

This shows that the answer in the example problem should be expressed as 482.

A problem that is more involved can be solved by this method, as shown by the following example.

Example: $\dfrac{(12{,}560)(0.0387)}{(594{,}000)} = 819$ (decimal point to be determined)

Using simple numbers near in value to the problem numbers, write the same problem:

$$\dfrac{(12{,}000)(0.04)}{(600{,}000)} = 0.0008$$

By cancellation the numbers can be simplified still further to obtain an approximate answer of 0.0008. One way of doing this would be to divide 12,000 into 600,000, obtaining a value of 50 in the denominator. This value of 50 divided into 0.04 gives 0.0008. Referring to the original problem, the decimal point must be located to give an answer of 0.000819.

POWER-OF-TEN METHOD

The power-of-ten method is a varition of the characteristic method discussed later in this book. In this method the numbers in the problem are expressed as a single digit, a decimal point, the remaining digits, and followed by the number "10" raised to the appropriate power. This process simplifies the numbers, and the decimal point in the answer can be determined by inspection or by the approximation method.

Example:

$(15.9)(0.0077)(30500)(4660) = 1741$ (decimal point to be located)

Write the same problem with each number expressed as a digit, decimal point, and the remaining digits followed by the appropriate power of 10.

$(1.59 \times 10^1)(7.7 \times 10^{-3})(3.05 \times 10^4)(4.66 \times 10^3) = 174.1 \times 10^5$

Since all the numbers are now expressed as numbers between 1 and 10, followed by 10 to a power, the approximate value of the multiplication can be determined rapidly, by inspection, to be about 170. The power of 10 is obtained by adding algebraically the powers of 10 of each of the rewritten numbers. The answer to the original problem is therefore 174.1×10^5, or 17,410,000.

Example: $\dfrac{(28{,}500)(307)}{(0.552)} = 1585$ (decimal point to be located)

Rewrite the problem using powers of 10:

$$\dfrac{(2.85 \times 10^4)(3.07 \times 10^2)}{(5.52 \times 10^{-1})} = 1.585 \times 10^7$$

By inspection and approximation the product of the numerator will be found to be near 9, and dividing 5.52 into it will give about 1.6. This procedure determines the decimal point location for the digits of the answer. The powers of 10 are added algebraically to give 10^7, which completes the decimal point location in the answer. The answer may be rewritten as 15,850,000 if desired.

DIGIT METHOD

In this method the numbers of digits in each number are counted and the following rules apply.

Multiplication: Add the number of digits to the left of the decimal of each number to be multiplied. This will give the number of digits to the left of the decimal in the answer. If the slide projects to the right, subtract one from the number of digits to be pointed off.

Example: $(27,300)(15.1) = 412,000$

There are five digits to be counted in the first number and only two digits in the second number. Since the slide projects to the right, subtract 1. There will be six digits to the left of the decimal point in the answer.

Division: Subtract the number of digits to the left of the decimal in the denominator from the number of digits to the left of the decimal in the numerator to obtain the number of digits to the left of the decimal in the answer. If the slide projects to the right in division, add one digit more to be pointed off.

Example: $$\frac{(12.88)}{(466)} = 0.0276$$

Subtracting three digits in the denominator from two digits in the numerator gives (-1) digit to be located in the answer. Inspection shows that the answer will be a decimal quantity. In any case where decimal numbers are encountered, the method of counting the digits is to begin at the decimal point and count the number of zeroes between the decimal point and the first digit, which is not zero, to the right of the decimal. Since the digit difference shown above is (-1), there must be one zero between the decimal point and the first significant figure, which gives an answer of 0.0276. The student will observe that the digit count of decimal numbers is considered as a minus quantity and that the addition and subtraction of the digit count must take into account any minus signs.

Variations and extensions of these methods may readily be set up to solve problems involving roots and powers.

Many schools prefer the "characteristic" or "projection method" to determine decimal point location, and this method is given in detail in the discussions which follow.

Mathematical Tools Useful in Problem Solving

PROJECTION RULE FOR MULTIPLICATION

1. Before attempting to solve the problem, place the characteristic of each quantity above or below it.
2. Solve for the sum of the characteristics by simple addition and place this number above the space for the answer.
3. Begin the multiplication with the slide rule, and each time the left index of the C scale extends past the left index of the D scale, add a (+1) to the sum of the characteristics previously determined.
4. Add the original sum to the +1's obtained from left extensions. The total number is the characteristic of the answer.

Example:

one left extension ↓

CHARACTERISTICS. (0) + (0) → (0) + 1 = +1 ← characteristic of answer
(5)   (3) =   15   Answer

Example:

one left extension ↓

CHARACTERISTICS. (+2) + (−3) → (−1) + 1 = 0
(390)   (0.0030) =   1.17   Answer

Example:

two left extensions ↓

CHARACTERISTICS. (−3) + (+1) + (+2) + (+4) → (+4) + 2 = +6
(0.001633) (79.1) (144) (96,500) = 1,800,000   Answer

Example:

three left extensions ↓

CHARACTERISTICS. (+1) + (+3) + (−3) + (−4) → (−3) + 3 = 0
(73.7) (4460) (0.00704) (0.000853) =   1.975   Answer

Example:

two left extensions ↓

CHARACTERISTICS. (+2) + (+2) + (0) → (+4) + 1 + 1 =   +6
(861) (204) (9.0) = 1,580,000 or (1.58)(10)^6 Answer

Multiplication Problems

9-523. (46.8)(11.97)
9-524. (479.)(11.07)
9-525. (9.35)(77.8)
9-526. (10.09)(843,000,)
9-527. (77,900.)(0.467)
9-528. (123.9)(0.00556)
9-529. (214.9)(66.06)
9-530. (112.2)(0.953)
9-531. (87.0)(1.006)

9-532. (1,097,000)(1.984)
9-533. (43.8)(0.000779)
9-534. (31.05)(134.9)
9-535. (117.9)(98.9)
9-536. (55.6)(68.1)
9-537. (1.055)(85.3)
9-538. (33,050.)(16,900.)
9-539. (6.089)(44.87)
9-540. (34.8)(89.7)

9-541. (43,900.)(19.07)
9-542. (41.3)(87.9)
9-543. (99.7)(434,000.)
9-544. (10.68)(21.87)
9-545. (88,900.)(54.7)
9-546. (113,900.)(48.1)
9-547. (95,500.)(0.000479)
9-548. (0.0956)(147.2)(0.0778)
9-549. (15.47)(82.5)(975,000.)

9-550. (37.8)(22,490,000.)(0.15)
9-551. (1.048)(0.753)(0.933)
9-552. $(1.856)(10)^3(21.98)$
9-553. (57.7)(46.8)(3.08)
9-554. (0.045)(0.512)(115.4)
9-555. (0.307)(46.3)(7.94)
9-556. $(2.229)(86.05)(16,090.)(\pi)$
9-557. (44,090.)(38.9)(667.)(55.9)
9-558. (568.)(46.07)(3.41)(67.9)

9-559. (75.88)(0.0743)(0.1185)(0.429)
9-560. $(10)^{-4}(69.8)(11.03)(0.901)$
9-561. $(46.3)(0.865)(10)^{-9}(0.953)(\pi)$
9-562. (665.)(35,090)(0.1196)(0.469)
9-563. (888.)(35.9)(77.9)(0.652)
9-564. $(43.4)(0.898)(70.09)(0.113)(\pi)$
9-565. (0.0969)(0.1034)(0.1111)(0.1066)
9-566. $(1.084 \times 10^{-5})(0.1758 \times 10^{13})(66.4)(0.901)$
9-567. $(234.5)(10)^4(21.21)(0.874)(0.0100)$
9-568. $(\pi)(26.88)(0.1682)(0.1463)(45.2)(1.007)$
9-569. $(75.8)(0.1044 \times 10^8)(10)^{-2}(54,000)(0.769)$
9-570. $(34.5)(31.09)(10^{-6})(54.7)(0.677)(0.1003)$
9-571. $(6.08)(5.77)(46.8)(89.9)(3.02)(0.443)(\pi)$
9-572. $(1.055)(6.91)(31.9)(11.21)(\pi)(35.9)(4.09)$

Division

We see that multiplication is merely the process of mechanically adding the logarithms of the quantities involved. From the preceding section on logarithms it follows that division is merely the process of mechanically subtracting the logarithm of the divisor from the logarithm of the dividend.

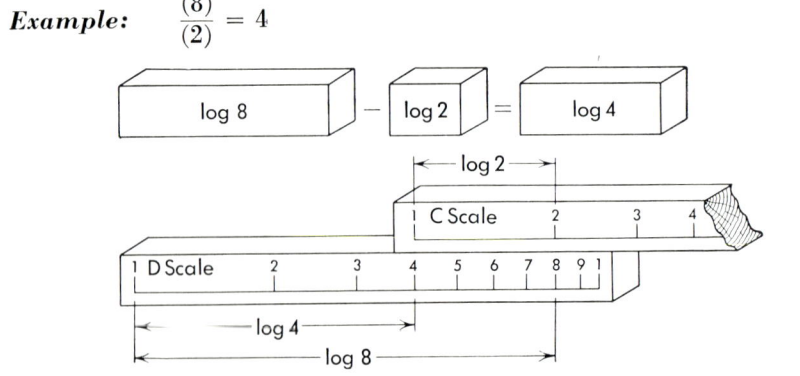

Example: $\quad \dfrac{(8)}{(2)} = 4$

Fig. 9-48

Mathematical Tools Useful in Problem Solving

Procedure:

1. Set the divisor (2) on the C scale directly above the dividend (8), which is located on the D scale.
2. Read the answer (4) on the D scale directly under the left index of the C scale.

For location of the decimal point in division problems the following *Projection Rule* should be observed.

PROJECTION RULE FOR DIVISION

1. Locate the characteristic of the dividend above it and the characteristic of the divisor below it.
2. Subtract the characteristic of the divisor from the characteristic of the dividend.
3. For every left extension of the C scale's left index, add a (-1) to the total characteristic already obtained.
4. The sum is the characteristic of the answer.

Example:

$$\frac{\overset{(+2)}{(575)}}{\underset{(0)}{(6.05)}} = (9.50)(10)^1 \qquad (+2) - (0) \to +2 - \overset{\text{left extension}}{1} = +\overset{\text{characteristic of answer}}{1}$$

Example:

$$\frac{\overset{(-1)}{(0.465)}}{\underset{(+1)}{(54)}} = (8.61)(10)^{-3} \qquad (-1) - (+1) \to -2 - \overset{\text{left extension}}{1} = -\overset{\text{characteristic of answer}}{3}$$

Problems in Division

9-573. $\dfrac{89.9}{45.}$

9-574. $\dfrac{147.}{22.}$

9-575. $\dfrac{9.06}{7.1}$

9-576. $\dfrac{1,985.}{78.55}$

9-577. $\dfrac{19,230.}{64.88}$

9-578. $\dfrac{87,600.}{43.8}$

9-579. $\dfrac{54.8}{9.10}$

9-580. $\dfrac{0.877}{33.07}$

9-581. $\dfrac{11.44}{24.9}$

9-582. $\dfrac{187,900.}{71.45}$

9-583. $\dfrac{0.00882}{87.04}$

9-584. $\dfrac{0.675}{54.8}$

9-585. $\dfrac{87.9}{45.7}$

9-586. $\dfrac{164,800.}{3.88}$

9-587. $\dfrac{7.09 \times 10^3}{18.45}$

Engineering: Elementary Problem Analysis

9-588. $\dfrac{(0.001755)}{(6.175)}$

9-589. $\dfrac{(0.0000559)}{(0.00659)}$

9-590. $\dfrac{(5.065)}{(0.0003375)}$

9-591. $\dfrac{(469,000)}{(793)}$

9-592. $\dfrac{(5,100,000)}{(933 \times 10^5)}$

9-593. $\dfrac{(3765 \times 10^3)}{(760.3)}$

9-594. $\dfrac{(4917)}{(0.391)}$

9-595. $\dfrac{(5516)}{(1.65)}$

9-596. $\dfrac{(0.0916)}{(0.331)}$

9-597. $\dfrac{(193.7)}{(5.06)}$

9-598. $\dfrac{(113.05)}{(72.35)}$

9-599. $\dfrac{(32.33)}{(46.77)}$

9-600. $\dfrac{(3.17)}{(3.1416)}$

9-601. $\dfrac{(0.221)}{(56.91)}$

9-602. $\dfrac{(233.17)}{(5506)}$

9-603. $\dfrac{(72.13)}{(52.03)}$

9-604. $\dfrac{(6607)}{(1.91 \times 10^5)}$

9-605. $\dfrac{(1.993 \times 10^{-8})}{(72.31 \times 10^{-6})}$

9-606. $\dfrac{(461 \times 10^3)}{(0.003617)}$

9-607. $\dfrac{(9903 \times 10^{-5})}{(47.31 \times 10^3)}$

9-608. $\dfrac{0.711}{11,980.}$

9-609. $\dfrac{0.01253}{66.8}$

9-610. $\dfrac{0.974}{1.058}$

9-611. $\dfrac{0.000497}{38.9 \times 10^{-5}}$

9-612. $\dfrac{48.6 \times 10^{-9}}{1.977 \times 10^5}$

9-613. $\dfrac{69,990. \times 10^{18}}{43.9 \times 10^{-2}}$

9-614. $\dfrac{5.06 \times 10^{-7}}{0.001853 \times 10^9}$

9-615. $\dfrac{1.097 \times 10^{-6}}{458. \times 10^{-1}}$

9-616. $\dfrac{89.99 \times 10^{-3}}{40.7 \times 10^{-6}}$

9-617. $\dfrac{659,000}{0.1148 \times 10^{-3}}$

9-618. $\dfrac{883.8}{3.89 \times 10^{-11}}$

9-619. $\dfrac{15.06 \times 10^{-7}}{33.8 \times 10^{-1}}$

9-620. $\dfrac{1.095}{24.66}$

9-621. $\dfrac{33.97 \times 10^7}{56.98 \times 10^3}$

9-622. $\dfrac{22,900. \times 10^{-6}}{76.4 \times 10^4}$

Combined Multiplication and Division

Since most engineering calculations involve both multiplication and division, the student should master the technique of combined multiplication and division. The projection rules for both multiplication and division apply in a combination problem.

Example:

$$\frac{(513)^{(+2)} \; (15,300)^{(+4)}}{(238)_{+2}} = 32,900,^{(+6) \; - \; (+2) \; \to \; +4} \text{ or } \underline{\underline{3.29 \times 10^4}}$$

In order to work the above problem, first set 513 divided by 238 on the C and D scales. Now, instead of reading this answer, move the hairline to 15,300 on the C scale (thus multiplying this latter quantity by the quotient of the first setting).

The student should always alternate the division and multiplication

Mathematical Tools Useful in Problem Solving

settings and should not try to take readings as he progresses with the steps. Only the final result is desired and, since each reading of the rule further magnifies any error, the fewest readings possible should be allowed.

Example:

$$\frac{(+1)\quad(-4)\quad(+2)}{(47.30)(0.000391)(693.5)} = \frac{(-1)\quad(+3)}{9.66 \times 10^{-5}} \rightarrow -4 - \overset{\downarrow}{1} = -5$$

(left extension from the division)

It must be remembered that when you want to divide, move the slide, and when you want to multiply, move the hairline.

A common error committed by many students is to multiply all the quantities in the dividend and all the quantities in the divisor and then divide these two results. This is a bad habit and such practice should not be followed. There are too many chances for mistakes, in addition to it being a slower method.

Problems

Solve by combined multiplication and division method.

9-623. $\dfrac{(0.916)}{(90.5)(13.06)}$

9-624. $\dfrac{(0.00908)}{(22.3)(33.2)}$

9-625. $\dfrac{(24.5)(43)}{(36)}$

9-626. $\dfrac{(82)(9.3)}{(56.5)}$

9-627. $\dfrac{(167)(842)}{(0.976)}$

9-628. $\dfrac{(5.72)(3690)}{(95.7)}$

9-629. $\dfrac{(925)(76.9)}{(37.6)}$

9-630. $\dfrac{(9.87)}{(1.76)(89)}$

9-631. $\dfrac{(85.4)}{(26.3)(213)}$

9-632. $\dfrac{(1525)}{(73.6)(0.007)}$

9-633. $\dfrac{(84,500)}{(126)(37.3)}$

9-634. $\dfrac{(76)(23.7)}{(13.5)(373)}$

9-635. $\dfrac{(6.23)(2.14)}{(0.00531)}$

9-636. $\dfrac{(21.3)(370)}{(10.9)(758)}$

9-637. $\dfrac{(0.00215)(2520)}{(7.57)(118)}$

9-638. $\dfrac{(755)(1.15)}{(51.4)(0.093)}$

9-639. $\dfrac{(916)(0.752)}{(5.16)}$

9-640. $\dfrac{(23.1)(1.506)}{(6.27)}$

9-641. $\dfrac{(42.6)(1.935)}{(750.3)}$

9-642. $\dfrac{(77.1)(10.53)}{(331.0)(73)}$

9-643. $\dfrac{(56.7)(0.00336)}{(15.06)(8.23)}$

9-644. $\dfrac{(14.5)(10)^3(6.22)}{(53.3)(0.00103)}$

9-645. $\dfrac{(42)(1000)}{(5.23)(0.00771)}$

9-646. $\dfrac{(1.331)}{(916)(506)}$

Engineering: Elementary Problem Analysis

9-647. $\dfrac{(4320)(0.7854)}{(134)(0.9)}$

9-648. $\dfrac{(0.00713)(329)}{(0.0105)(1000)}$

9-649. $\dfrac{(103.4)(0.028)}{(0.0798)}$

9-650. $\dfrac{(1573)(4618)}{(3935)(97)}$

9-651. $\dfrac{(47.2)(0.0973)}{(85)(37.6)}$

9-652. $\dfrac{(0.0445)(0.0972)}{(0.218)(0.318)}$

9-653. $\dfrac{(39.1)(680,000)(3.52)(1.1 \times 10^6)}{(0.0316)(9.6 \times 10^6)(26.3)}$

9-654. $\dfrac{(7.69)(76,000)(5.63)(0.00314)}{(0.00365)(10 \times 10^6)}$

9-655. $\dfrac{(3.97)(6.71 \times 10^{-3})(0.067)}{(63.1)(3 \times 10^7)(7.61)(80,175)}$

9-656. $\dfrac{(697)(0.000713)(68.1)}{(234)(9.68)(5.1 \times 10^4)}$

9-657. $\dfrac{(43,400)(9.16)(8.1 \times 10^{-6})}{(0.00613)(67,000)(0.416)}$

9-658. $\dfrac{(691.6)(7.191)(3 \times 10^7)}{(410,000)(6.39)(0.0876)}$

9-659. $\dfrac{(37.615)(81.4)(9.687)(0.0017)}{(13.13)(0.076)(43)}$

9-660. $\dfrac{(51.2 \times 10^{-6})(3.41 \times 10^5)(36.1)}{(96.69)(7 \times 10^{-2})(0.134)}$

9-661. $\dfrac{(6.716)(3.2 \times 10^3)(0.0173)(413)}{(0.0000787)(6.6 \times 10^4)}$

9-662. $\dfrac{(1.061 \times 10^{-1})(96,000)(3.717)}{(7.34 \times 10^{-6})(3.9 \times 10^4)(13.5)}$

9-663. $\dfrac{(361)(482)(5.816)(38.91)(0.00616)}{(0.07181)(3 \times 10^3)(39.36)}$

9-664. $\dfrac{(0.019 \times 10^8)(111.15)(0.0168)}{(7.96)(58.6)(0.0987)(3,000)}$

9-665. $\dfrac{(21.4)(0.82)(39.6 \times 10^{-1})}{(10.86)(6.7 \times 10^{-2})(37,613)}$

9-666. $\dfrac{(63,761)(43,890)(0.00761)}{(8 \times 10^6)(0.0781)(67.17)}$

9-667. $\dfrac{(516.7)(212 \times 10^3)(0.967)(34)}{(76,516)(2 \times 10^{-6})(618)}$

9-668. $\dfrac{(5.1 \times 10^8)(370)(8.71)(3,698)}{(0.00176)(36,170)}$

9-669. $\dfrac{(59.71 \times 10^{-6})(0.00916)(0.1695)(55.61)}{(17.33 \times 10^5)(0.3165)(10.56)(1.105)}$

9-670. $\dfrac{(773.6)(57.17)(0.316)(912.3)}{(56,000)(715,000)(471.3)}$

Mathematical Tools Useful in Problem Solving

9-671. $\dfrac{(51.33)(461.3)(919)(5.03)}{(66{,}000)(71.52)(0.3316)(12.39)}$

9-672. $\dfrac{(0.6617)(75.391)(0.6577)(91.33)}{(0.3305)(5.69 \times 10)(0.00317 \times 10^{-5})}$

Squares and Square Roots

The A and B scales have been so constructed that their lengths are one-half those of the C and D scales. This means that the logarithm of 3 as represented on the D scale would be equivalent in length to the logarithm of 9 on the A scale.

Example:

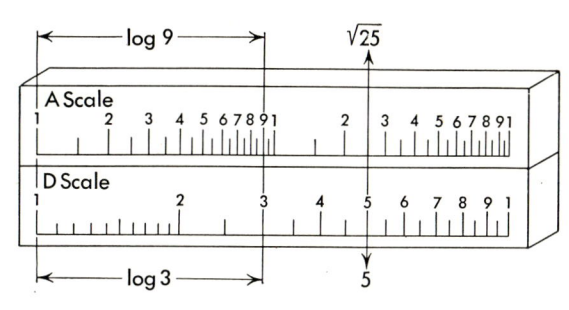

Fig. 9-49

TO FIND THE SQUARE ROOT OF A NUMBER

1. Get an estimate of the intended answer by placing a bar over every two digits, starting at the decimal point and working outward. There will be a digit in the answer for each bar marked.

2. Set the number on the A scale and read the square root on the D scale under the hairline. Note that the estimated answer will always indicate which A scale to use, since only one of the scales will give a square root near the estimated value.

Examples for Finding the Location of Decimal Points

a. $\sqrt{\overline{97}\,\overline{65}}^{\,9\ x}$ The estimated answer is somewhere between 90–100.

b. $\sqrt{.\overline{00}\,\overline{30}}^{\,.0\ 5}$ The estimated answer is approximately 0.05.

NOTE: In the last example, since the given value was 0.003, an extra zero would have to be added after the 3 to complete the digits beneath the bar.

Examples for Finding the Square Root of a Number

a. $\sqrt{\overline{1}\ \overline{03}\ \overline{57}}$ ⎯ $\overset{1\quad x\quad x}{}$ The estimated answer is somewhere between 100–200.

$\sqrt{\overline{1}\ \overline{03}\ \overline{57}} = 101.9 = \underline{1.019 \times 10^2}$

b. $\sqrt{\overline{0.00}\ \overline{05}\ \overline{20}}$ ⎯ $\overset{0.\ 0\ 2\ \ x}{}$ The estimated answer is approximately 0.02.

$\sqrt{\overline{0.00}\ \overline{05}\ \overline{20}} = 0.02285 = \underline{2.285 \times 10^{-2}}$

Examples for Finding Squares

1. Express the number in scientific notation.

   a. $(0.0000956)^2 = (9.56 \times 10^{-5})^2$

2. Square each part of the converted term by setting the number to be squared on the D scale and reading its square on the A scale under the hairline.

   a. $(9.56)^2 \times (10^{-5})^2 = 91.4 \times 10^{-10} = \underline{9.14 \times 10^{-9}}$

   b. $(90100)^2 = (9.01 \times 10^4)^2$
   $(9.01)^2 \times (10^4)^2 = 81 \times 10^8 = \underline{8.1 \times 10^9}$

   c. $(357000000)^2 = (3.57 \times 10^8)^2$
   $(3.57)^2 \times (10^8)^2 = 12.7 \times 10^{16} = \underline{1.27 \times 10^{17}}$

   d. $(0.00000001050)^2 = (1.05 \times 10^{-8})^2$
   $(1.05)^2 \times (10^{-8})^2 = \underline{1.10 \times 10^{-16}}$

Problems

Solve by method of squares and square roots.

9-673. $(1468.)^2$
9-674. $(0.886)^2$
9-675. $(67.4)^2$
9-676. $(11.96)^2$
9-677. $(0.00448)^2$
9-678. $(0.000551)^2$
9-679. $(9.22)^2$
9-680. $(64,800.)^2$
9-681. $(0.0668)^2$
9-682. $(16.85)^2$

9-683. $(1.802 \times 10^9)^2$
9-684. $(0.00358)^2$
9-685. $(5089)^2$
9-686. $(44,900.)^2$
9-687. $(64.88)^2$
9-688. $\sqrt{11.81}$
9-689. $\sqrt{4567.}$
9-690. $\sqrt{0.01844}$
9-691. $\sqrt{0.9953}$
9-692. $\sqrt{1395.}$

9-693. $\sqrt{0.0001288}$
9-694. $\sqrt{1.082 \times 10^2}$
9-695. $\sqrt{75.9}$
9-696. $\sqrt{\pi}$
9-697. $\sqrt{73,800.}$
9-698. $\sqrt{13.38}$
9-699. $\sqrt{93.07}$
9-700. $\sqrt{0.1148}$
9-701. $\sqrt{0.2776}$
9-702. $\sqrt{9.31}$

9-703. $(0.774)^2(11.47)^{\frac{1}{2}}$
9-704. $(0.1442)^{\frac{1}{2}}(33.89)^{\frac{1}{2}}$
9-705. $(54.23)^2(88,900)^{\frac{1}{2}}$
9-706. $\sqrt{234.5}\ \sqrt{55,900.}$
9-707. $\sqrt{16.38}\ \sqrt{45.6}\ \sqrt{0.9}$

9-708. $\sqrt{415.}\ \sqrt{\pi}\ \sqrt{86.4}$
9-709. $\sqrt{15.66}\ \sqrt{0.1904}\ \sqrt{\pi}$
9-710. $(34.77)^2(54.8)^2(0.772)^{\frac{1}{2}}$
9-711. $\sqrt{7.90}\ \sqrt{7.02}\ \sqrt{11.54}$
9-712. $\sqrt{31.19}\ \sqrt{56.7}\ \sqrt{54.8}$

Mathematical Tools Useful in Problem Solving 185

Cubes and Cube Roots

The D and K scales are used to find the cube or cube root of a number. The same general procedure is used as that followed for squaring numbers and taking the square root of a number. The K scale is divided into scales K_1, K_2, and K_3 which are each one-third the length of the D scale. Thus, if a number is located on the D scale, the cube of the number will be indicated on the K scale. It follows that if a number is located on one of the K scales, the root of the number would appear on the D scale.

Example:

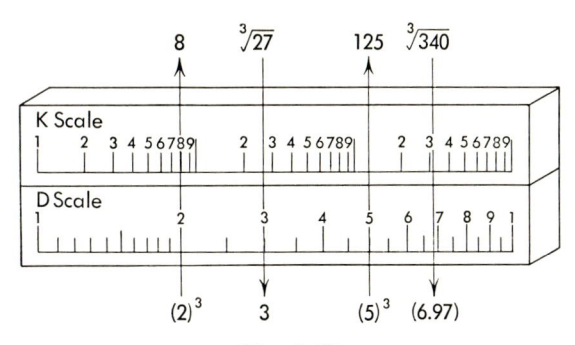

Fig. 9-50

TO FIND THE CUBE ROOT OF A NUMBER

1. Get an estimate of the intended answer by placing a bar over every three digits, starting at the decimal point and working outward. There will be a digit in the answer for each bar marked.

2. Set the number on the K scale and read the cube root on the D scale under the hairline.

Examples for Finding the Location of Decimal Points

a. $\sqrt[3]{\overline{44,}\overline{800.}}$ The estimated answer is somewhere between 30–40.

b. $\sqrt[3]{\overline{0.}\,\overline{000}\,\overline{011}}$ The estimated answer is approximately 0.02.

NOTE: In estimating the answer by marking bars over the digit groupings, be sure that the bars cover three digits instead of two, as was the case in square roots.

Since an estimated answer [see example (a) above] has been obtained, it is easy to pick the proper K scale (K_1, K_2, or K_3) to use. Remember that only one of these will give an answer between 30 and 40 [see example (a)].

Engineering: Elementary Problem Analysis

Examples for Finding the Cube Roots of a Number

a. $\sqrt[3]{1\ 490\ 000}$. The estimated answer is somewhere between 100–200.
$$\sqrt[3]{\overset{1}{1}\ \overset{x}{490}\ \overset{x}{000}} = 114.1 = \underline{(1.141)(10)^2}.$$

b. $\sqrt[3]{0.000\ 156\ 9}$ The estimated answer is approximately 0.06.
$$\sqrt[3]{\overset{0.}{0.000}\ \overset{0}{156}\ \overset{6}{9}} = 0.0537 = \underline{(5.37)(10)^{-2}}.$$

Examples for Finding Cubes

1. Convert the number to a number between 1 and 10 (scientific notation) which must be multiplied by 10 raised to some power.

   a. $(0.00641)^3 = (6.41 \times 10^{-3})^3$

2. Cube each part of the converted term by setting the number to be cubed on the D scale and reading its cube on the K scale under the hairline.

   a. $(6.41 \times 10^{-3})^3 = (264)(10)^{-9} = \underline{2.64 \times 10^{-7}}$

   b. $(93.88)^3 = (9.388 \times 10^1)^3$
   $(9.388)^3(10^1)^3 = 830 \times 10^3 = \underline{8.30 \times 10^5}$

   c. $(2{,}618{,}000.)^3 = (2.618 \times 10^6)^3$
   $(2.618)^3(10^6)^3 = (17.95 \times 10)^{18} = \underline{1.795 \times 10^{19}}$

   d. $(0.000001194)^3 = (1.194 \times 10^{-6})^3$
   $(1.194)^3(10^{-6})^3 = \underline{1.71 \times 10^{-18}}$

Problems

Solve by Method of Cubes and Cube Roots.

9-713. $(86)^3$
9-714. $(148)^3$
9-715. $(395{,}000)^3$
9-716. $(47.6)^3$
9-717. $(1.074)^3$
9-718. $(76.9)^3$
9-719. $(220.8)^3$
9-720. $(9.72)^3$
9-721. $(110.7)^3$
9-722. $(91.3)^3$
9-723. $(1.757 \times 10^4)^3$
9-724. $(3.06 \times 10^{-7})^3$

9-725. $(44.8 \times 10^{-1})^3$
9-726. $(0.933 \times 10^{-2})^3$
9-727. $(0.1184 \times 10^8)^3$
9-728. $(51.5 \times 10^2)^3$
9-729. $\sqrt[3]{118}$
9-730. $\sqrt[3]{2{,}197}$
9-731. $\sqrt[3]{9}$
9-732. $\sqrt[3]{0.0689}$
9-733. $\sqrt[3]{0.001338}$
9-734. $\sqrt[3]{0.1794}$
9-735. $\sqrt[3]{0.0891}$
9-736. $\sqrt[3]{34{,}690}$

9-737. $\sqrt[3]{0.3329}$
9-738. $\sqrt[3]{1{,}258{,}000}$
9-739. $\sqrt[3]{0.1853}$
9-740. $\sqrt[3]{12.88}$
9-741. $\sqrt[3]{4.98 \times 10^7}$
9-742. $\sqrt[3]{1.844 \times 10^{-5}}$
9-743. $\sqrt[3]{3.86 \times 10^{-1}}$
9-744. $(9.94)(0.886)^{\frac{1}{3}}$
9-745. $(248.)(11.98)^{\frac{1}{3}}$
9-746. $(0.1170.)(0964)^{\frac{1}{3}}$
9-747. $(\pi)^3(44.89)^3$

Mathematical Tools Useful in Problem Solving

9-748. $(6.88)^3(0.00799)^3$
9-749. $(0.915)^{\frac{1}{2}}(0.366)^{\frac{1}{3}} \sqrt[3]{11,250} \ (36.12)^{\frac{1}{3}}$
9-750. $(2.34)^3(3.34)^3(4.56)^3(5.67)^3$
9-751. $(8.26)^{\frac{1}{2}}(8.26)^3(1000)^{\frac{1}{2}}(10)^3$
9-752. $\sqrt[3]{2670} \ \sqrt[3]{3165} \ \sqrt[3]{1065} \ \sqrt[3]{7776}$
9-753. $\sqrt[3]{206} \ \sqrt[3]{0.791} \ (12.35)^3(26.3)^3$

Trigonometric Functions

Finding trigonometric functions on a log-log rule is a rather simple process. The angle may be read on the S (sine), ST (sine and tangent of small angles), or T (tangent) scales. The functions may be read under the hairline on the C, D, or DI scales without any movement of the indicator.

SINE 0°—0.574°

It is not often that the engineer needs to know the function of extremely small angles, but if he does need them, it is possible to get approximate values for these functions without consulting tables.

Method 1 (Based on the relation that the sine of small angles is approximately equal to the angle in radians)

1. This method is more accurate than the following Method 2 and is preferable.
2. Express the angle in question in degrees.
3. Change the degrees to radians by dividing by 57.3.

NOTE: $\quad 57.3° = 1$ radian (approximately)

4. The value obtained is the approximate answer.

Example: $\qquad \sin 6' = ?$
$$6' = \tfrac{6}{60} = 0.10°$$
$$\sin 6' = \frac{0.10}{57.3}$$
$$\sin 6' = 0.00174 \text{ approximately}$$

Method 2

1. Keep in mind the following values:

$\sin 1'' = 0.000005$ (five zeros-five) approximately
$\sin 1' = 0.0003$ (three zeros-three) approximately

2. For small angles, multiply the value of 1' or 1'', as the case may be, by the number of minutes or seconds in question.
3. The value obtained is the approximate answer.

Example: sin 6' = ?
sin 6' = (6) (sin 1')
sin 6' = (6) (0.0003)
sin 6' = 0.0018 approximately

SINE 0.574°—5.74°

To find the sine of an angle between 0.574° and 5.74°, the ST and D scales are used.

Example: sin 1.5° = ?

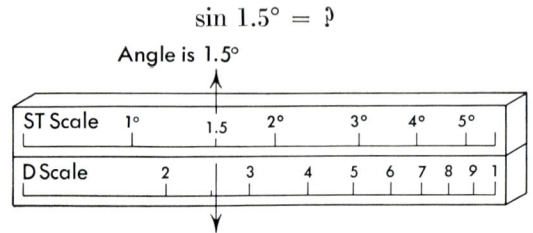

Angle is 1.5°

ST Scale 1° 1.5 2° 3° 4° 5°
D Scale 2 3 4 5 6 7 8 9 1

Sine of the angle is 0.0262

Fig. 9-51

Instructions

1. Be certain that the left index of the D scale is directly under the left index of the ST scale.
2. Set the hairline to the angle on the ST scale.
3. Read the answer on the D scale. The answer will be a decimal number and will have one zero preceding the digits read from the rule.

SINE 5.74°—90°

To find the sine of an angle between 5.74° and 90°, the S and D scales are used.

Example: sin 45° = ?

Angle is 45°

S Scale 10° 20° 30° 40° 50° 60° 80°
D Scale 2 3 4 5 6 7 8 9 1

Sine of the angle is 0.707

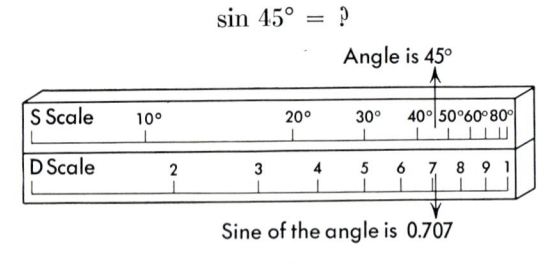

Fig. 9-52

Instructions

1. Be certain that the left index of the D scale is directly under the left index of the S scale.

Mathematical Tools Useful in Problem Solving

2. Set the hairline to the angle on the S scale. If the rule has more than one set of figures on the S scale, the angles for sine functions are usually shown to the right of the longer graduations.

3. Read the answer on the D scale. Place the decimal preceding the first digit read from the rule.

COSINE 0°—84.26°

To find the cosine of an angle between 0° and 84.26°, the markings to the left of the long graduations on the S scale are used in conjunction with the D scale. Note that the markings begin with 0° at the right end of the scale and progress to 84.26° at the left end of the scale.

Example: $\cos 74.1° = ?$

Angle is 74.1°

| S Scale | 80° | | 70° | | 60° | 50° | 40° 30° | 0 |
| D Scale | | 2 | 3 | 4 | 5 | 6 | 7 8 9 | 1 |

Cosine of the angle is 0.274

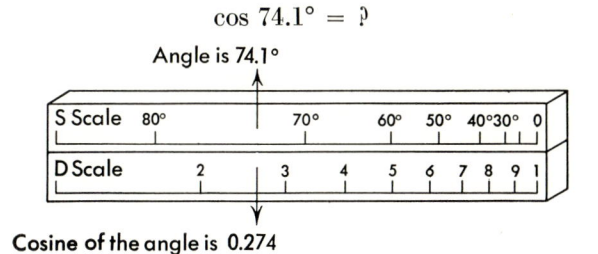

Fig. 9-53

COSINE 84.26°—89.4°

To find the cosine of an angle between 84.26 and 89.4°, the complement of the angle on the ST scale is used in conjunction with the D scale.

Example:
$$\cos 88.5° = ?$$
$$\text{complement of } 88.5° = 1.5°$$
$$\sin 1.5° = 0.0262$$
$$\cos 88.5° = 0.0262$$

COSINE 89.4°—90°

To find the cosine of an angle between 89.4° and 90°, determine the complement of the angle and find the value of the sine of this angle as previously discussed.

Example:
$$\cos 89.94° = ?$$
$$\text{complement of } 89.94° = 0.06°$$
$$\sin 0.06° = \frac{0.06}{57.3} = 0.001048$$
$$\cos 89.94° = 0.001048$$

NOTE: In finding the cosine of any angle, it is sometimes more convenient to look up the sine of the complement of the angle.

Example:
$$\cos 60° = ?$$
$$\text{complement of } 60° = 30°$$
$$\sin 30° = 0.500$$

Therefore
$$\cos 60° = 0.500$$

TANGENT 0°—5.74°

For small angles (0° to 5.74°) the tangent of the angle may be considered to be the same value as the sine of that angle.

TANGENT 5.74°—45°

To find the tangent of an angle between 5.74° and 45°, the T scale is used in conjunction with the D scale.

Example: Find tan 30°.

Angle is 30°

| T Scale | 10° | | 20° | | 30° | | 40° 45° |

| D Scale | 2 | 3 | 4 | 5 | 6 | 7 | 8 | 9 | 1 |

Tangent of the angle is 0.577

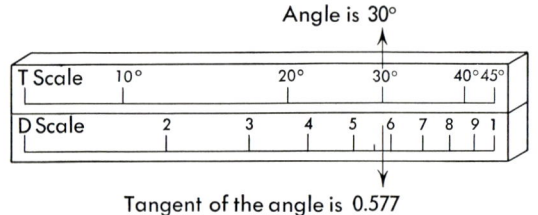

Fig. 9-54

Instructions

1. Be certain that the left index of the D scale is directly under the left index of the T scale.
2. Set the hairline to the angle on the T scale. If the T scale has more than one set of markings, be certain that the correct markings are used.
3. Read the answer on the D scale. Place the decimal preceding the first digit read from the rule.

TANGENT 45°—84.26°

To find the tangent of an angle between 45° and 84.26°, the markings to the left of the longer graduations on the T scale are used in conjunction with the CI or DI scales.

Example:
$$\tan 70° = ?$$

Angle is 70°

| T Scale | 80° | | 70° | | 60° | | 50° 45° |

| 9 8 7 6 5 | 4 | 3 | | 2 | | DI Scale |

Tangent of the angle is 2.74

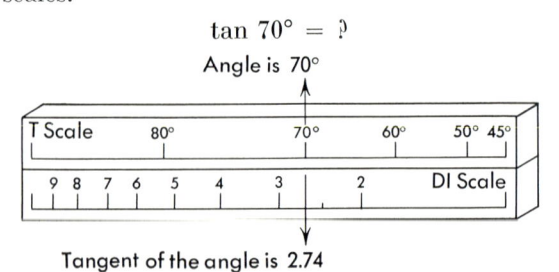

Fig. 9-55

Mathematical Tools Useful in Problem Solving

Instructions

1. Be certain that the left index of the DI or CI scale is aligned with the left index of the T scale.
2. Set the hairline to the angle on the T scale.
3. Read the answer on the CI or DI scale. Note that these scales read from right to left. Place the decimal after the first digit read from the rule.

TANGENT 84.26°—89.426°

To find the tangent of an angle between 84.26° and 89.426°, the complement of the angle on the ST scale is used in conjunction with the CI or DI scales.

Example: $\tan 88° = ?$

Complement of angle is 2°

Tangent of the angle is 28.6

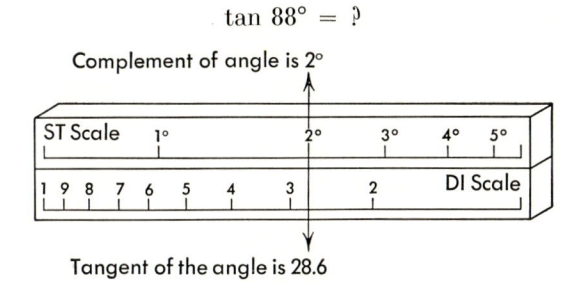

Fig. 9-56

Instructions

1. Be certain that the left index of the DI or CI scale is aligned with the left index of the ST scale.
2. Complement of 88° = 2°.
3. Read the answer on the DI or CI scale. Note that these scales read from right to left.
4. Place the decimal point after the first two digits read from the rule.

Frequently the value of the function of an angle is known and it is desired to find the value of the angle.

Example: $\sin \theta = 0.53;$
$\theta = ?$

This may be written in the inverse form in either of two ways:

$$\text{Arc sin } 0.53 = \theta$$
or
$$\text{Sin}^{-1} 0.53 = \theta$$
then
$$\theta = 32°$$

The forms arc sin, arc cos, and arc tan are preferred in present-day practice.

Trigonometric Functions

Problems

Solve, using the slide rule.

9-754. sin 35°	9-782. cot 18.7°	9-810. arc cos 0.238
9-755. sin 14°	9-783. cot 3.77°	9-811. cos 0.75°
9-756. sin 78°	9-784. cot 66.4°	9-812. cos 36.6°
9-757. sin 3.7°	9-785. csc 38.1°	9-813. tan 32.6°
9-758. sin 88.3°	9-786. csc 75.2°	9-814. tan 16.34°
9-759. sin 55.3°	9-787. csc 88.3°	9-815. tan 88°30′
9-760. cos 35°	9-788. csc 12.8°	9-816. arc tan 0.62
9-761. cos 66°	9-789. csc 46.4°	9-817. $\tan^{-1}$ 0.75
9-762. cos 21.3°	8-790. csc 81.1°	9-818. arc tan 0.392
9-763. cos 11.1°	9-791. csc 32.6°	9-819. $\tan^{-1}$ 1.53
9-764. cos 7.9°	9-792. csc 9.03°	9-820. tan 37°24′
9-765. cos 43.8°	9-793. sec 6.14°	9-821. arc tan 0.567
9-766. tan 33.8°	9-794. sec 59.2°	9-822. $\tan^{-1}$ 0.0321
9-767. tan 9.4°	9-795. sec 79.4°	9-823. cot 19°33′
9-768. tan 37.7°	9-796. sec 19.5°	9-824. sec 46°46′
9-769. tan 22.5°	9-797. sec 2.77°	9-825. csc 32°12′
9-770. tan 86.1°	9-798. sec 45.9°	9-826. sin 37°
9-771. tan 54.4°	9-799. arc sin 0.771	9-827. sin 51°50′
9-772. tan 70.3°	9-800. arc cos 0.119	9-828. sin 68°37′
9-773. tan 29.7°	9-801. arc tan 34.8	9-829. sin 75°10′
9-774. tan 36.5°	9-802. arc sec 7.18	9-830. arc sin 0.622
9-775. tan 13.3°	9-803. arc csc 1.05	9-831. sin 13.6°
9-776. tan 45.8°	9-804. cos 33.4°	9-832. $\sin^{-1}$ 0.068
9-777. cot 14.7°	9-805. cos 3.6°	9-833. sin 14.6°
9-778. cot 81.8°	9-806. arc cos 0.992	9-834. arc sin 0.169
9-779. cot 36.9°	9-807. cos 24.67°	9-835. sin 34.67°
9-780. cot 61.2°	9-808. $\cos^{-1}$ 0.496	9-836. cos 26.26°
9-781. cot 54.3°	9-809. cos 36°6′	9-837. csc 20°20′

9-838. $(\csc 20°)(\sin 46°)$

9-839. $(\cos 32°)(\tan 43°)$

9-840. $\dfrac{(\sin 13.9°)}{(\cot 13.9°)}$

9-841. $\dfrac{\cot 33°22'}{\sec 4°53'}$

9-842. $\dfrac{(\cos 33°15')}{(\cot 46°19')}$

9-843. $\dfrac{(\sec 10°)(\cot 10°)}{(\sin 10°)(\csc 10°)}$

9-844. $\dfrac{(\sin 35°)(\tan 22°)}{(\sqrt[3]{\sin 5.96°})}$

9-845. $\dfrac{(\sec 11°)(\tan 4°)}{(\cot 49°)}$

9-846. $\dfrac{(\sin 8°)(\tan 9°)}{(\cot 82°)}$

9-847. $\dfrac{(\sin 1.36°)(\cot 26°)}{(\sqrt[3]{0.00916})}$

9-848. $\dfrac{\cot \sin^{-1} 0.916}{(1.32)(5.061)}$

9-849. $\dfrac{(77.19)(\sec 46°)}{(\tan 3.91°)}$

Mathematical Tools Useful in Problem Solving

9-850. $\dfrac{(\sqrt[3]{\tan 25.9°})(\sin \cos^{-1} 0.5)}{(\sin 5.16°)(\tan 22°)}$

9-851. $\dfrac{(0.0311)(\sec 69°)\sqrt[3]{9.0}}{(\sin 9°)(\cos 9°)}$

9-852. $\dfrac{(1.916)(\sqrt[3]{1.916})(\sqrt[3]{\sin 20°})}{(\sqrt[3]{\sec 40°})(\tan 10° 22')}$

9-853. $\dfrac{(6.17)(\tan 6.17°)(\sqrt[3]{6.17})}{(6.17)^2(\sin 61.7°)(\cos 6.17°)}$

The following tables have been prepared for trigonometric values. The student should check all the examples with his rule as he proceeds.

	ANGLE	READ ANGLE ON	READ FUNCTION ON	DECIMAL	EXAMPLES
sine or tangent	0°—0.574° Convert the angle to radians (1 radian = 57.3°), and this value is assumed to be equal to the sine or tangent of the angle.			
sine or tangent	0.574°—5.74°	ST	D	0.0xxx	$\tan 2° = 0.0349$ $\sin 3° = 0.0523$
sine	5.74°—90°	S (right markings)	D	0.xxxx	$\sin 29° = 0.485$
cosine	0°—84.26°	S (left markings)	D	0.xxxx	$\cos 43° = 0.7314$
tangent	5.74°—45°	T (right markings)	D	0.xxxx	$\tan 13° = 0.231$
tangent	45°—84.26°	T (left markings)	DI	x.xxx	$\tan 78° = 4.70$
tangent	84.26°—89.426°	Set complement on ST	DI	xx.xxx	$\tan 89° = 57.3$
cosecant	5.74°—90°	S (right markings)	DI	x.xxx	$\csc 63° = 1.122$
secant	0°—84.26°	S (left markings)	DI	x.xxx	$\sec 48° = 1.496$
cotangent	0.574°—5.74°	ST	DI	xx.xx	$\cot 3.5° = 16.35$
cotangent	5.74°—45°	T (right markings)	DI	x.xxx	$\cot 23° = 2.36$
cotangent	45°—84.26°	T (left markings)	D	0.xxxx	$\cot 68° = 0.404$

THE LOG-LOG SCALES

There are two groups of log-log scales on the slide rule. One group, composed of the LL_1, LL_2, and LL_3 scales, concerns numbers larger than one, while the other group, composed of the LL_{01}, LL_{02}, and LL_{03} scales, concerns numbers less than one. These scales are used to obtain the roots, powers, and logarithms of numbers.

Rules manufactured by some companies have the LL_{01}, LL_{02}, and LL_{03} scales directly under the corresponding LL_1, LL_2, and LL_3 scales, and the LL_0 scales are not designated by separate markings. The C and D scales are used in conjunction with these log-log scales. Other rules are manufactured with only two LL_0 scales, and these are marked as LL_0 and LL_{00}. The A and B scales must be used with the LL_0 and LL_{00} scales on this type of rule. The general principles discussed below apply to all types of log-log slide rules.

As an example, the following problems are types that may be solved by using the log-log scales:

$$(2.35)^{0.67} = ? \qquad (63.1)^{\frac{1}{5.33}} = ?$$
$$(59.3)^{1.26} = ? \qquad \sqrt[4.3]{95.3} = ?$$
$$(0.569)^{0.97} = ? \qquad \log_\epsilon 2.36 = ?$$

If the scales LL_1, LL_2, and LL_3 were placed end to end, they would form a continuous scale. Similarly, if the scales LL_{01}, LL_{02}, and LL_{03}, (or LL_0, LL_{00}) were placed end to end, they would form a continuous scale. The LL_0 scales are graduated from approximately 0.00005 to 0.99, while the LL scales are graduated from approximately 1.01 to 22,026.

Example:

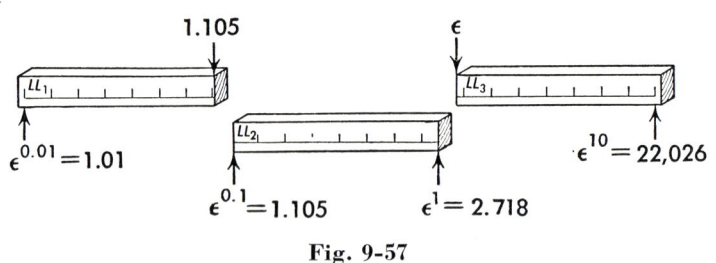

Fig. 9-57

The decimal point is already marked on the scales for all numbers on the LL_0 and LL scales. For example, there is only one place on the LL scales that 125.0 may be found. The number 125.0 is found on the LL_3 scale, while the number 1.25 is found on the LL_2 scale. Since the manner in which settings are read on the log-log scales is distinctly different from the method of reading the scales previously studied, the student should be very careful in making his slide rule settings.

Mathematical Tools Useful in Problem Solving

RECIPROCAL VALUES

The only case where the LL and LL$_0$ scales may be used together is in the finding of reciprocals of numbers. The reciprocal of any number on the LL scales can be read on the corresponding LL$_0$ scale.

Examples:

a. Find 1.25 on the LL$_2$ scale. On the LL$_{02}$ scale its reciprocal can be read as 0.80.

b. Find 236 on the LL$_3$ scale. On the LL$_{03}$ scale its reciprocal can be read as 0.00424.

RAISING A NUMBER TO A POWER

If such problems as $(5.3)^3 = ?$ were worked entirely by logarithms, the following procedure would be required:

1. $(5.3)^3 = ?$
2. log ans. = 3 log 5.3
3. log [log ans.] = log 3 + log (log 5.3)
4. Answer = $(1.488)(10)^2$

Step 3 is rather involved in many instances. It is for this reason that the log-log scales have been added to the slide rule. Since log-log values of numbers are recorded on the LL scales, and the log values of numbers have been recorded on the C and D scales, it is quite convenient to perform Step 3 in the preceding example.

The LL and LL$_0$ scales are also used in conjunction with the C and D scales to find powers, roots, and logarithms to the base ϵ of numbers.

In order to raise any number greater than 1.01 to any power:

$$(X)^n = A$$

1. Set the index of the C scale over the value X found on the appropriate LL scales (LL$_1$, LL$_2$, or LL$_3$).
2. Move the hairline to the value n on the C scale.
3. Read the answer A on the appropriate LL scale.

Example:

$(1.02)^{2.5} = ?$

log [log ans.] = log 2.5 + log (log 1.02)

Answer = 1.0507

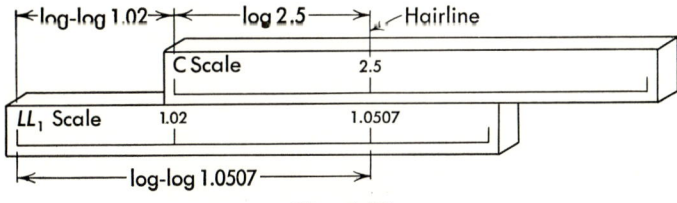

Fig. 9-58

Solution

1. Set the index of the C scale over the value 1.02 on the LL_1 scale.
2. Move the hairline to the value 2.5 on the C scale.
3. Read the answer 1.0507 on the LL_1 scale.

Upon investigation it will be found that these scales are arranged so that a number on the LL_3 scale is the tenth power of the number directly below it on the LL_2 scale, and the LL_2 scale gives the tenth power of a number in the corresponding position on the LL_1 scale. Therefore the LL_3 scale would give the one-hundredth power of a number in the corresponding position on the LL_1 scale. However, there is no such correlation between the LL and LL_0 scales, and the student should not attempt to go from one group of scales to the other.

There are no definite rules to follow in determining the proper log-log scale upon which to read the answer. However, the student should be able to estimate the approximate answer and thereby know on which scale the answer will be found.

Example:
$(1.034)^{2.3}$ = 1.0799 ans. on the LL_1
$(1.034)^{23.}$ = 2.156 ans. on the LL_2
$(1.034)^{230.}$ = 2160 ans. on the LL_3

The following suggestions are presented so that the student can more easily decide whether the answer is to be larger or smaller than the original quantity.

$$(\text{Number})^{\text{power}} = \text{answer}$$

1. If the number is larger than 1.00 and the power is larger than 1.00, the answer will be greater than the number.
2. If the number is less than 1.00 and the power is less than 1.00, the answer will be greater than the number.
3. If the number is less than 1.00 and the power is greater than 1.00, the answer will be less than the number.
4. If the number is greater than 1.00 and the power is less than 1.00, the answer will be less than the number.

In order to raise any number less than 0.99 to any power:

$$(X)^n = A$$

1. Set the index of the C scale over the value X found on the appropriate LL_0 scale (LL_{01}, LL_{02}, or LL_{03}).
2. Move the hairline to the value n on the C scale.
3. Read the answer A on the appropriate LL_0 scale.

Mathematical Tools Useful in Problem Solving

Example: $(0.855)^{4.8} = A$

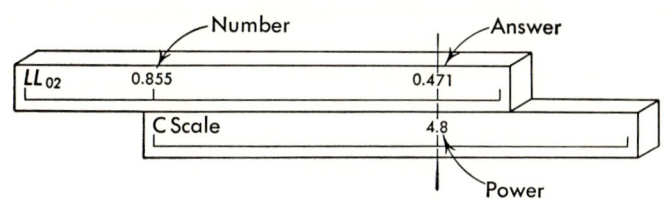

Fig. 9-59

Then $\qquad A = 0.471$

RESULTS WHICH DO NOT FALL WITHIN THE LIMITS OF THE SCALES

In many computations the final answer may be larger than 22,026 and hence cannot be read within the limits of the scales. In such cases the original expression must be factored before attempting to use the log-log scales. Several such methods of factoring are explained below.

Method 1: Express the number in scientific notation and raise each part to the given power.

Example:
$$(35.3)^4 = ?$$
$$(35.3)^4 = (3.53 \times 10)^4$$
$$= (3.53)^4 \times (10)^4$$

Now, using the LL scales, and since $(3.53)^4 = 155$, we obtain

$$(35.3)^4 = 155. \times 10^4$$
$$= \underline{1.55 \times 10^6} \quad \text{(Answer)}$$

Method 2: Factor the number which is to be raised to a power and then treat each part separately, as in Method 1.

Example:
$$(15)^5 = ?$$
$$(15)^5 = (3 \times 5)^5$$
$$= (3)^5 \times (5)^5$$
$$= (243)(3125)$$
$$= \underline{7.59 \times 10^5} \quad \text{(Answer)}$$

Method 3: Divide the exponent into two or more smaller parts and, using the log-log scales, compute each part separately. A final computation is made using the C and D scales as in Method 1 and Method 2.

Engineering: Elementary Problem Analysis

Example: $(2.36)^{15} = ?$
$$(2.36)^{15} = (2.36)^5 \times (2.36)^5 \times (2.36)^5$$
$$= (73.2)(73.2)(73.2)$$
$$= \underline{3.93 \times 10^5} \qquad \text{(Answer)}$$

or
$$(2.36)^{15} = (2.36)^8 \times (2.36)^7$$
$$= (960)(410)$$
$$= \underline{3.93 \times 10^5} \qquad \text{(Answer)}$$

or
$$(2.36)^{15} = (2.36)^{7.5} \times (2.36)^{7.5}$$
$$= (620)^2$$
$$= \underline{3.93 \times 10^5} \qquad \text{(Answer)}$$

Example: $(0.000025)^{1.3} = ?$
$$(0.000025)^{1.3} = (2.5 \times 10^{-5})^{1.3}$$
$$= (2.5)^{1.3} \times (10^{-5})^{1.3}$$
$$= 3.29 \times (10)^{-6.5}$$
$$= (3.29)(10)^{-6}(10)^{-0.5}$$
$$= (3.29)(10)^{-6} \left(\frac{1}{3.16}\right)$$
$$= (3.29)(10)^{-6}(0.316)$$
$$= \underline{1.041 \times 10^{-6}} \qquad \text{(Answer)}$$

Method 4: Express the number in scientific notation and then express the power of 10 in logarithmic form.

Example: $(250)^{3.2} = ?$
$$(250)^{3.2} = (2.50 \times 10^2)^{3.2} = (2.50)^{3.2}(10)^{6.4}$$

where $(10)^{6.4} = x$ may be expressed as $\log_{10} x = 6.4$ or $x = (2.51)(10)^6$. Then
$$(2.50)^{3.2}(10)^{6.4} = (1.87 \times 10^1)(2.51 \times 10^6)$$
and
$$(1.87 \times 10^1)(2.51 \times 10^6) = \underline{4.71 \times 10^7}$$

Method 1 is generally preferred over the other methods because it usually is possible to obtain greater accuracy in the final answer.

NEGATIVE EXPONENTS

In solving problems which involve raising numbers to a negative power, either of two methods may be employed.

Method 1: Set the number and its exponent on the proper scales in the usual manner. Instead of reading the answer on the usual log-log scale, read it on the corresponding scale of the other group.

Mathematical Tools Useful in Problem Solving 199

Example: $(9.2)^{-3.5} = ?$

Instead of reading the answer as 2355 on the LL_3 scale, read its reciprocal value on the LL_{03} as 0.000425; therefore,

$$(9.2)^{-3.5} = \underline{\underline{4.25 \times 10^{-4}}} \quad \text{(Answer)}$$

Method 2: Set the numbers on the rule in the usual manner, ignoring the negative exponent. When the answer by this operation has been obtained, determine its reciprocal, using the CI scale.

On the slide rules that have the LL_0 and LL_{00} scales, Method 2 is the only method that can be used.

FINDING ROOTS OF NUMBERS

The process of finding the roots of numbers is easier to understand if the student remembers that

$$\sqrt[2.1]{576} = X$$

may be written as

$$(X)^{2.1} = 576$$

Therefore it is possible to "work backwards" and apply the principles learned in raising a number to a power.

Example: $\sqrt[3.2]{120} = 4.46$ ans. on LL_3

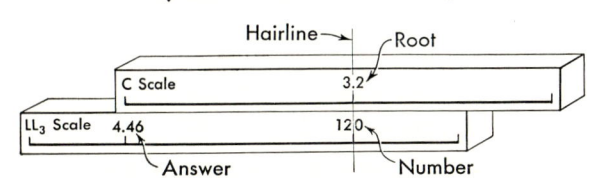

Fig. 9-60

Also
$$\sqrt[32]{120} = 1.1615 \text{ ans. on } LL_2$$
$$\sqrt[320]{120} = 1.0152 \text{ ans. on } LL_1$$

FINDING THE NATURAL LOGARITHM OF A NUMBER

The natural base for logarithms is ϵ (2.71828—). The logarithm of any number (to the base ϵ) may be found as follows:

For Numbers Greater than 1.00

$$\log_\epsilon X = A$$

1. Locate the number X on the LL_1, LL_2, or LL_3 scale.

2. Read the logarithm of the number under the hairline on the D scale.

Location of Decimal Point

If the number X is on	Decimal point in the answer
LL_3	x.xxx
LL_2	0.xxx
LL_1	0.0xxx

Examples:

$\log_\epsilon 62 = 4.13$
$\log_\epsilon 1.271 = 0.240$
$\log_\epsilon 1.026 = 0.0257$

For Numbers Less than 1.00

$\log_\epsilon X = A$

1. Locate the number X on the LL_{01}, LL_{02}, or LL_{03} scales.
2. Read the logarithm (to the base ϵ) of the number A directly above X on the D scale.

Location of Decimal Point

If the number X is on	Decimal point in the answer
LL_{03}	−x.xxx
LL_{02}	−0.xxx
LL_{01}	−0.0xxx

3. The logarithm (to the base ϵ) of all numbers less than 1.000 is a negative number.

Examples:

$\log_\epsilon 0.0045 = -5.40$
$\log_\epsilon 0.745 = -0.294$
$\log_\epsilon 0.954 = -0.0471$

Problems

Solve, using the log-log scales.

9-854. $(2.89)^6$
9-855. $(4.11)^{5.2}$
9-856. $(19.01)^{1.6}$
9-857. $(1.185)^{2.7}$
9-858. $(1.033)^{5.8}$
9-859. $(1.0134)^{25}$
9-860. $(3.95)^{0.65}$
9-861. $(8.46)^{0.134}$
9-862. $(81.2)^{0.118}$
9-863. $(7850.)^{0.0775}$
9-864. $(1.399)^{0.883}$
9-865. $(10.06)^{0.0621}$

9-866. $(0.569)^4$
9-867. $(0.157)^8$
9-868. $(0.985)^{1.568}$
9-869. $(0.318)^{4.65}$
9-870. $(0.078)^{0.458}$
9-871. $(17.91)^{0.012}$
9-872. $(4780.)^{0.913}$
9-873. $(253.)^{0.269}$
9-874. $(0.428)^{0.559}$
9-875. $(4.08)^{24}$
9-876. $(3.91)^{20}$
9-877. $(8.45)^{16}$

9-878. $(7.77)^{42}$
9-879. $(16.89)^{1.402}$
9-880. $(87.8)^8$
9-881. $(0.1164)^{0.33}$
9-882. $(0.779)^{0.43}$
9-883. $(867.)^6$
9-884. $(91.05)^{14}$
9-885. $(0.775)^{0.0259}$
9-886. $\sqrt[6]{8.69}$
9-887. $\sqrt[5]{1.094}$
9-888. $\sqrt[1.3]{8.74}$
9-889. $\sqrt[0.6]{19.77}$

Mathematical Tools Useful in Problem Solving

9-890. $\sqrt[18]{54.8}$
9-891. $\sqrt[7]{1.004}$
9-892. $\sqrt[1.95]{0.642}$
9-893. $\sqrt[14]{0.1438}$
9-894. $\sqrt[3.6]{0.952}$

9-895. $\sqrt[2.4]{0.469}$
9-896. $\sqrt[1.7]{0.1975}$
9-897. $\sqrt[0.55]{0.2218}$
9-898. $\sqrt[0.46]{16,430}$
9-899. $\sqrt[0.133]{507}$

9-900. $\sqrt[0.57]{0.964}$
9-901. $\sqrt[5.09]{6.49}$
9-902. $\sqrt[13.6]{0.1574}$
9-903. $\sqrt[2.09]{0.1268}$

Solve for X.

9-904. $X = (43.8)^{6.4}$
9-905. $X = (1.853)^{0.447}$
9-906. $(15.84)^x = 4.87$
9-907. $(0.679)^x = 0.337$
9-908. $(31.77)^x = 1.164$
9-909. $(2.388)^{3x} = 3.066$
9-910. $(1.064)^{0.2x} = 4.99$
9-911. $(X)^{5.8} = 8.57$
9-912. $(4.92)^{0.66x} = 24.1$
9-913. $(0.899)^{4.7x} = (1.552)(10)^{-8}$
9-914. $(0.1135)^{0.77x} = 0.775$
9-915. $(11.774)^{8.31x} = 12.88$
9-916. $(18.73)^{6.4x} = 8688$

9-917. $(34.86)^{1.117x} = 9.44$
9-918. $(0.631)^{0.64x} = 0.318$
9-919. $(0.1299)^{0.68x} = 0.443$
9-920. $(1.461)^{19.66x} = 9.07$
9-921. $(0.766)^{5.8x} = 0.239$
9-922. $(X)^{7.99} = 0.775$
9-923. $(X)^{0.175} = 8.53$
9-924. $(X)^{3.33} = 1.055$
9-925. $(X)^{0.871} = 0.1557$
9-926. $(X)^{4.77} = 1.088$
9-927. $(X)^{0.771} = 0.0521$
9-928. $(4.51)^{0.199} = \dfrac{X}{3}$

Solve for the natural logarithms of the following numbers:

9-929. 15.77
9-930. 19,850.
9-931. 0.7789
9-932. 0.1845
9-933. 1.896
9-934. 56.87
9-935. 13.09
9-936. 33.4
9-937. 8.09

9-938. 1.571
9-939. 0.1345
9-940. 0.915
9-941. 0.001233
9-942. 13,890.
9-943. 2.066
9-944. 1.3157
9-945. 1.0047

9-946. 89.78
9-947. 0.664
9-948. 0.459
9-949. 0.1175
9-950. 1.9974
9-951. 0.9974
9-952. 0.2378
9-953. 0.01663

Right Triangle Solution (Log-Log Rule)

In the study of truss design, moments, and free body diagrams, the right triangle plays an important role. Since the Pythagorean theorem is sometimes awkward to use, and mistakes in arithmetic are more likely to occur, it is suggested that the following method be used to solve right triangles.

Given: Right triangle with sides a, b, and c and angles A, B, and C (90°).

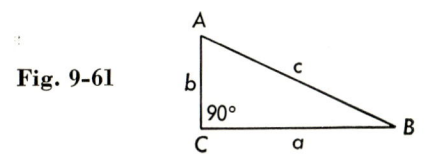

Fig. 9-61

If the smaller side (*b*) is divided by the longer side (*a*) and the quotient is greater than 0.100, use *Solution 1*. If the quotient is between 0.100 and 0.0100, use *Solution 2*. If the quotient is less than 0.0100, assume that the hypotenuse (*c*) is equal in length to the longest side (*a*) and that angle $B \cong 0°$.

Solution 1

1. Set the index of the T scale above the larger side (*a*) on the D scale.
2. Move the hairline to the smaller side (*b*) on the D scale.
3. Read the two angles of the right triangle on the T scale. The larger angle is always opposite the larger side.
4. Move the slide until the smaller of the two angles just read is under the hairline on the sine scale.
5. Read the hypotenuse (*c*) on the D scale as indicated by the index of the sine scale.

Example:
$a = 4 \quad A = ?$
$b = 3 \quad B = ?$
$c = ?$

  a. Set right index of T to 4 on D scale.
  b. Move the hairline to 3 on D scale.
  c. Read $B = 36.9°$, $A = 53.1°$ on the T scale. (Note that the smaller angle is opposite the smaller side.)
  d. Move the slide so that 36.9° on the S scale is under the hairline.
  e. Read side $c = 5$ at right index of S on the D scale.

Solution 2

1. Set the index of the T scale above the largest side (*a*) on the D scale.
2. Move the hairline to the smaller side (*b*) on the D scale.
3. Read the smaller angle (*B*) on the ST scale. The other angle (*A*) is the complement of *B*.
4. The hypotenuse is assumed to be equal in length to the largest side.

Solution 3: This solution is used where the hypotenuse is given with one side.

Example:
$a = 5.26 \quad A = ?$
$b = ? \quad B = ?$
$c = 8.75$

  a. Set index over 8.75 on D scale.
  b. Move hairline to 5.26 on D scale.
  c. Read $A = 37.0°$; $B = 53.0°$ on the S scale. (Note that angle read on sine scale is opposite the given side.)
  d. Set hairline to 37° on cosine scale.
  e. Read $b = 7.0$ on D scale.

Mathematical Tools Useful in Problem Solving

Problems

Solve by right triangle method.

9-954.	$a = 53$	$B = ?$		9-964.	$a = 11.33$	$b = ?$
	$b = 4$	$c = ?$			$B = 26.1°$	$c = ?$
9-955.	$a = 69.3$	$b = ?$		9-965.	$a = 0.00197$	$b = ?$
	$c = 95$	$A = ?$			$A = 11.36°$	$c = ?$
9-956.	$a = 37$	$b = ?$		9-966.	$c = 1904$	$a = ?$
	$c = 40.3$	$B = ?$			$A = 18.33°$	$b = ?$
9-957.	$a = 1.97$	$B = ?$		9-967.	$c = 4.0059$	$a = ?$
	$c = 2.33$	$b = ?$			$B = 86.3°$	$b = ?$
9-958.	$a = 29.3$	$b = ?$		9-968.	$c = 4.266$	$a = ?$
	$c = 55.3$	$A = ?$			$B = 31.06°$	$b = ?$
9-959.	$a = 49.3$	$c = ?$		9-969.	$a = 0.00397$	$b = ?$
	$b = 29.6$	$A = ?$			$c = 0.00512$	$A = ?$
9-960.	$a = 57.3$	$c = ?$		9-970.	$a = 1069$	$b = ?$
	$b = 42.1$	$A = ?$			$A = 85.3°$	$c = ?$
9-961.	$a = 3.95$	$c = ?$		9-971.	$b = 42.1$	$a = ?$
	$b = 1.06$	$B = ?$			$B = 3.56°$	$c = ?$
9-962.	$a = 333$	$A = ?$		9-972.	$a = 0.0317$	$b = ?$
	$b = 20$	$c = ?$			$c = 0.0444$	$B = ?$
9-963.	$a = 591$	$c = ?$		9-973.	$a = 21.67$	$c = ?$
	$b = 25$	$B = ?$			$b = 20.06$	$B = ?$

Folded Scales

The CF and DF scales are called *folded scales*. They are identical with the C and D scales except that their indices are in a different position. On the majority of slide rules, the CF and DF scales begin at the left end with the value π, which means that their indices will be located near the center of the rule. On some rules the CF and DF scales may be folded at ϵ (2.718) or at some other number.

Since the CF and DF scales are identical in graduations with the C and D scales, they can be used in multiplication and division just as the C and D scales are. Another important fact may be noticed when the scales are examined; that is, if a number such as 2 on the C scale is set over a number such as 3 on the D scale, then 2 on the CF scale coincides with 3 on the DF scale. This means that operations may be begun or answers obtained on either the C and D scales or on the CF and DF scales.

For example, if we wish to multiply 2 by 6, and we set the left index of the C scale over 2 on the D scale, we observe that the product cannot be read on the D scale because 6 on the C scale projects past the right end of the rule. Ordinarily this would mean that the slide would need to be run to the left so that the right index of the C scale could be used. However, by using the folded scales, we notice that the 6 on the CF scale coincides with 12 on the DF scale, thereby eliminating an extra movement of the slide.

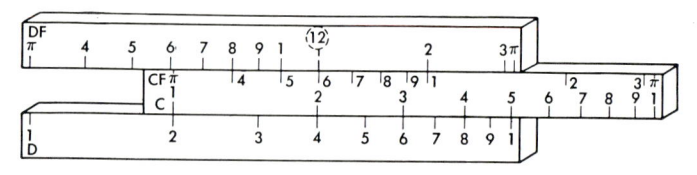

Fig. 9-62

In many cases the use of the folded scales will reduce the number of times the slide must be shifted to the left because an answer would fall beyond the right end of the D scale.

There are several methods by which the location of the decimal point in the answer can be determined. The projection rule can be used if it is always remembered that an answer read on the DF scale to the right of the index (near the center of the rule) corresponds to a left projection. Since in many operations the decimal point location in the answer can be determined by inspection, the decimal point can often be placed without reference to projection rules.

A convenient method of multiplying or dividing by π is afforded by the use of the folded scales. For example, to find the product 2π, set the hairline over 2 on the D scale. The product 6.28 is read on the DF scale under the hairline. Of course this same operation may be performed by using either index of the slide.

Reciprocal Scales

The CI, DI, and CIF scales are known as *reciprocal scales* or *inverted scales*. They are identical with the C, D, and CF scales, respectively, except that they are inverted; that is, the numbers represented by the graduations on these scales increase from right to left. On some slide rules, the inverted scale graduations are printed in red to help distinguish them from the other scale markings.

An important principle to remember when using these scales is that a number on the C scale will have its reciprocal in the same position on the CI scale. Conversely, when the hairline is set to a number on the CI scale, its reciprocal is under the hairline on the C scale.

The inverted scales are useful in problems involving repeated multiplication or division because some movements of the slide may be eliminated.

Example: Find the product:

$$(1.71)(8.30)(0.252)(4910)(53.8)$$

Mathematical Tools Useful in Problem Solving

In order to perform this operation, using the inverted scales, the following steps are used:
1. Set the hairline to 1.71 on the D scale.
2. Move the slide until 83 on the CI scale is under the hairline.
3. Move the hairline until it is set on 252 on the C scale.
4. Move the slide until 491 on the CI scale is under the hairline.
5. Move the hairline until it is set on 538 on the C scale.
6. Read the product 946000 under the hairline on the D scale.

The actual process has involved the use of reciprocal quantities in division in Steps 2 and 4 of the above sequence. Rewritten as the operation is actually performed, the problem appears as follows:

$$\frac{(1.71)(0.252)(53.8)}{(1/8.30)(1/4910)}$$

In finding the location of the decimal point in the answer when the inverted scales are used, the number of left projections are sometimes difficult to determine. It is recommended that the projection rule not be used but rather that the decimal point be determined by inspection or by using simple numbers having values near the given numbers, and then obtaining the decimal location by a trial multiplication or division, using the simple numbers. For example, in the above problem, using simple numbers of approximately the same values as those in the problem, the product would be determined as follows:

$$(2)(8)(0.3)(5000)(50) = 1{,}200{,}000, \quad \text{or} \quad (1.20)(10)^6$$

Since the digits determined on the slide rule were 946, the actual product would be 946,000, or $(9.46)(10)^5$.

Review Problems

Solve by general slide rule methods.

9-974. $(51)(9)$
9-975. $(426)(51)$
9-976. $(6.03)(5.16)$
9-977. $(561)(4956)$
9-978. $(43.2)(0.617)$
9-979. $(6617)(0.00155)$
9-980. $(99{,}043)(3.091)$
9-981. $(0.0617)(0.4417)$
9-982. $(1.035)(2.31 \times 10^5)$
9-983. $(79.81 \times 10^{-4})(0.617)$
9-984. $(516 \times 10^{-8})(0.391 \times 10^{-2})$
9-985. $(51)(97)(32)$

9-986. $(52.3)(759.3)$
9-987. $(716.5)(0.03166)$
9-988. $(11.65)(-0.9213)$
9-989. $(76.2)(-31.45)$
9-990. $(-0.6175)(-12{,}391)$
9-991. $\dfrac{(-759.6)}{(0.6175)}$
9-992. $\dfrac{(-19.96)}{(3346)}$
9-993. $\dfrac{(-1.0366)}{(29.31)}$
9-994. $\dfrac{(7575)}{(695.2)}$

Engineering: Elementary Problem Analysis

9-995. $\dfrac{(-516.6)}{(0.06052)}$

9-996. $(116.5)(4619)(0.317)$

9-997. $(210.9)(151.3)(7716)$

9-998. $(706.5)(1.695 \times 10^{-6})(0.006695)$
9-999. $(1033)(7.339 \times 10^{-6})(0.0317 \times 10^{-3})$
9-1000. $(4.017 \times 10^{-8})(0.0991)(0.1756)$
9-1001. $(5.576)(0.0917)(1.669 \times 10^{4})$
9-1002. $(6.991)(0.75)(0.993)(4.217)$
9-1003. $(56.88)(0.971 \times 10^{-5})$
9-1004. $(59.17)(0.3617)(0.5916)(0.00552)$
9-1005. $(5.691)(0.3316)(0.991)(0.00554)(0.1712)$
9-1006. $(6.523)(71.22)(4.091)(591)(600)(0.1332)$
9-1007. $(43.06)(0.2361)(0.905 \times 10^{-4})(3.617 \times 10^{-3})$

9-1008. $(1917)^{2.16}$
9-1009. $(4.216)^{1.517}$
9-1010. $(2.571)^{2.91}$

9-1011. $(0.3177)^{2.06}$
9-1012. $\sqrt[5]{26.31}$
9-1013. $\sqrt[3]{0.03175}$

9-1014. $\sqrt{116.75}$
9-1015. $\sqrt[3]{0.6177}$
9-1016. $\sqrt{3167}$

9-1017. $(179 \times 10^{3})(0.3165)$
9-1018. $(5033 \times 10^{-4})(0.9116)$
9-1019. $(0.06105)(77.165)$
9-1020. $(\sqrt{216})(34)(\pi)^{2}$
9-1021. $(\sqrt{819})(107)(\sqrt{\pi})$
9-1022. $\dfrac{(\sqrt{616})(6.767)}{(\sqrt{39.6})}$
9-1023. $\dfrac{(20.5)^{2}(7.49)(\sin 49°)}{(30.5)(0.0987)}$
9-1024. $\sqrt{\dfrac{(38)^{2}(6.71)^{2}}{\pi}}$
9-1025. $(7.61)(\sqrt[3]{7.61})(\pi)$

9-1026. $\dfrac{(13.1)(\sin 3.12°)}{(\tan 41.9°)}$
9-1027. $\dfrac{2}{3} = \dfrac{(X)(\pi)}{8.37}$
9-1028. $\dfrac{(9616)}{X} = \dfrac{(3.1416)}{(0.0142)}$
9-1029. $\dfrac{(1045)}{(X)} = \dfrac{(0.0278)}{(0.0798)}$
9-1030. $\dfrac{(1.486)}{(33)} = \dfrac{(0.37)(X)}{467}$
9-1031. $(816) = \dfrac{(244)(2\pi)}{(0.049)(X)}$
9-1032. $\dfrac{(0.0036)(\sin 49.8°)}{(\sqrt[3]{64.9})(2.1 \times 10^{3})}$

9-1033. $(4 \times 10^{6})(0.007) = (X)(10{,}980)$

9-1034. $Y = \left(\dfrac{1}{4}\right)\left(\dfrac{16}{6}\right)\left(\dfrac{1}{17}\right)$
9-1035. $\dfrac{X}{\pi} = \dfrac{(\sqrt{46.2})(3.14)^{2}}{(\sin 3.7°)}$
9-1036. $\dfrac{(3.98)(X)}{(1.07)(38)} = \dfrac{(3 \times 10^{6})}{(17{,}680)}$

9-1037. $\dfrac{(\sqrt[3]{986})}{X} = \dfrac{(14)}{(1/116)}$
9-1038. $\dfrac{(X)^{2}}{(9.2)} = \dfrac{(18.17)(3.4)}{(166)}$
9-1039. $\dfrac{(X)^{\frac{1}{2}}}{(31.1)} = \dfrac{(\sqrt{196})(189.1)}{4/76}$

9-1040. $\dfrac{(3.6)}{(X)^{2}} = \dfrac{(9.6 \times 10^{2})}{(67.4)} = \dfrac{(Y)^{\frac{1}{2}}}{(64)}$

Mathematical Tools Useful in Problem Solving

9-1041. $\dfrac{(96.5)}{(3.9)} = \dfrac{X}{(\sin 46.6°)} = \dfrac{(Y)^2}{(3.14 \times 10^{-2})}$

9-1042. $\dfrac{(X)^2}{Y} = \dfrac{(67.3)^2(Y)}{(96.61)} = \dfrac{(497.1)}{\tan 75°}$

9-1043. $\dfrac{(3.7)(4.9)}{X} = \dfrac{(46.7)}{564}$

9-1044. $\dfrac{Y}{(28)} = \dfrac{(3.2)}{(4/118)}$

9-1045. $\dfrac{Y}{42} = \dfrac{(39.1)}{(1/45)}$

9-1046. $(37.3)(X)(46.6) = (175)(\pi)$

9-1047. $(\sqrt{256})(3) = (X)(197.6)$

9-1048. $\dfrac{(54.6)(\tan 10.6°)}{(\sqrt{0.0967})(8.1 \times 10^3)}$

9-1049. $\dfrac{\sqrt[3]{(15.1)^2}(31.4)^2}{(\sin \arccos 0.617)}$

9-1050. $\dfrac{(0.954)(0.06 \times 10^3)}{(\tan 59°)^{\frac{1}{2}}(6.5)^2}$

9-1051. $\dfrac{\sqrt[3]{(15.6)^2}(0.9618)}{(0.08173)(61{,}508)(2\pi)}$

9-1052. $\dfrac{(68)(765)(391)(0.0093 \times 10^3)}{(571)^2(\sqrt[3]{(64)})}$

9-1053. $\dfrac{(\cos 11.5°)(\sqrt{6.87})}{(0.00081)(7.7 \times 10^4)}$

9-1054. $\dfrac{\sqrt[4]{(1.71)^5}\,(6.87)}{(\tan 53°)(5.1)^2}$

9-1055. $\dfrac{(0.000817)(\tan 81°)}{(0.00763)(\tan 81°)}$

9-1056. $(273)^{\frac{1}{2}}(46.9)(\cos 61°)(\pi^3)$

9-1057. $\dfrac{(\sin \arctan 3.17)(71.7)}{(\sqrt{89.6})(\sqrt[3]{(76.5)^2})}$

9-1058. $\dfrac{(\sqrt{(16)^3})(\log_{10} 100)}{(6.71 \times 10^{-1})(3.71)^3}$

9-1059. $\dfrac{(6.93)(\sin \operatorname{Cos}^{-1} 0.98)}{(0.937)^2(39.6)}$

9-1060. $\dfrac{(\sqrt{91.68})\,(\sqrt[3]{65.9})}{(\tan 68.7°)(0.671)^2}$

9-1061. $\dfrac{(4.5)^4(\sqrt{98.71})(\sin 56.4°)}{(0.09 \times 10)(38.6)^{3/2}}$

9-1062. $\dfrac{(\sqrt{285})(\cos 36.6°)(1.64)^2}{(67.1 \times 10^{-1})(5780)}$

9-1063. $\dfrac{(\tan \operatorname{Sin}^{-1} 0.87)(61.7)}{(5.64)^{0.98}(3.65)^2}$

9-1064. $\dfrac{(3174)(\tan 64°)}{(81.6)^2(\sqrt[3]{18})}$

9-1065. $\dfrac{(44.6)(0.09 \times 10^3)(\sin 80.9°)}{(\sqrt[3]{96.7})(51.6)^2}$

9-1066. $\dfrac{(\tan 50.6°)(3.4)^2}{(\sqrt{9681})(171)}$

9-1067. $\dfrac{(296)(0.197 \times 10^5)}{\sqrt[4]{(76.1)}(\sin 49.6°)}$

9-1068. $\dfrac{(\sin 22.6°)(9.918)}{(\tan 31.6°)(98.71)}$

9-1069. $\dfrac{(68.7 \times 10^2)(\tan 56.1°)}{(96.7)^{0.86}(18{,}614)}$

9-1070. $\dfrac{(0.0098)(\sin 17.6°)\,\sqrt{(0.186)}}{(41.6)^2(689.0)}$

9-1071. $\dfrac{(\tan 19.8°)^2(6.71 \times 10^3)}{(1{,}876)(\sqrt[4]{59})}$

9-1072. $\dfrac{(\sqrt{\sin 40°})(17)^2(4\pi^2)}{(0.643)(\tan 60°)}$

chapter ten

Unit Systems and Dimensional Analysis

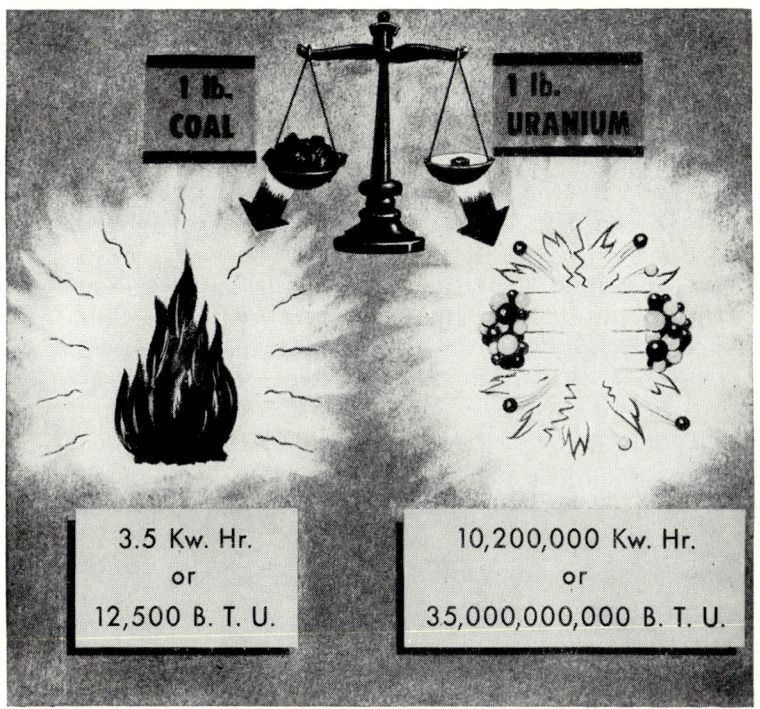

Courtesy Westinghouse Electric Corporation

The contrast of energy sources is depicted in this picture which shows the relative energy conversion from coal and nuclear fuels. In working with such energy sources, the engineer must be able to convert from one unit system to another.

chapter ten

Unit Systems and Dimensional Analysis

Engineering and scientific calculations make use of measurements of all types. Some measurements are made with precise instruments, while others are the result of crude approximations. Regardless of the accuracy of the measurements or of the particular type of measuring instrument used, the measurements are themselves merely representative of certain comparisons previously agreed upon.

The length of a metal cylinder, for example, can be determined by laying it alongside a calibrated scale or ruler. The 12-in. ruler is known to represent one-third of a yard, and a yard is recognized as being equivalent to 36.00/39.37 of a meter—the distance between two marks on a platinum-iridium bar which is kept in a vault in Troyes, France. All these methods of measurements are comparisons. Other similar standards exist for the measurement of temperature, time, force, etc.

Physical quantities to be measured may be of two types: those which are concerned with *fundamental dimensions* of length (L), time (T), force (F), mass (m), temperature (θ), etc.; and those which are concerned with *derived dimensions* of area, volume, pressure, density, etc. *Fundamental dimensions* may be subdivided into various sized parts, called *units*. The dimension *time* (T), for example, can be expressed in the units of seconds, hours, days, etc., depending upon the application to be made or the magnitude of the measurement. *Derived dimensions* are the result of combining *fundamental dimensions*. Area, therefore, is expressed dimensionally as length squared (L^2); pressure, as force per unit area $(F/L^2$, or $FL^{-2})$; acceleration as length per time squared $(L/T^2$, or $LT^{-2})$, etc.

Most measured quantities must be expressed in both magnitude and units. To state that an area was 146 would have no meaning. For example an area could be tabulated as 146 sq. miles or 146 cm^2; a pressure could be recorded as 0.0015 dyne per square centimeter or 0.0015 lb$_f$ per in.^{2}; an acceleration could be indicated as 159 in./sec^2 or 159 ft/sec^2, etc. However, there are some values used in engineering computations which are dimensionally sterile (without dimensions). These should be ignored in the unit balancing of an equation. *Radians*, π, *coefficient of friction*, *ratios*, and *per cent error* are examples of *sterile* values.

Equations involving measured quantities must be balanced dimensionally as well as numerically. Both dimensions and units can be multiplied and divided or raised to powers just like ordinary algebraic quantities. When all of the dimensions (or units) in an equation balance, the equation is said to be dimensionally homogeneous.

Unit Systems and Dimensional Analysis

Example: An alloy has a specific weight of 400 pcf. What is the weight of 2 ft³ of the alloy? Show the numerical and dimensional solutions to the problem.

$$W = V\rho$$

or

(Weight of metal) = (volume of metal)(specific weight of metal)

Fundamental Dimensions: $F = (L^3)\left(\dfrac{F}{L^3}\right)$ (Dimensional solution)

Units: $F = (2 \text{ ft}^3)\left(400 \dfrac{\text{lb}_f}{\text{ft}^3}\right) = 800 \text{ lb}_f$ (Numerical solution)

Check: $\text{lb}_f = \text{lb}_f$

Frequently it will be necessary to change unit systems, i.e., feet to inches, hours to seconds, pounds to grams, etc. This process can be accomplished by the use of unity conversion factors which are multiplied by the expression to be changed. Refer to pages 368 to 370 for a listing of commonly used conversion factors.

Example: Change a speed of 3000 miles per hour (miles/hr) to feet per second (ft/sec).

Fundamental dimensions: $\dfrac{L}{T} = \dfrac{L}{T}$

Units: $V = \left(3000 \dfrac{\text{miles}}{\text{hr}}\right)\left(\dfrac{5280 \text{ ft}}{1 \text{ mile}}\right)\left(\dfrac{1 \text{ hr}}{3600 \text{ sec}}\right) = \left(4400 \dfrac{\text{ft}}{\text{sec}}\right)$

The two conversion factors, (5280 ft/1 mile) and (1 hr/3600 sec), are each equivalent to unity, since the numerator of each fraction is equal to its denominator (5280 ft = 1 mile, and 1 hr = 3600 sec).

It should also be noted that the word *per* means *divided by*. To avoid misunderstandings in computations, the units should be expressed in fractional form.

Example:

(a) $(X \text{ per } Y) \text{ per } Z = (X \div Y) \div Z = [(X/Y)/Z] = \dfrac{(X/Y)}{Z} = \dfrac{X}{YZ}$

(b) Acceleration = 156 ft per sec per min = 156 ft/sec/min

$$= 156 \dfrac{\text{ft}}{(\text{sec})(\text{min})}$$

(c) Pressure = 14.7 lb$_f$ per square inch = $14.7 \dfrac{\text{lb}_f}{\text{in.}^2}$

Example: Solve for the conversion factor k.

(a) $$\frac{c^2 b^3 d}{a^4} = (k)\left(\frac{c^5 ba^2}{e^2}\right)$$

Solving for k: $$k = \frac{b^2 de^2}{a^6 c^3}$$

and $$\left(\frac{c^2 b^3 d}{a^4}\right) = \left(\frac{b^2 de^2}{a^6 c^3}\right)\left(\frac{c^5 ba^2}{e^2}\right)$$

Check: $$\frac{c^2 b^3 d}{a^4} = \frac{c^2 b^3 d}{a^4} = c^2 b^3 d a^{-4}$$

(b) $$\left(\frac{XR^3 d^3 e}{(f/T)(h^5)}\right)(k) = \left(\frac{Rd}{X^5 hT^2}\right)$$

$$(k) = \left(\frac{fh^4}{X^6 eR^2 d^2 T^3}\right)$$

Check: $$\left[\frac{XR^3 d^3 e}{(f/T)(h^5)}\right]\left[\frac{fh^4}{X^6 eR^2 d^2 T^3}\right] = \frac{Rd}{X^5 hT^2} \quad \text{or} \quad RdX^{-5}h^{-1}T^{-2}$$

Example: Solve for the fundamental dimensions of Q and P in the following dimensionally homogeneous equation if C is a velocity and B is an area.

$$Q = C(B - P)$$

Fundamental Dimensions: $$Q = \frac{L}{T}(L^2 - P)$$

Since the equation is dimensionally homogeneous, P must also be length squared (L^2) in order that the subtraction can be carried out. If this is true, the units of Q are

$$Q = \frac{L}{T}(L^2 - L^2)^* = \frac{L}{T}(L^2) = \frac{L^3}{T}$$

Problems

Solve for the conversion factor k.

10-1. $k\left(\dfrac{c^3 dxe^5}{hR}\right) = \dfrac{R^3 d^5 e}{c^2}$

10-2. $\dfrac{ABC^2}{DM^3} = k\dfrac{D^5 M}{B^2}$

10-3. $k\left(\dfrac{HRM}{BA^2}\right) = \sqrt{C^4 EHR^8}$

10-4. $D^2 \sqrt{CX^5} = k\left(\dfrac{AB^2}{X^3}\right)$

10-5. $k(GJ^2 NT^{-2}R^{-3}) = R^5 TJG^{-3}$

10-6. $D^2 EH^{-5}B^{-2} = k\sqrt{DH^2 E}$

10-7. $\sqrt{TS^3 F^{-2}B} = k\sqrt{SF^3 B^6}$

10-8. $k\dfrac{\sqrt{B^3 E}}{C^2 F^{-2}} = R^3 BCF^2$

10-9. $k(A^2 B\sqrt{CX^{-2}}) = X^{-3}B^{-2}$

10-10. $YC^3 R^{-1}M^{-3} = k\sqrt{C^2 R^{-1}}$

* It should be remembered that the terms L^2 represent a particular length squared in each instance. Thus the remainder (depending on the numerical magnitude of each term) will also be length squared or will be zero for the special case of the original lengths being equal.

Unit Systems and Dimensional Analysis

10-11. Is the equation $a = (2S/t^2) - (2V_1/t)$ dimensionally homogeneous if a is an acceleration, V_1 is a velocity, t is a time, and S is a distance? Prove your answer by writing the equation with fundamental dimensions.

10-12. Is the equation $V_2^2 = V_1^2 + 2as$ dimensionally correct if V_1 and V_2 are velocities and S is a distance? Prove your answer by rewriting the equation in fundamental dimensions.

10-13. In the homogeneous equation $R = B + \frac{1}{2}CX$, what are the fundamental dimensions of R and B if C is an acceleration and X is a time?

10-14. Determine the fundamental dimensions of the expression $B/g\sqrt{D} - m^2$, where B is a force, m is a length, D is an area, and g is the acceleration of gravity at a particular location.

10-15. The relationship $M = \sigma I/c$ pertains to the bending moment for a beam under compressive stress. σ is a stress in F/L^2, C is a length L, and I is a moment of inertia L^4. What are the fundamental dimensions of M?

*10-16. The expression $V/K = (B - 7/3A)A^{2/3}$ is dimensionally homogeneous. A is a length and V is a volume of flow per unit of time. Solve for the fundamental dimensions of K and B.

*10-17. Is the expression $S = 0.031 V^2/fB$ dimensionally homogeneous if S is a distance, V is a velocity, f is the coefficient of friction, and B is a ratio of two weights? Is it possible that the numerical value 0.031 has fundamental dimensions? Prove your solution.

*10-18. If the following heat-transfer equation is dimensionally homogeneous, what are the units of k?

$$Q = \frac{-kA(T_1 - T_2)}{L}$$

A is a cross-sectional area in square feet, L is a length in feet, T_1 and T_2 are temperatures (°F), and Q is the amount of heat (energy) conducted in Btu per unit of time.

*10-19. In the dimensionally homogeneous equation

$$F = \frac{4Ey}{(1-\mu^2)(Md^2)}\left[(h-y)\left(h-\frac{y}{2}\right)t - t^3\right]$$

F is a force, E is a force per (length)^2, y, d, and h are lengths, μ is Poisson's ratio, and M is a ratio of diameters. What are the fundamental dimensions of t?

*10-20. In the equation

$$F = \frac{12WV^2}{gr}\left(\cos\alpha + \frac{r}{l}\cos 2\alpha\right)$$

F represents a force, W is a weight, V is a crank velocity, g is the acceleration of gravity at the place of experimentation, α is an angle, and l is a connecting rod length. What must be the fundamental dimensions of r if the equation is to be dimensionally homogeneous?

Solve the following:

10-21. Change 5030 $\frac{\text{miles}}{\text{hr}}$ to $\frac{\text{ft}}{\text{sec}}$.

10-22. Change 762 in. per sec to miles per day.

10-23. Change $(26)(10)^5$ gal of gasoline per sec to ft³ of gasoline per hr.

10-24. Change 0.0972 cm³ of water per sec to ton of water per hr.

10-25. Change 1.59×10^8 board-feet to ft³.

10-26. Change 6,910,000 $\frac{\text{dynes}}{\text{cm}^3}$ to tons per ft³

10-27. Change 2770 acres to cm².

10-28. Change 0.0033 $\frac{\text{miles}}{\text{sec}}$ per day to ft per sec².

10-29. Change (0.0139×10^{-7}) knots per sec to $\frac{\text{miles}}{(\text{hr})(\text{day})}$.

10-30. It takes the earth 365 days, 5 hr, 46 min, and 46 sec to make one complete trip around the sun. The orbit is approximately $(5.84)(10)^8$ miles. Find the speed of the earth in (a) miles per hour, (b) feet per second, (c) meters per second, and (d) kilometers per minute.

*10-31. The kinetic energy of a moving body in space may be expressed as follows:

$$KE = \frac{MV^2}{2}$$

where KE = kinetic energy of the moving body
M = mass of the moving body
V = velocity of the moving body

   a. Given: $M = 539 \frac{\text{lb}_f \text{ sec}^2}{\text{ft}}$; $V = 2900 \frac{\text{ft}}{\text{sec}}$

     Find: KE in (ft)(lb$_f$)

   b. Given: $M = 42.6 \frac{\text{lb}_f \text{ sec}^2}{\text{ft}}$; $KE = 1.20(10^{11})$(ft)(lb$_f$)

     Find: V in $\frac{\text{ft}}{\text{sec}}$

   c. Given: $KE = 16,900$ (in.)(lb); $V = 3960 \frac{\text{in.}}{\text{min}}$

     Find: M in slugs.

   d. Given: $M = 143$ grams; $KE = 2690$ (in.)(lb)

     Find: V in $\frac{\text{mile}}{\text{hr}}$

*10-32. The inertia force due to the acceleration of a rocket may be expressed as follows:

$$F = Ma$$

Unit Systems and Dimensional Analysis 215

where F = unbalanced force
a = acceleration of the body
M = mass of the body

a. Given: $a = 439 \dfrac{\text{ft}}{\text{sec}^2}$; $M = 89.6 \dfrac{\text{lb}_f \text{ sec}^2}{\text{ft}}$
Find: F in lb$_f$.

b. Given: $F = 1500$ lb$_f$; $M = 26.4 \dfrac{\text{lb}_f \text{ sec}^2}{\text{ft}}$
Find: a in $\dfrac{\text{ft}}{\text{sec}^2}$

c. Given: $F = (49.3)(10)^5$ lb$_f$; $a = 32.2 \dfrac{\text{ft}}{\text{sec}^2}$
Find: M in $\dfrac{\text{lb}_f \text{ sec}^2}{\text{ft}}$

d. Given: $M = 9650 \dfrac{\text{lb}_f \text{ sec}^2}{\text{ft}}$; $a = 980 \dfrac{\text{cm}}{\text{sec}^2}$
Find: F in lb$_f$

*10-33. The force required to assemble a force-fit joint on a particular piece of machinery may be expressed by the following equation:

$$F = \dfrac{\pi d l f P}{2000}$$

where d = shaft diameter, in.
l = hub length, in.
f = coefficient of friction
P = radial pressure, psi
F = force of press required, tons

a. Given: $d = 9.05$ in.; $l = 15.1$ in.; $f = 0.10$; $P = 10{,}250$ psi.
Find: F in lb$_f$.

b. Given: $F = 4.21 \times 10^5$ lb$_f$; $f = 0.162$; $P = 8.32(10^8)$ psf; $l = 1.62$ ft.
Find: d in ft.

c. Given: $d = 25$ cm; $l = 30.2$ cm; $f = 0.08$; $P = 9260$ psi.
Find: F in tons.

d. Given: $F = 206$ tons; $d = 6.23$ in.; $l = 20.4$ in.; $f = 0.153$.
Find: P in lb$_f$./ft^2.

*10-34. The dynamic stress in the rim of a certain flywheel has been expressed by the following equation:

$$\sigma = 0.0000284 \rho r^2 n^2$$

where σ = tensile stress, $\frac{\text{lb}_f}{\text{in.}^2}$

ρ = specific weight of material, $\frac{\text{lb}_f}{\text{in.}^3}$

r = radius of curvature, in.

n = number of rpm

a. Given: $\sigma = 200$ psi; $\rho = 0.282 \frac{\text{lb}_f}{\text{in.}^3}$; $r = 9$ in.

Find: n in rpm.

b. Given: $\rho = 0.332 \frac{\text{lb}_f}{\text{in.}^3}$; $r = 23.1$ cm; $n = 200$ rpm.

Find: σ in psi.

c. Given: $\rho = 540 \frac{\text{lb}_f}{\text{ft}^3}$; $n = 186$ rpm; $\sigma = (31.2)(10)^3$ psf.

Find: r in ft.

d. Given: $\rho = 326 \frac{\text{lb}_f}{\text{ft}^3}$; $n = 250$ rpm; $r = 0.632$ ft.

Find: σ in psf.

*10-35. The stress in a certain column may be calculated by the following relationship:

$$\sigma = \frac{F}{A}\left[1 + \left(\frac{l}{k}\right)^2 \frac{R}{\pi^2 nE}\right]$$

where σ = induced stress, psi

F = applied force, lb$_f$

A = cross-sectional area of member, in.^{2}

l = length of bar, in.

k = radius of gyration, in.

R = elastic limit, lb$_f$/in.^{2}

E = modulus of elasticity, lb$_f$/in.^{2}

n = coefficient for different end conditions

a. Given: $n = 1$; $E = (3)(10)^7$ psi; $R = (4.2)(10)^4$ psi; $k = 0.29$ in.; $l = 20.3$ in.; $A = 17.5$ in.^{2}; $F = 12,000$ lb$_f$.

Find: σ in psi.

b. Given: $\sigma = 11,500$ psi; $F = 6.3$ tons; $l = 2.11$ ft; $k = 0.41$ in.; $R = 40,000$ psi; $E = (3.16)(10)^7$ psi; $n = 2$

Find: A in ft^2.

c. Given: $n = \frac{1}{4}$; $E = (2.65)(10)^7$ psi; $R = (3.21)(10)^4$ psi; $k = 0.026$ ft; $A = 102$ cm^2; $F = 5.9$ tons; $\sigma = 10,000$ psi.

Find: l in ft.

d. Given: $\sigma = (1.72)(10)^6$ psf; $F = (1.33)(10)^4$ lb$_f$; $l = 1.67$ ft; $k = 0.331$ in.; $E = (7.87)(10)^7$ psi; $n = 4$; $A = 14.2$ in.^{2}

Find: R in psi.

Unit Systems and Dimensional Analysis

UNIT SYSTEMS

There are a number of systems of units that have been used in scientific and engineering calculations. Variations in the preference of unit systems may depend not only upon the language spoken by a particular researcher but also upon whether or not he has been educated as an engineer or as a scientist.

The need for unit systems was first evident when it became necessary to explain the fundamental relationships between force, mass, and acceleration. Sir Isaac Newton (1642–1727) expressed several basic laws which he believed to govern the motion of particles. Only recently has it become evident that in studying the motion of atoms and certain planets, Einstein's theory of relativity must supplant Newton's previous concepts. However, Newton's "second law" still serves as a basis for much of today's engineering mechanics. Briefly this law may be stated as follows:

When an external unbalanced force F acts on a rigid particle of mass, the motion of the particle will be changed. The particle will be accelerated. Its rate of change in motion will be in the direction of the unbalanced force and will be proportional to it.

Stated mathematically: $$\frac{F_1}{a_1} = \frac{F_2}{a_2} = \frac{F_3}{a_3} = \frac{F_n}{a_n} = \text{a constant}$$

where F_1, F_2, F_3, etc., are external unbalanced forces acting on a particle.

a_1, a_2, a_3, etc., are consequential accelerations of the particle.

The quotient of (F/a) is a quantity which is invariant. The units of this term depend upon the units aribitrarily chosen to define F and a. This constant has been called the *mass* of the particle under consideration. It is properly designated by the symbol M, or in some cases by the product of the two symbols, km. In this latter case, k could be a value of 1, or it could be some other dimensional expression of unity. The mass M of a particular body is independent of the location of the body in the universe. Thus

$$F = Ma$$
or
$$F = kma$$

The Foot-Pound-Second (FPS) Gravitational System of Units

Engineers and scientists have in general differed upon the method of defining the respective parts of the preceding relationship. Engineers work primarily with measured forces, and consequently they have usually preferred to consider *length* (L), *force* (F), and *time* (T) as fundamental dimensions.

In Newton's equation, $F = Ma$, dimensional homogeneity must be maintained. If length, force, and time are taken as fundamental dimensions, the dimensions of mass must be derived. This can be accomplished as follows:

$$F = Ma$$

Then
$$M = \frac{F}{a}$$

$$M = \frac{(F)}{(L/T^2)} = FL^{-1}T^2$$

and
$$M = \text{lb ft}^{-1} \text{ sec}^2$$

For convenience, this derived unit of mass (1 lb sec^2)/ft is called a *slug*. Thus, a force of 1 lb will cause a mass of 1 slug to have an acceleration of 1 ft/sec^2.

It should be noted that, with the FPS system, a unity conversion factor must be used if a mass unit other than the slug is used. Since the acceleration of gravity varies with both latitude and altitude, the use of a gravitational system is sometimes inconvenient. A 100,000-lb rocket on the earth, for example, would not weigh 100,000 lb$_f$ on the moon—where gravitational forces are smaller. The mass of the rocket, on the other hand, is a fixed quantity and will be a constant amount, regardless of its location in space.

For a freely falling body at sea level and 45° latitude, the acceleration g* of the body is 32.17 (approximately 32.2) ft/sec^2. As the mass is attracted to the earth, the only force then acting on it is its own weight.

If
$$F = Ma$$
then
$$W = Mg$$
and
$$M = \frac{W}{g}$$
where
$$a = g \quad \text{and} \quad F = W$$

In this particular system of units, then, the mass of a body in slugs may be calculated by dividing the weight of the body in pounds by the local acceleration of gravity in ft/sec^2.

The Engineering System of Units

Early in the development of engineering analysis a system of units was developed which defined both the units of mass and the units of force. It is perhaps unfortunate that the same word, pounds, was chosen to represent both quantities, since they are physically different. In order to help differentiate the quantities, the pound-mass may be designated as lb$_{mass}$ (or lb$_m$) and the pound-force as lb$_{force}$ (or lb$_f$).

* The value of the acceleration of gravity, g, at any latitude θ on the earth may be approximated from the following relationship: $g = 32.09(1 + 0.0053 \sin^2 \theta)$ ft/sec^2.

Unit Systems and Dimensional Analysis

For many engineering applications the numerical values of lb$_{mass}$ and lb$_{force}$ are very nearly the same. However, in expressions such as $F = Ma$, it is necessary that the difference between lb$_{mass}$ and lb$_{force}$ be maintained. By definition, a mass of 1 lb$_{mass}$ will be attracted to the earth by a force of 1 lb$_{force}$ at a place where the acceleration of gravity is 32.17 ft/sec^2. If the acceleration of gravity changes to some other value, the force must change in proportion, since mass is invariant.

Although the pound subscripts, *force* and *mass*, are frequently omitted in engineering and scientific literature, it is nevertheless true that lb$_{force}$ is not the same as lb$_{mass}$. Their numerical values are equal, however, in the case of sea level, 45° latitude calculations. Their values may be widely different, as would be the case in an analysis involving satellite design and space travel.

The engineer frequently works in several systems of units in the same calculation. For this reason, most engineers have preferred to express Newton's second law as $F = Ma$ rather than $F = kma$.*

In this case, it is only necessary that the force, mass, and acceleration units all be expressed in some valid set of units from any unit system. Numerical equality and unit homogeneity may be determined by applying unity conversion factors to the individual terms of the expression (see page 211).

Example: Solve for the lb$_{mass}$ which is being accelerated at 3.07 ft/sec^2 by a force of 392 lb$_{force}$.

Solution:
$$F = Ma \quad \text{or} \quad M = \frac{F}{a}$$

$$M = \frac{392 \text{ lb}_{force}}{3.07 \text{ ft/sec}^2} = 127.8 \frac{\text{lb}_{force} \text{ sec}^2}{\text{ft}}$$

The direct substitution has given mass in the units of slugs instead of lb$_{mass}$ units. This is a perfectly proper set of units for mass, although not in lb$_{mass}$ units as desired. Consequently the final equation must be altered by applying the unity conversion factor $\left(\frac{32.2 \text{ lb}_{mass}}{1 \text{ lb}_{force} \text{ sec}^2 \text{ ft}^{-1}} \right)$. The object, of course, is to cancel units until the desired units appear in the answer. Thus

$$M = \left(\frac{127.8 \text{ lb}_{force} \text{ sec}^2}{\text{ft}} \right) \left(\frac{32.2 \text{ lb}_{mass} \text{ ft}}{1 \text{ lb}_{force} \text{ sec}^2} \right) = (4.11)(10)^3 \text{ lb}_{mass}$$

Example: Solve for the mass in slugs which is being accelerated at 13.6 meters/sec by a force of 1782 lb$_{force}$.

---

* The expression $F = kma$ is most properly used when all the analysis being done is in a particular unit system such as the CGS system (see page 221).

Solution: $F = Ma$

$$M = \frac{F}{a} = \frac{(1782 \text{ lb}_{force})}{(13.6 \text{ meters}/\text{sec}^2)} = \left(\frac{1782 \text{ lb}_{force} \text{ sec}^2}{13.6 \text{ meters}}\right)\left(\frac{1}{3.28}\frac{\text{meter}}{\text{ft}}\right)$$

$$M = 40 \frac{\text{lb}_{force} \text{ sec}^2}{\text{ft}} = 40 \text{ slugs}$$

Handling all units and dimensional systems as simple algebraic equations, and then solving for the particular set of units which may be desired, has the distinct advantage of simplicity over the $F = kma$ concept. It is recommended that in writing a mathematical expression to represent some physical phenomena, the engineer should avoid using stereotyped conversion symbols such as g, g_c, k, J, etc. in the equation. If one of these, or any other conversion factor, is needed in an equation to achieve unit balance, it can *then* be added. Since many different unit systems may be used from time to time, it is best to add unity conversion factors *only* as they are needed. Unfortunately much of the engineering literature has been written such that the equations used in a particular instance include one or more unity conversion factors. Considerable care must be exercised, therefore, in using these expressions since they represent a "special case" rather than a "general condition." The engineer should form a habit of always checking the unit balance of all equations.

Referring above to the discussion of the FPS system of units, it can be shown that

$$1 \text{ slug} = 1 \frac{\text{lb}_{force} \text{ sec}^2}{\text{ft}} = 32.2 \text{ lb}_{mass}$$

The foregoing discussion shows that:

1. If mass units in slugs are used in the expression $F = Ma$, the force units will come out in the usual units of pounds (lb_{force}).

2. If mass units in pounds (lb_{mass}) are used in the expression $F = Ma$, force units will come out in an absolute system unit called the *poundal* (see Table 10-1).

Absolute Unit Systems

Scientists the world over have chosen to use dimensional or unit systems which are *absolute*. That is, the fundamental units chosen do not depend upon gravitational effects on the earth or other planets. In absolute systems the dimensions of force are derived, and the magnitude of the proportionality constant k (in $F = kma$) is taken as unity.

Three such absolute systems are in scientific use today. These are the MKS (meter, kilogram, second) absolute system, the CGS (centimeter, gram, second) absolute system, and the FPS (foot, pound$_m$, second) absolute system. No attempt will be made here to discuss these systems in detail. However, the corresponding units of each system may be noted in Table 10-1.

Table 10-1. Unit Systems

FUNDAMENTAL DIMENSIONS	GRAVITATIONAL (1) FPS	GRAVITATIONAL (2) MKS	(3) ENGINEERING	(4) FPS	ABSOLUTE (5) MKS	ABSOLUTE (6) CGS
Force (F)	lb$_{force}$	kg	lb$_{force}$	...	...	...
Length (L)	ft	meter	ft	ft	meter	cm
Time (T)	sec	sec	sec	sec	sec	sec
Mass (M)	...	...	lb$_{mass}$	lb$_{mass}$	kg	gram

DERIVED DIMENSIONS	(1)	(2)	(3)	(4)	(5)	(6)
Force (F)	...	...	...	lb$_{mass}$ ft sec^{-2} (called a *poundal*)	kg meter sec^{-2} (called a *newton**)	gram cm sec^{-2} (called a *dyne*)
Mass (M)	lb$_{force}$ sec^2 ft^{-1} (called a *slug*)	kg sec^2 meter^{-1}	...	...	...	...
Energy (LF)	ft-lb$_{force}$	meter-kg	ft-lb$_{force}$	ft-poundal	meter-newton	cm-dyne (called an *erg*)
Power ($\frac{LF}{T}$)	$\frac{\text{ft-lb}_{force}}{\text{sec}}$	$\frac{\text{meter-kg}}{\text{sec}}$	$\frac{\text{ft-lb}_{force}}{\text{sec}}$	$\frac{\text{ft-poundal}}{\text{sec}}$	$\frac{\text{meter-newton}}{\text{sec}}$	$\frac{\text{erg}}{\text{sec}}$
Velocity ($\frac{L}{T}$)	$\frac{\text{ft}}{\text{sec}}$	$\frac{\text{meter}}{\text{sec}}$	$\frac{\text{ft}}{\text{sec}}$	$\frac{\text{ft}}{\text{sec}}$	$\frac{\text{meter}}{\text{sec}}$	$\frac{\text{cm}}{\text{sec}}$
Acceleration ($\frac{L}{T^2}$)	$\frac{\text{ft}}{\text{sec}^2}$	$\frac{\text{meter}}{\text{sec}^2}$	$\frac{\text{ft}}{\text{sec}^2}$	$\frac{\text{ft}}{\text{sec}^2}$	$\frac{\text{meter}}{\text{sec}^2}$	$\frac{\text{cm}}{\text{sec}^2}$
Area (L^2)	ft^2	meter^2	ft^2	ft^2	meter^2	cm^2
Volume (L^3)	ft^3	meter^3	ft^3	ft^3	meter^3	cm^3

* A newton is the force required to accelerate a 1-kg mass at 1 meter/sec^2. The acceleration of gravity at sea level and 45° latitude has the measured value of 9.807 meters/sec^2. A force of 1 kg equals 9.807 newtons of force.

Problems on Unit Systems

10-36. In the FPS gravitational system, what mass in slugs is necessary to produce 15.6 lb_{force} at standard conditions?

10-37. In the engineering gravitational system, what mass in lb_{mass} is necessary to produce a 195.3 lb_{force} at standard conditions?

10-38. Using the FPS gravitational system, calculate the fundamental dimensions of E in Einstein's equation,

$$E = mc^2 \left[\frac{1}{\sqrt{1 - (V^2/c^2)}} - 1 \right]$$

if m is a mass, V is a velocity, and c is the speed of light. What would be the fundamental dimensions of E in the CGS absolute system of units?

10-39. Using the relationship for g on page 218 and the FPS gravitational system of units, determine the weight, at the latitude 0°, of a stainless steel sphere whose mass is defined as 150 (lb_{force} sec^2/ft).

10-40. The mass of solid propellant in a certain container is 5 kg. What is the weight of this material in newtons at a location in Greenland, where the acceleration of gravity is 9.83 meters/sec^2? What is the weight in kg?

10-41. Change 100 newtons of force to lb_{force}.

10-42. If a gold sphere has a mass of 89.3 lb_{mass} on the earth, what would be its weight in lb_{force} on the moon, where the acceleration of gravity is 5.31 fps²?

10-43. Assuming that the acceleration due to gravitation is 5.31 fps² on the moon, what is the mass in slug units of a 100 lb_{mass} which is located on the moon?

10-44. A silver bar weighs 382 lb_{force} at a point on the earth where the acceleration of gravity is measured to be 32.1 fps². Calculate the mass of the bar in lb_{mass} and slug units.

10-45. The acceleration of gravity can be approximated by the following relationship:

$$g = 980.6 - (3.086)(10)^{-6} A$$

where g is expressed in cm/sec^2, and A is an altitude in cm. If a rocket weighs 10,370 lb_{force} at sea level and standard conditions, what will be its weight in dynes at 50,000 ft elevation?

10-46. At a certain point on the moon the acceleration due to gravitation is 5.35 fps². A rocket resting on the moon's surface at this point weighs 23,500 lb_{force}. What is its mass in slugs? (b) In lb_{mass}?

10-47. If a 10-lb weight on the moon (where g = 5.33 fps²) is returned to the earth and deposited at a latitude of 90° (see page 218), how much would it weigh in the new location?

Unit Systems and Dimensional Analysis

10-48. A 4.37-slug mass is taken from the earth to the moon and located at a point where $g = 5.33$ fps². What is the magnitude of its mass in the new location?

10-49. Is the equation $F = WV^2/2g$ a homogenous expression if W is a weight, V is a velocity, F is a force, and g is the linear acceleration of gravity? Prove your answer, using the FPS absolute system of units.

*10-50. Sir Isaac Newton expressed the belief that all particles in space, regardless of their mass, are each attracted to every other particle in space by a specific force of attraction. For spherical bodies, whose separation is very large compared with the physical dimensions of either particle, the force of attraction may be calculated from the relationship $F = Gm_1m_2/d^2$, where F is the existing gravitational force, d is the distance separating the two masses m_1 and m_2, and G is a gravitational constant, whose magnitude depends upon the unit system being used. Using the CGS absolute system of units [$G = 6.67 \times 10^{-8}$ (cm³/gm sec²)], calculate the mass of the earth if it attracts a mass of 1 gram with a force of 980 dynes. Assume that the distance from the center of the earth to the gram mass is 6370 km.

*10-51. Referring to Problem 10-50, calculate the mass of the sun if the earth (6×10^{24} kg mass) has an orbital diameter of 1.49×10^7 kms and the force of attraction between the two celestial bodies is $(1.44)(10)^{25}$ newtons.

*10-52. From Problem 10-50 calculate the acceleration of gravity on the earth in CGS absolute units.

*10-53. An interstellar explorer is accelerating uniformly at 58.6 fps² in a spherical space ship which has a total mass of 100,000 slugs. What is the force acting on the ship?

*10-54. At a certain instant in time a space vehicle is being acted on by a vertically upward thrust of 497,000 lb$_{force}$. The mass of the space vehicle is 400,000 lb$_{mass}$, and the acceleration of gravity is 32.1 fps². Is the vehicle rising or descending? What is its acceleration? (Assume "up" means radially outward from the center of the earth.)

*10-55. Some interstellar adventurers land their space craft on a certain celestial body. Explain how they could calculate the acceleration of gravity at the point where they landed.

chapter eleven

The Engineering Method of Analysis

Courtesy Westinghouse Electric Corporation

Engineers make use of models of various kinds to aid in the analysis and evaluation of problems. Here an idealized model system in the form of a nuclear power plant simulator is being used by an engineer to predict the behavior of a full scale system.

chapter eleven

The Engineering Method of Analysis

METHODS OF REASONING

Problem solving may be considered to be both an art and a science. The *art* of problem solving is generally developed over a period of continuous practice, while the *science* of problem solving comes about through a study of the engineering method of problem analysis. Both engineers and scientists must be "problem-solvers." However, in many instances, the end product of the engineer's analysis, which is a working system economically devised, is considerably different from that of the scientist's, which may be a solution without regard to economics or usefulness. Also, different processes of reasoning (deductive or inductive) may be used, depending upon the type of problem encountered.

Deductive Reasoning

The laws of reasoning by deduction, sometimes called *syllogism*, were defined by Aristotle (384–322 BC), a Greek philosopher. This form of reasoning makes use of (1) a statement of a general law (called a *major premise*), (2) a statement assigning a particular zone of interest to the general law (called a *minor premise*), and (3) a statement of *conclusion* which applies the general law to the specific zone of interest.

Example: Major Premise. The volume of all spheres can be determined by the relationship $V = \pi D^3/6$, where D is the diameter of the sphere.
Minor Premise. A ball is a sphere.
Conclusion. The volume of a ball can be found by applying the relationship $V = \pi D^3/6$, where D is the diameter of the ball.

An obvious limitation of this form of reasoning is that the statements of the *major* and *minor premises* may not always be free from error. If an untruth is assumed as a *major* or *minor premise*, for example, the *conclusion* will most likely also be in error. Only by chance could the *conclusion* be a true statement. Thus this form of reasoning is most useful when the *major* and *minor premises* have been proved by experimentation for all possible situations. It also follows that deductive reasoning is not useful for the discovering of new truths. It is, however, of considerable usefulness in the finding of new applications to proven laws.

Undoubtedly complete adherence to the doctrine of deductive reasoning during the Middle Ages was a primary reason for the barrenness of achievement in physical sciences and engineering during this particular period of history. However, mathematics was not so limited. Mathematics is a process of reasoning which is based upon fundamental concepts or premises, the parts of which are connected by the process of syllogism, or deductive reasoning.

Inductive Reasoning

Methods of inductive reasoning, or *truth by experiment*, have been practiced to some degree since the beginning of man. However, Aristotelian logic was long the accepted authority, and it was not until the thirteenth century that a revolt against deductive logic was successfully launched. Processes of inductive reasoning were first set forth by Roger Bacon (1214–1294) and later amplified by Francis Bacon (1561–1626). This form of reasoning is based upon the premise that if two or more things agree with one another in one or more respects, they will likely agree in still other respects; that things which are true of certain individual items within a class will be true of the entire class; and phenomena which are true at certain times will be true in similar environments at all other times. This is reasoning from a part to a whole, from the particular to the general, and from the individual to the universal.

It is only by processes of inductive reasoning that general laws and new scientific truths can be discovered. Consequently it is only in this way that the major premises necessary for deduction can be found.

Reasoning and Problem Solving

Engineers and scientists must master both the inductive or experimental method and the deductive method of logic, since the two processes of reasoning are complementary. Ordinarily one does not by choice think only by deduction or induction. Rather, he will alternate from one form of logic to the other as he moves through an analysis. It is of considerable value, however, to know which type of reasoning to use in a given situation. Perhaps of even more value to one is the ability to recognize false premises or improper experimental methods which may have been employed in the processes of analysis.

PROCESSES OF ANALYSIS

Engineers who have mastered the engineering method of problem analysis are considerably more successful in their work than those persons who have not been trained in this technique. In the past, many engineering problems were of such routine nature that a resort to deductive reasoning would suffice, and premises of deduction could be taken from handbooks. However, many of the engineering problems of today cannot be solved by mere "handbook techniques." Experimentation, research, and development are significant aspects of today's world. In any problem analysis some definite sequence, or procedure, should be employed, regardless of the type of situation encountered. The first step in this procedure is to define the problem.

Defining the Problem

Undoubtedly the most critical step in problem analysis is in understanding and defining the problem. All too frequently the novice analyst will begin his solution without first really identifying the real problem. Then, after laboriously working for several hours, he will finally realize that his answers are meaningless. In fact, he may have been working on facets of the general situation which bear only indirectly, and have no significant import, on the real problem.

Separation and identification of the problem, from amid great assortments of data and physical phenomena, is not easy. Seldom, if ever, will the problem be as clearly defined as those given in most textbook situations. It is for this reason that there is no substitute for *experience* in problem solving.

Example: The chief engineer of a helicopter plant has received notification from the FAA that ship Model 7-A5Z will not receive clearance for licensing due to instability of the ship at certain flight parameters.

In this particular case, the general statement of the situation is easy (ship Model 7-A5Z is unstable), but the particular problem or problems which must be solved to get FAA approval may be exceedingly difficult and involved. Thus it becomes necessary for the chief engineer to select the *strategic factors* before beginning his analysis.

Selection of the Strategic Factors

A *strategic factor* is that particular question or group of questions selected from within the framework of a general situation which when answered will enable one to solve the problem at hand. The *strategic factor* will probably not be a single statement or question. In fact it frequently has several parts, each of which must be solved individually. It is important that the problem analyst identify these parts by verbal or mathematical statements *before beginning his solution.*

A statement of the *strategic factors* may be set apart by such identifying words as "To Find," "Required," "Find," etc., on the problem sheet (see pages 82 to 85). If the *strategic factor* is composed of several parts, the parts should be solved individually in logical and systematic sequence. This sequence will depend largely upon the *assumptions* and *idealized model system* which are selected by the engineer.

Assumptions and the Idealized Model System

The engineer never attempts to find the perfect solution to a given physical problem. Like the scientist he must understand basic laws of nature, but

The Engineering Method of Analysis

unlike the scientist, he must also strive for a compromise between "*theory*" and "*reality*." At the present time, man does not possess enough tools (for example: mathematics and science) to solve any given physical problem with a *perfect* solution. Therefore approximate solutions are necessary. Also, engineers are professional people who work for employers and clients. These people support the engineer's analyses with financial renumeration. Since a meticulously detailed analysis (taking into consideration a great number of variables) would cost many times that of an acceptable and workable solution, mere economics forces the engineer to use an approximate solution.

Example: Solve for the best design of a highway bridge across Honey Creek on Highway 97, between Sweetville and Sourtown.

It should be apparent that an infinite number of solutions are possible. Any engineer could spend an entire lifetime investigating and testing all types of materials and loading conditions for the bridge, not to speak of the unlimited methods of problem solution which could be utilized and the varied sites which could be considered. Thus the engineer must make some basic assumptions and then proceed with a proven method of analysis.

An *idealized model system* must also be selected for any given problem solution. An *idealized model system* is actually an image (as visualized by the engineer) of the real situation. An *idealized model system* may take the form of a simplified drawing, model, sketch, chart, diagram, or other similiar device representing a system or series of interrelated parts which has been removed from its surroundings for purposes of simplifying an analysis. Such a model system may emphasize the whole of a system and minimize its component parts, or it may detail only some particular part of the system and ignore the remainder.

In solving a problem by using an *idealized model system*, the decision must be made, based upon simplifying assumptions, as to how much of the system to include within the boundaries of the analysis. Should the entire problem situation, called the *complex*, be analyzed, or would it be sufficient, perhaps, to examine only some portion of the complex? Will the examination be macroscopic or microscopic in nature? Are the boundaries of the *idealized model system* chosen to be fixed or flexible? Such are the questions which must be answered by the engineer.

In selecting an *idealized model system*, one must realize that he is merely simplifying or limiting the complex (or part of the complex) so that proven laws of science can be applied in the analysis. In actuality, the idealization chosen may vary considerably from the true state. Consequently any solution found will be only a solution for the particular *idealized model system* being used. The answer that culminates from such analysis must also be viewed with respect to the assumptions which were made initially by the engineer. If the assumptions made were in error, or if their importance

Fig. 11-1. The Golden Gate Bridge

Courtesy Bethlehem Steel Company

The Engineering Method of Analysis

was underestimated, then it follows that the engineer's analysis will probably not approximate or predict true conditions very closely.

The Free-Body Diagram

One form of *idealized model system* used by engineers is the "free-body diagram." A free-body diagram is a diagrammatical representation or model of a body or system, or some part of it, which has been separated from all surrounding bodies or systems for purposes of examination. It may be drawn to represent an entire complex or any part of a complex. It may also be drawn to represent the effect of various force actions at a single point in space.

The boundaries of an *idealized model system* should be drawn such that they enclose the system under study. All force actions external to the boundaries that act on the *idealized model system* (or free-body diagram) should be represented by force vectors on the drawing. Force actions internal to the system should be ignored, since the system is analyzed as a whole. Extraneous detail of the complex must not appear on the free-body diagram. Rather, the diagram should include only those force actions which are believed to be of significant import.

It must be realized that a free-body diagram is merely an *idealized* model system and that it is imaginary in every sense. Such an idealized condition does not exist in nature, but it is assumed to so exist for purposes of the analysis. The following example problems are typical of some problem types which the student may encounter in engineering problem analyses.

Example: Draw a free-body diagram of the ship shown in Fig. 11-1.

Solution: It is not necessary that the free-body diagram be drawn to exact scale, since the shape of the *idealized model system* is only an imaginary concept. Proceed in two steps as shown in Fig. 11-2.

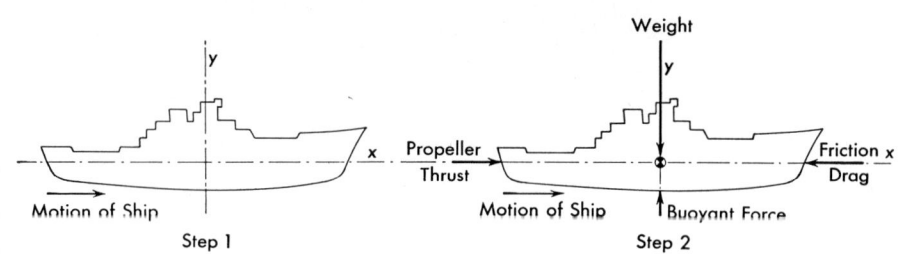

Fig. 11-2. Step 1. Draw the boundaries of the system. Step 2. Show on the same figure external forces which are acting on the boundaries.

Explanation: In the most general sense, the external forces acting on the *idealized model system* are four in number: a forward thrust, which acts at the ship's propeller; a friction drag, which acts in such manner as to retard

Fig. 11-3. Testing a new automobile at General Motors Proving Ground.

Courtesy General Motors Corporation.

232

The Engineering Method of Analysis

motion; a buoyant force, which keeps the ship afloat; and the ship's weight, which may be considered to be acting through the center of gravity of the ship.

NOTE: The symbol ⊙ is used to denote the location of the center of gravity of an *idealized model system*. Also notice that a co-ordinate system, as applied to the free-body diagram, is very useful for purposes of orientation.

Example: Draw a free-body diagram of the test automobile shown in Fig. 11-3.

Solution:

Explanation: Always show the system under consideration in its true and realistic position in space. For example, it would have been incorrect to have shown the automobile in Fig. 11-3, as being on a horizontal surface, since it is in actuality moving up an incline.

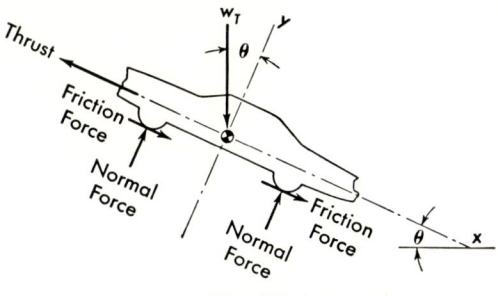

Fig. 11-4

Example: Draw a free-body diagram of the bridge shown in Fig. 11-5 to include only vertical forces which may be acting.

Courtesy Gulf, Colorado and Santa Fe Railway Company

Fig. 11-5. Railroad bridge across Canyon Diablo near Winslow, Arizona. The fundamental principles of mechanics must be used in the design of bridges and other types of truss systems.

Solution:

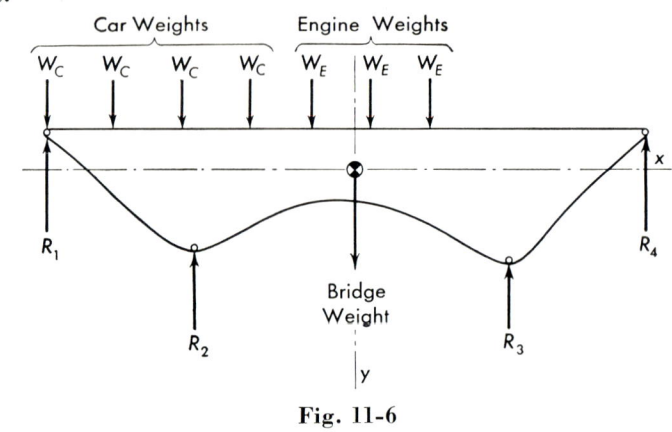

Fig. 11-6

Explanation: The bridge reactions have all been shown as acting vertically upward. An analysis may show that some of these reactions are actually acting downward. It has also been assumed that the bridge is pin-connected at four points.

General Suggestions for Drawing Free-Body Diagrams

To aid the student in learning to draw free-body diagrams, the following suggestions are given:

   1. *Free Bodies.* Be certain that the body is *free*. Draw the body so it is *free*. Do not show a supporting surface but rather show only the force vector which replaces that surface. Do not rotate the body from its original position but rather rotate the axes if necessary. Show all forces and label them. Show all needed dimensions and angles.

   2. *Force Components.* Forces are often best shown in their component forms. When replacing a force by its components, select the most convenient directions for the components. Never show both a force and its components by solid-line vectors; use broken-line vectors for one or the other (see pages 272 to 274 for a discussion of vectors).

   3. *Weight Vectors.* Show the weight vector as a vertical line with its tail or point at the center of gravity, and place it so that it interferes least with the remainder of the drawing. It should always be drawn vertically.

   4. *Refer to the Free-Body Diagram.* Each step of the solution should have a clear cross reference to the free body to which it pertains.

   5. *Direction of Vectors.* The free-body diagram should represent the facts as nearly as possible. If a pull on the free body occurs, place the tail of the vector at the actual point of application and let the point of the vector be in the true direction of the pull. Likewise, if a push occurs on the free body, the vector should show the true direction and the point of the arrow

The Engineering Method of Analysis 235

should be placed at the point of application. Force vectors on free-body diagrams are not usually drawn to scale but may be drawn proportionate to their respective magnitudes.

6. *Free-Body Diagram of Whole Structure.* This should habitually be the first free-body examined in the solution of any problem. Many problems cannot be solved without this first consideration. After the free-body of the whole structure or complex has been considered, select such members or subassemblies for further free-body diagrams as may lead to a direct solution.

7. *Two Force Members.* When a two-force member is in equilibrium, the forces are equal, opposite, and collinear. If the member is in compression, the vectors should point toward each other; if a member is in tension, they should point away from each other.

8. *Three-Force Members.* When a member is in equilibrium and has only three forces acting on it, the three forces are always concurrent, if they are not parallel. In analyzing a problem involving a three-force member, one should recall that any set of concurrent forces may be replaced by a resultant force. Hence, if a member in equilibrium has forces acting at three points, it is a three-force member regardless of the fact that the force applied at one or more points may be replaced by two or more components.

9. *Concurrent Force System.* For a concurrent force system the size, shape, and dimensions of the body are neglected, and the body is considered to be a particle.

Example: Draw a free body of point A.

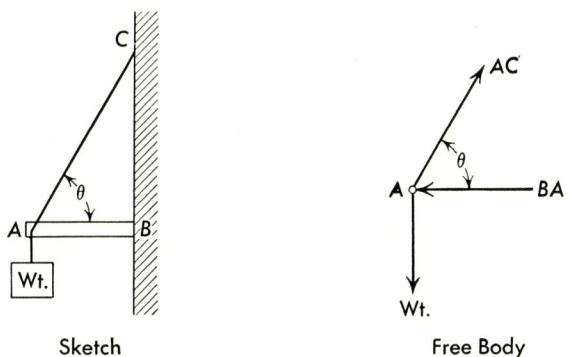

Sketch   Free Body

Fig. 11-7

10. *Pin Joints.* A free-body diagram of the pin itself should be drawn when it lends to simplicity of the solution. Pin connections may be considered to be frictionless.

11. *Reaction between Surfaces.* Some problems involve *smooth surfaces* (an imaginary concept) which are considered to offer no frictional resistance to motion. For bodies in equilibrium at rest, this concept is both a useful

and practical approximation. Pins and the members they join are in contact on a surface, and the reaction between the surfaces is perpendicular to the common tangent plane at the point of contact. Thus, if a cylinder rests on a plane, the reaction at the point of contact will pass through the center of the cylinder.

Example:

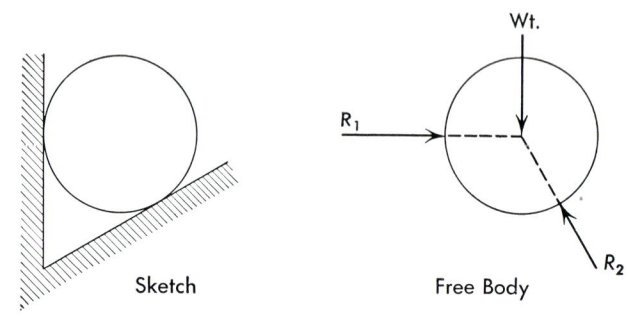

Fig. 11-8

Additional examples are given in Figs. 11-9 and 11-10 to illustrate situations which the engineer may encounter, together with the resulting free-body diagrams which may be drawn to represent the situations.

The Engineering Method of Analysis

SITUATION	FREE-BODY	EXPLANATION
A box resting on a plane 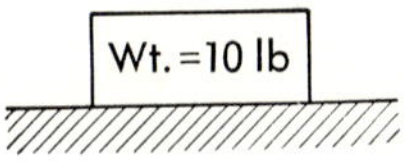 (Wt. = 10 lb on ground)	 10 lb downward, N upward	The normal force always acts at an angle of 90° with the surfaces in contact. This force N usually is considered to act through the center of gravity of the body.
A weight hanging from a ring 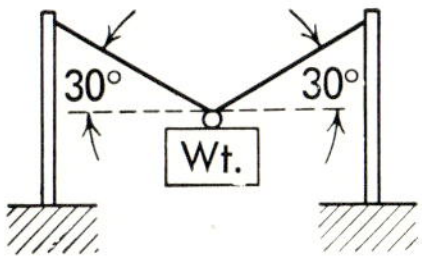 (two cables at 30° from vertical supporting Wt.)	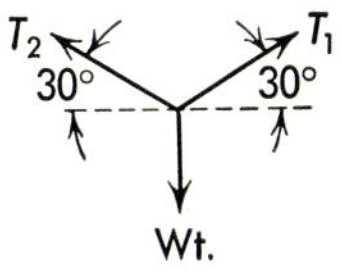 T_2 and T_1 each at 30° above horizontal, Wt. downward	Since the ring is of negligible size, it may be considered to be a point. All of the forces would act through this point. The downward force W is balanced by the tensions T_1 and T_2. The numerical sum of these tensions will be greater than the weight. This is true since T_1 is pulling against T_2.
A box on a frictionless surface 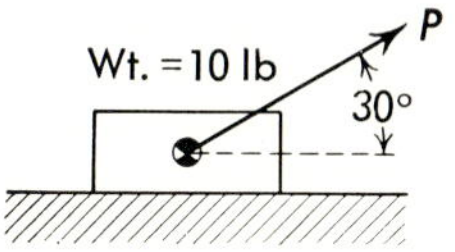 (Wt. = 10 lb, force P at 30°)	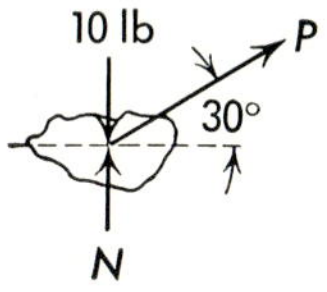 10 lb down, P at 30°, N up	In problem work some surfaces are considered frictionless although in reality, no surface is frictionless. The force P is an unbalanced force and it will produce an acceleration. The symbol ⊗ denotes the location of the center of gravity of the body.
A small box on a rough surface 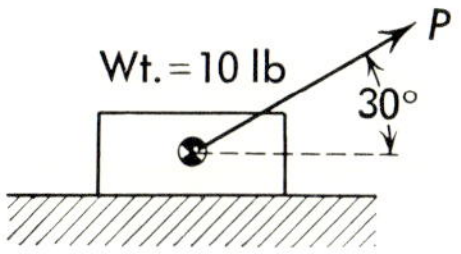 (Wt. = 10 lb, force P at 30°)	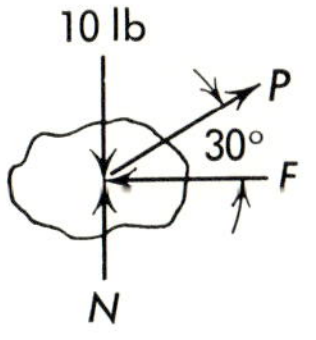 10 lb down, P at 30°, F horizontal, N up	The force of friction will always oppose motion or will oppose the tendency to move. For bodies of small size, the *moment effect* of the friction force may be disregarded and the friction and normal forces may be considered to act through the center of gravity of the body.

Fig. 11-9

238   Engineering: Elementary Problem Analysis

SITUATION	FREE-BODY	EXPLANATION
A beam resting on fixed supports 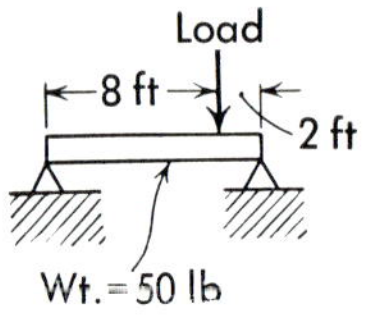 Load, 8 ft, 2 ft, Wt. = 50 lb	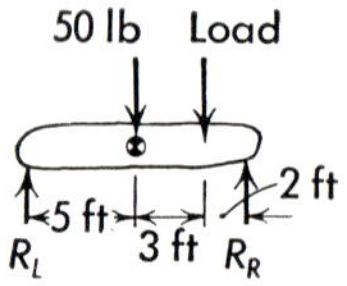 50 lb Load R_L, 5 ft, 3 ft, 2 ft, R_R	For a uniform beam, the weight acts at the midpoint of the beam regardless of where the supports are located.
A pivoted beam resting on a roller 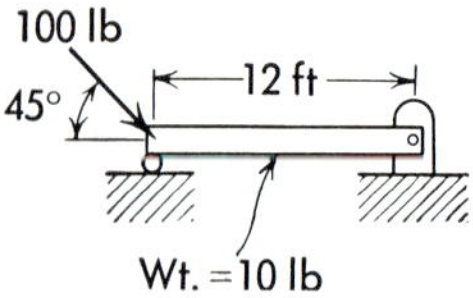 100 lb, 45°, 12 ft, Wt. = 10 lb	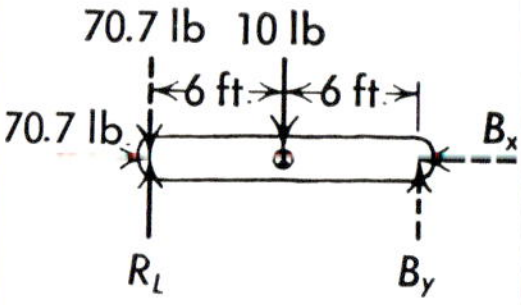 70.7 lb, 10 lb 6 ft, 6 ft 70.7 lb, B_x R_L, B_y	Since a roller cannot produce a horizontal reaction, the horizontal component of any force must be counteracted by the horizontal component of the reaction at the pivoted end.
A ladder resting against a frictionless wall 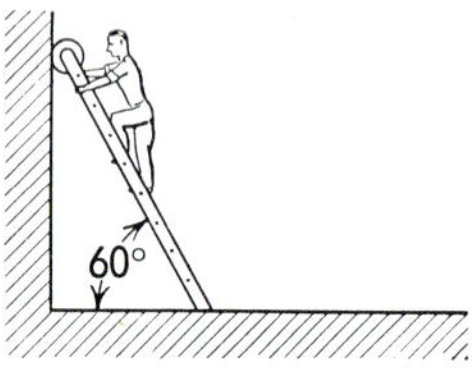 60°	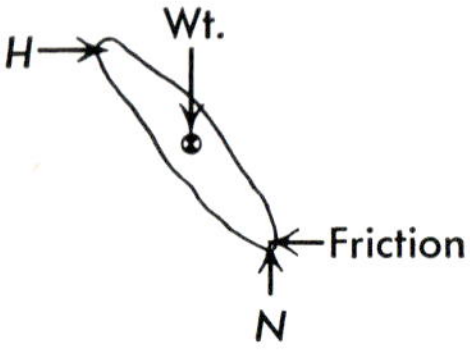 H, Wt., Friction, N	At the upper end of the ladder, the only reaction possible is perpendicular to the wall since the surface is considered to be frictionless.
Pulling a barrel over a curb 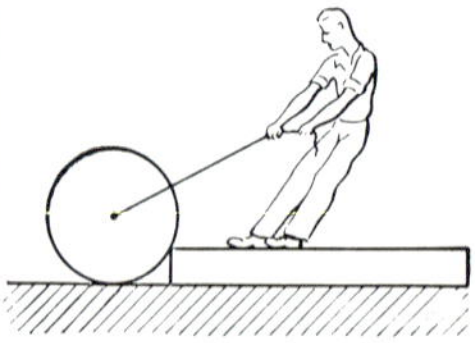	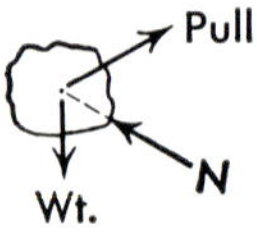 Pull, Wt., N	All of the forces are acting through the center of the barrel. For additional discussion, see paragraphs 8 and 11, page 235.

Fig. 11-10

The Thermodynamic System

Many specializations in engineering have occasion to use variations of the free-body diagram. One such variation may be called the *thermodynamic system*. The basic principles of drawing idealized model systems as previously discussed should be followed in drawing thermodynamic systems; for example: simplifying assumptions, selection of boundaries, and operating conditions. In general the thermodynamic system is most useful in analyzing processes of systems involving mass and heat flow, rather than in static analyses which are essentially concerned with mechanics and vectors.

Example: A quantity of high-temperature steam flows into a turbine at high pressure, expands in the turbine while doing work on the turbine rotor, and then is exhausted at low pressure. Draw a thermodynamic system of this situation (see Fig. 11-11).

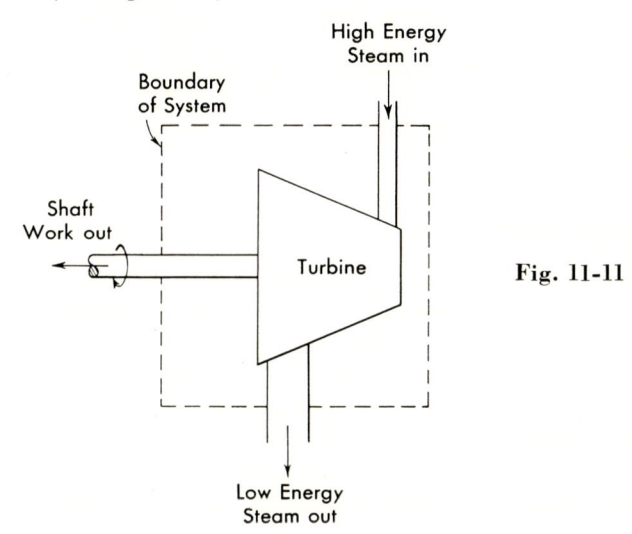

Fig. 11-11

Example: Draw a thermodynamic system of a typical steam-powered electrical generating station which burns natural gas in a boiler and utilizes the heat to produce electric energy by means of a steam turbine (see Fig. 11-12).

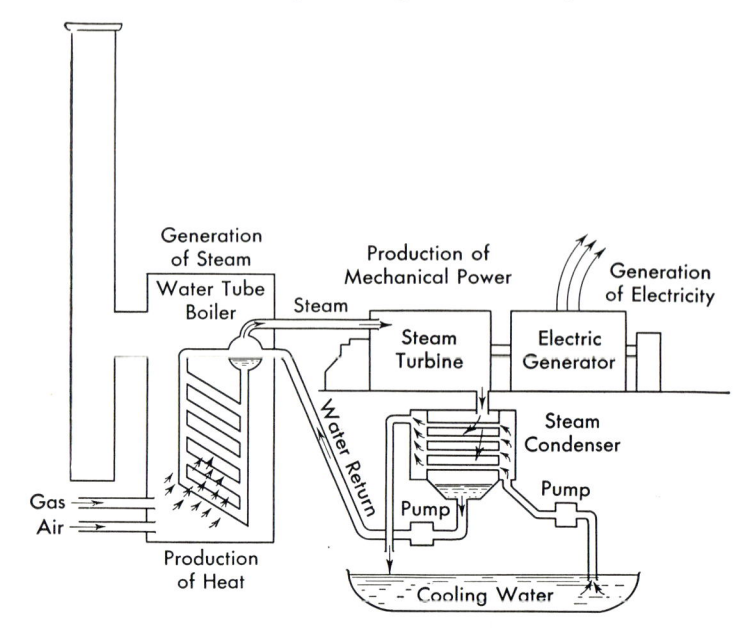

Fig. 11-12. Thermodynamic system of a steam-powered electrical generating station.

The Electrical Diagram

A special form of idealized model system is used in the analyses of electrical problems. In electrical diagrams extensive use is made of specialized symbols. This has been developed to such an extent that electrical symbols on diagrams almost form a language within themselves.

Electrical diagrams may be classified into two categories. One class, called *block diagrams*, includes charts and diagrams of systems involving electrical equipment. In this class, components such as transducers, power supplies, switching units, servo equipment, and recorders are shown as blocks, with flow lines designating the relation of one component to another.

Figure 11-13 is an example of a block diagram in which electrical subassemblies are drawn as blocks, and the connecting lines between blocks indicate the flow of information in the whole assembly. This type of presentation is widely used to lay out large or complicated systems—particularly those involving servo-electrical and mechanical devices. No attempt is made on the drawing to detail the inner circuits of any of the subassemblies pictured.

Another class of electrical diagram is the *circuit diagram*. This idealized model includes wiring diagrams of particular electrical items by utilizing conventional symbols for brevity. These diagrams may be of the most

The Engineering Method of Analysis

Courtesy Texas Instruments Incorporated

Fig. 11-13. The relation of component parts of a transistorized telemetering system are best shown by means of a block diagram.

elementary type, or they may be highly complicated and require many hours of engineering time in preparation. In any case, however, they are representations or models in symbolic language of an electrical assembly.

In Fig. 11-14 is shown an electrical diagram of a photoelectric tube which is arranged to operate a relay. Notice that the diagram details only the

242 Engineering: Elementary Problem Analysis

essential parts in order to provide for electrical continuity and thus is an idealization which has been selected for purposes of simplification.

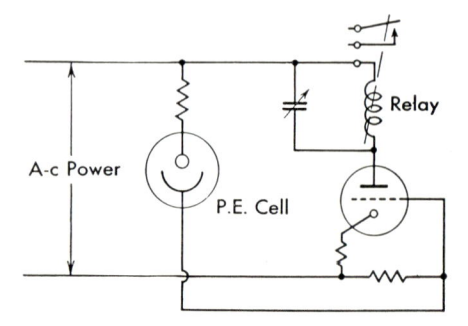

Fig. 11-14. A simple photoelectric tube relay circuit.

The Industrial Model

Another type of idealized model system which is often useful in problem solving and in analyzing the results of studies already completed is the *industrial model*. Such a device is most useful in those cases where a mathematical-type model is either impossible or impractical. An *industrial model* is usually a three-dimensional scale model of the complex, or of certain parts of the complex, which the engineer wishes to examine within its natural

Courtesy Oldsmobile Division, General Motors Corporation

Fig. 11-15. With the aid of lifelike, three-dimensional models the engineer can check the results of his analysis and design. Such industrial models are most useful in determining the effectiveness of new methods of manufacture and assembly in mass-production facilities.

The Engineering Method of Analysis 243

environment. The idealization that he may construct is a scaled replica of the actual situation. The model scale chosen can be varied in such manner that the industrial model will be larger in size, the same size, or much smaller in size than the actual design.

Such projects as dam or reservoir construction, highway and freeway interchange design, factory layout, and aerodynamic analyses are particularly adaptable to study by using this type of idealized model. In some

Courtesy State of California Department of Public Works

Fig. 11-16. Models of super-highways and freeway systems are useful to engineers and city planners who must design for an ever increasing volume of traffic. This model shows a freeway interchange which is located near East Los Angeles.

cases the industrial model is not instrumented (see Fig. 11-15 and 11-16); but component parts of the model can be moved about to represent changing conditions within the system. Of considerable more usefulness, however, are those industrial models which are instrumented and subjected to static and dynamic load conditions that approximate reality (see Figs. 4-1 and 11-13). In such cases the models are tested and experimental data are recorded by the engineer. From an analysis of these data, final conclusions are made.

By using an industrial model, the final design can be checked for accuracy prior to actual construction of the system or complex. Although industrial models often cost many thousands of dollars, they are of relatively minor expense, considering the total cost of a particular design. Also, an industrial model frequently may be constructed and tested in a fraction of the time necessary to build the original system.

Problems

11-1. Draw a free-body diagram of the container for radioactive materials as shown in Fig. 11-17.

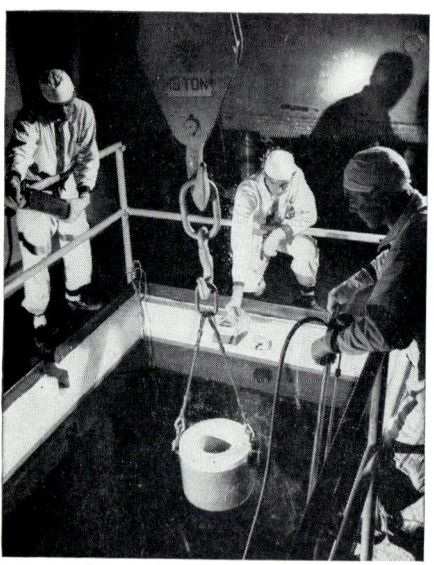

Fig. 11-17. Since radioactive materials must be handled with extreme care, the lowering of a container of radioactive products must be monitored continuously, using precision instruments.

Courtesy Westinghouse Electric Corporation

Fig. 11-18. Test stands for launching rockets and missiles are complex structures which have been designed so that all parts of the missile will be accessible for instrumentation checks prior to launching.

Reprinted from Missiles and Rockets. *American Aviation Publications, Inc.*

The Engineering Method of Analysis 245

11-2. Draw a free-body diagram of the ballistic missile as shown in Fig. 11-18.

11-3. Draw a free-body diagram of point Q as shown in Fig. 11-19.

11-4. Draw a free-body diagram of the sphere shown in Fig. 11-20.

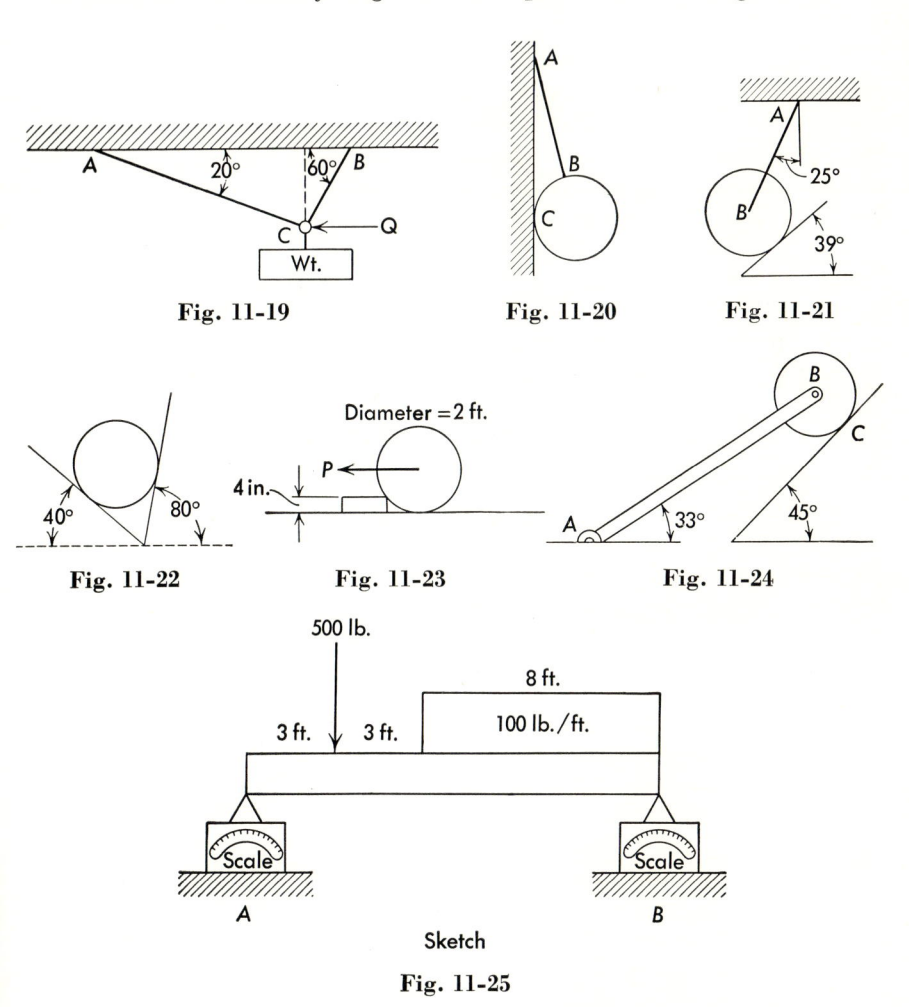

Fig. 11-19

Fig. 11-20

Fig. 11-21

Fig. 11-22

Fig. 11-23

Fig. 11-24

Sketch

Fig. 11-25

11-5. Draw a free-body diagram of the sphere shown in Fig. 11-21.

11-6. Draw a free-body diagram of the sphere shown in Fig. 11-22.

11-7. Draw a free-body diagram of the sphere shown in Fig. 11-23.

11-8. Draw the free-body diagram of the sphere shown in Fig. 11-24.

11-9. Draw the free-body diagram of the horizontal beam shown in Fig. 11-25.

11-10. Draw a free-body diagram of the horizontal bar shown in Fig. 11-26.

11-11. (a) Draw a free-body diagram of ball No. 1 as shown in Fig. 11-27. (b) Draw a free-body diagram of ball No. 2 as shown in Fig. 11-27.

11-12. Draw a free-body diagram of the horizontal member as shown in Fig. 11-28. Draw a free-body diagram of the diagonal member as shown in Fig. 11-28.

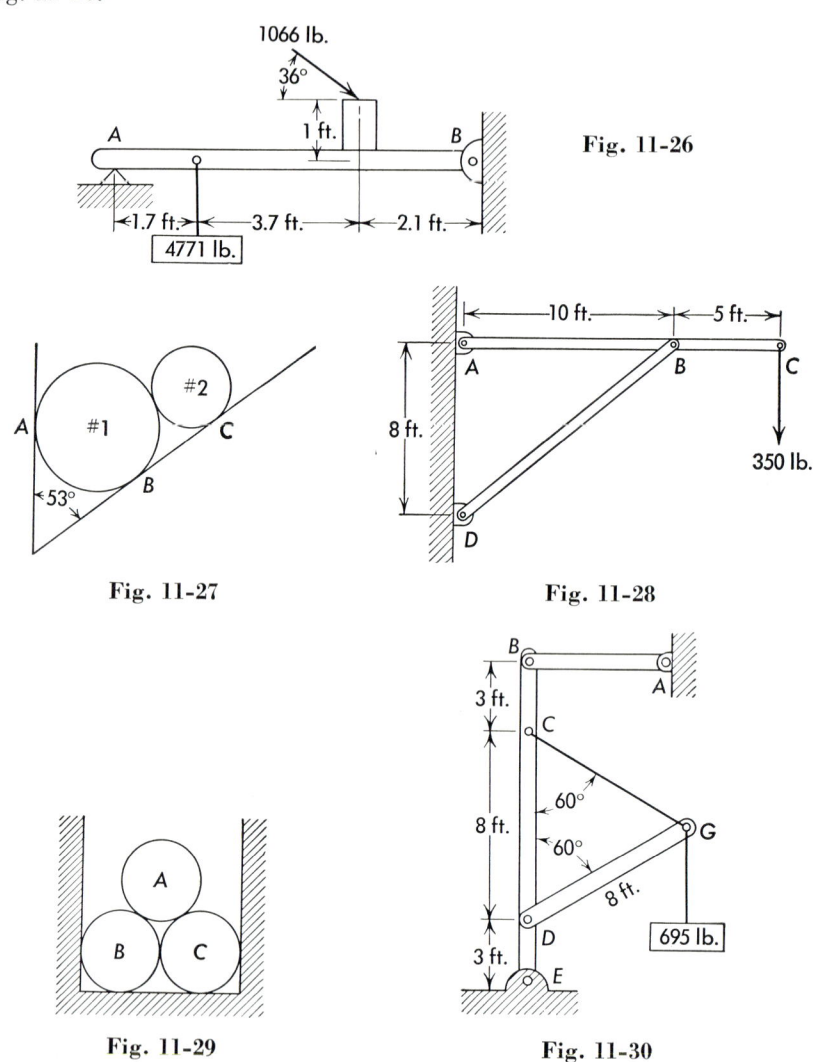

Fig. 11-26

Fig. 11-27

Fig. 11-28

Fig. 11-29

Fig. 11-30

11-13. Draw free-body diagrams of balls A, B, and C as shown in Fig. 11-29.

11-14. Draw a free-body diagram of members DG, EB, and AB as shown in Fig. 11-30.

The Engineering Method of Analysis

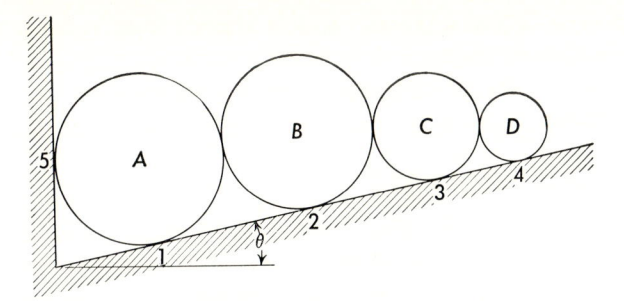

Fig. 11-31

11-15. Draw a free-body diagram of balls D, C, B, and A as shown in the sketch in Fig. 11-31. The angle θ is 20°.

Diameters

$A = 24$ in.
$B = 20$ in.
$C = 12$ in.
$D = 6$ in.

11-16. Draw a thermodynamic system of an ordinary gas-fired hot water heater.

11-17. A water heater operates under steady-flow conditions such that a quantity of entering low-temperature water is mixed with steam. The mixing takes place inside the heater and leaves the exit as one fluid. Draw a thermodynamic system to represent this process.

*11-18. Draw a thermodynamic system of a vapor-compression refrigeration cycle.

11-19. A water heater operates under steady flow such that low-temperature water enters the heater, extracts heat from steam while inside the heater, and leaves the heater at an elevated temperature. The water and steam do not come in direct contact with each other. Draw a thermodynamic system to represent this process.

11-20. Draw an electrical circuit diagram containing two single-pole double-throw switches in such manner that a single light bulb may be turned on or off at either switch location.

*11-21. Arrange three single-pole single-throw switches in an electrical circuit containing three light bulbs in such manner that one switch will turn on one of the bulbs, another switch will turn on two of the bulbs, and the third switch will turn on all three bulbs.

11-22. Show a thermodynamic system representing a simple refrigeration cycle.

11-23. Show a thermodynamic system representing a Freon condenser.

*11-24. Show a thermodynamic system representing a heat engine that operates on a Carnot cycle.

*11-25. Show a thermodynamic system representing a "perpetual-motion" machine.

THE PROBLEM SOLUTION

The engineer will utilize an idealized model system to aid him in solving the problem at hand. Within itself the free-body diagram, thermodynamic system, or electrical diagram is of little value except, perhaps, to serve as a means of communicating ideas between engineers or scientists. However, in the hands of a competent problem analyst such diagrams can be powerful tools.

It is necessary, of course, that the analyst apply mathematical relationships to the idealized model system whenever possible. An analysis should be logical in nature and neat in presentation, since the work may be used for other purposes in future design. In many industries it is common practice to have a second person check the analysis to uncover any arithmetical mistakes or incorrect assumptions in reasoning which may have entered into the calculation.

The engineer should check his work as he proceeds in an analysis, and he should never lose sight of the criterion that "there is no substitute for common sense." After solving for an answer, regardless of its apparent importance, he should ask himself the question: "Does this answer seem reasonable?" If it seems unreasonable, he should first check his work until he is satisfied that there have been no arithmetic mistakes. If the result is still in doubt, he should reexamine the basic assumptions and boundary conditions within which he has been operating. Quite often these may be in error, although this fact may have been hidden at the beginning of the problem analysis.

CONCLUSIONS

When the final answer to the problem is obtained, it must be examined in the light of the idealized model system which was originally chosen. It must be remembered that the solution *is not* a solution to the real problem but only to the idealized case which was considered.

All conclusions should emphasize and summarize the facts that have been determined in the problem analysis.

PART THREE
applications of the engineering method of analysis

Courtesy Texas Instruments Incorporated

After test data have been collected, the engineer must identify the significant items and proceed to solve the given problem, using the engineering method of analysis. This engineer is acquiring test data concerning the operation of silicon power transistors at elevated temperatures.

chapter twelve

Problem Analysis

In the preceding chapter, methods of reasoning necessary in engineering problem solving were discussed. These methods have been explained in order to provide a positive, logical, and vigorous approach to problem analysis. These techniques should eliminate much of the indecision as to method and the distraction of extraneous detail that complicates any physical situation. It is expected that the student will apply the techniques learned in the preceding chapter to the analysis of problems in this and following chapters.

A brief discussion is given below to review some basic principles involved in the solution of several different types of problems. These notes are not intended to be complete discussions of the subjects, so if the student finds that his background is insufficient in any of the material discussed, it is recommended that he review other books specifically concerned with the subject matter.

MENSURATION

In solving many types of engineering problems, the method of solution will be simple and straightforward. In these cases the student should proceed from one logical step to another, being certain to show enough detail so that another person can follow the work without difficulty. It cannot be emphasized too greatly that a step-by-step presentation is necessary in any solution. The habits gained in presenting solutions in sequence is essential training in developing the scientific approach to more difficult problems, which may require much thought to determine a method of solution.

In simple problems in which measurements are involved, it is usually desirable to begin the solution with a sketch showing the known data. As the solution is developed, it is good practice to include not only formulas but also dimensional equations in places where the units or dimensions involved may not be immediately evident. The habit of showing all computations on the problem sheet should be developed. In industry the use of "scratch paper" is not considered good practice, since all calculations should be capable of being checked by others.

In this section a number of different types of problems will be presented which will require a wider background of scientific training than was necessary in the problems previously encountered. Some brief explanations of some of the principles involved in the problems are included as an aid.

Problem Analysis

For more detailed explanations, books on physics, chemistry, electricity, and economics should be consulted.

TEMPERATURE SCALES

The earliest attempts to make use of a thermometer type of temperature-measuring device is credited to Galileo, who used a long, closed tube partly filled with water. While this device indicated temperature changes resulting from heating or cooling of the air in the upper end of the closed tube, it was erratic because barometric pressure changes also affected it. It was not until about 1659 that mercury was used as a thermometric substance.

Many temperature scales were developed in the years following, but only two are in common use in this country at the present time. The Fahrenheit scale uses 32° as the freezing point of water and 212° as the boiling point. The centigrade scale uses 0° and 100° for the same points. The Fahrenheit scale is used for usual temperature measurements in English-speaking countries, while the centigrade scale is used for laboratory work and scientific work the world over.

To convert from one scale to another, remember that the Fahrenheit scale has 180° divisions between the freezing and boiling points of water, while the centigrade scale has 100° divisions. Also, the 0° location on the centigrade scale corresponds to the 32° location on the Fahrenheit scale. The expression of the relation of the scales in an equation may be written as

$$F - 32° = 1.8°C$$

By algebra
$$F = 1.8°C + 32°$$

and
$$C = \frac{F - 32°}{1.8°}$$

where F is the temperature in degrees Fahrenheit and C is the temperature in degrees centigrade.

PRESSURE LAW OF GASES

In 1660 Robert Boyle published the result of investigations of pressure-volume relations of gases and formulated what is now known as Boyle's law. This law stated that there is an inverse proportionality between pressure and volume of a given mass of a gas. As an equation this can be written as

$$P = \frac{K}{V} \quad \text{or} \quad PV = K$$

where P is the total pressure of the gas, V is the volume of the given mass of gas, and K is a constant of proportionality. This relation is represented graphically in Fig. 12-1. This graph shows that as the volume of a confined gas increases, its absolute or total pressure decreases, and as the pressure increases, the volume decreases.

Mariotte further defined the relationship by showing that this expression was true only at constant temperature, and van der Waals showed that the relation must be further modified when larger changes in pressures are involved, due to the attraction of the gas molecules for each other, and to account for the space actually occupied by the molecules themselves.

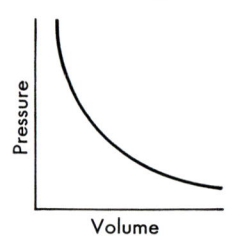

Fig. 12-1. Pressure-volume relation of a confined gas which follows Boyle's law.

In the problems in this section we shall deal with those pressure-volume relations of a gas at constant temperatures which approach Boyle's law in their behavior closely enough so that we may neglect secondary variations.

In using Boyle's law, we must remember that the pressures and volumes involved are total values, and in the case of atmospheric conditions, normal atmospheric pressure (14.7 psi) must be added to gauge pressures to obtain total or absolute pressures of a gas.

Example: A steel cylinder having a volume of 3.70 ft³ is to have air pumped into it until the gauge pressure reaches 63 psig. How many cubic feet of air at atmospheric pressure will have to be pumped into it? (psig means "pounds per square inch gauge pressure.")

Analysis: Assuming constant temperature conditions, $PV = K$ at any time. Let P_1 and V_1 be the starting pressure and volume conditions, respectively, and P_2 and V_2 be pressure and volume conditions when the air pressure in the tank is built up to 63 psig. Then $P_1 V_1 = K$ and $P_2 V_2 = K$. Therefore

$$P_1 V_1 = P_2 V_2$$

Solution: $P_1 = 14.7$ psia (absolute pressure of the air prior to being pumped)
$V_1 = ?$ ft³ (volume of air to be compressed)
$P_2 = 14.7 + 63$ psia (total or absolute pressure of the air after compressing)
$V_2 = 3.70$ ft³ (volume of the air after being compressed)
$(14.7)(V_1) = (14.7 + 63)(3.70)$
$V_1 = 19.58$ ft³

Problem Analysis

The volume of air to be added to the tank will be 19.58 − 3.70 = 15.88 ft³, since the tank already contained air at atmospheric pressure.

Example: A truck tire has a volume of 4.17 ft³ when inflated to a pressure of 55 psig. What additional volume of air at atmospheric pressure must be added to raise the pressure to 112 psig?

Analysis: Pressures involved must all be reduced to atmospheric to permit calculation of volumes.

Solution: Determine the volume of air at atmospheric pressure now in the tire.

$$P_1 V_1 = P_2 V_2$$
$$(55 + 14.7)(4.17) = 14.7 V_2$$
$$V_2 = 19.8 \text{ ft}^3 \text{ of air at atmospheric pressure}$$

Then the volume of air to produce 112 psig in the tire, assuming the tire volume does not change, will be

$$P_3 V_3 = P_4 V_4$$
$$(14.7)(V_3) = (14.7 + 112)(4.17)$$
$$V_3 = 35.8 \text{ ft}^3 \text{ of air at atmospheric pressure}$$

Volume of air to be added is 35.8 − 19.8 = 16.0 ft³ at atmospheric pressure.

TEMPERATURE LAW OF GASES

As the temperature of a confined gas increases, the kinetic energy of the molecules increases; this results in an increase of pressure on the walls of the containing vessel. The relation that expresses this property of a gas is known either as Charles' law or Gay-Lussac's law. By means of carefully conducted experiments during the period 1787 to 1800, it was found that most gases changed their volume at a constant pressure by 1/273 for each 1°C temperature change, or they changed their pressure at constant volume by 1/273 for each 1°C change in temperature.

In equation form,

$$P_2 = P_1(1 + \tfrac{1}{273}t)$$

where P_2 and P_1 are the final and initial pressures, respectively, and t is the change in temperature expressed in degrees centigrade. The value 273 also serves another useful purpose in that it may be considered as an absolute or beginning point for temperature relations for gases. If a gas at some given pressure could continue to be cooled continuously from its original temperature until it reached −273°C, it would have zero pressure. Of course there are a number of practical reasons why this cannot be done physically, but the idea of an absolute zero of −273°C is a useful concept in dealing with gases. For instance, since pressures within reasonable limits vary with absolute temperatures, we may write the equation of pressures and temperatures as

$$\frac{P_2}{P_1} = \frac{T_2}{T_1}$$

where P_2 and P_1 are the respective final and initial pressures and T_2 and T_1 are the final and initial respective absolute temperatures. The numerical values of T_2 and T_1 are found by adding 273 to the given centigrade temperatures.

For constant-pressure conditions, we may write in a manner similar to the above:

$$V_2 = V_1(1 + \tfrac{1}{273}t)$$

and

$$\frac{V_2}{V_1} = \frac{T_2}{T_1}$$

The condition of both a changing pressure and a changing volume with temperature change may be expressed by combining the equations into the form

$$\frac{P_2 V_2}{P_1 V_1} = \frac{T_2}{T_1}$$

or

$$\frac{P_2 V_2}{T_2} = \frac{P_1 V_1}{T_1}$$

where all values of pressure, volume, and temperature must be expressed in absolute terms.

Example: A tank having a volume of 10.8 ft³ contains air at a pressure of 78.5 psig and a temperature of 32°F. What will be its pressure at a temperature of 112°F?

Analysis: Convert the temperatures to centigrade or use the value of absolute zero on the Fahrenheit scale (−459.6°F). Solve for the new pressure, using Charles' law.

Solution:
$$\frac{P_2}{P_1} = \frac{T_2}{T_1} \qquad 112°F = 44.4°C$$
$$32°F = 0°C$$
$$P_2 = \frac{(78.5 + 14.7)(273 + 44.4)}{273 + 0}$$
$$P_2 = 108.2 \text{ psia}$$
Gauge pressure = 108.2 − 14.7 = 93.5 psig

ELECTRICITY

The beginnings of current electricity, as it is commonly referred to today, began with the discovery by Stephen Gray early in the eighteenth century

Problem Analysis

that electric charges could be conducted from one place to another. A century elapsed before enough had been discovered about the behavior of electricity to assign names to the measured quantities. Due to the work of André Ampère on a study of the magnetic conditions around a current-carrying conductor, the name *ampere* was given to the unit of rate of flow of electric charges.

Current

Modern ideas concerning the nature of the electric current are that the flow of large quantities of negative electrons through a conducting material constitutes what we call *electric current*. The electric current cannot exist without a continuous path for the electrons to flow. The number of electrons flowing, or the strength of the electric current, depends upon the opposition encountered and upon the driving force applied.

The unit of current flow is the *ampere*, and it is defined in various ways, one of the ways being that an ampere will deposit 0.001118 grams of silver per second in a standard plating solution. For our purpose we shall use the ampere to define a flow of a quantity of electrons past any given point in a second. An ammeter is an instrument used to measure electric-current flow in a conducting circuit.

Resistance

The flow of electric current in a conductor is affected by the opposition offered by the conductor. This opposition is determined by variation in the length (directly), the cross-sectional area (inversely), and the material (a constant). Temperature also affects the resistance of conducting materials, but this effect will not be considered here.

All materials may be grouped broadly into two classes, those having relatively low opposition to current flow, called *conductors*, and those having high opposition to current flow, called *insulators*. The unit of measure of opposition to current flow is called the *ohm* in honor of George S. Ohm who performed basic investigations of the electrical properties of conductors. This unit of resistance, the ohm, may be expressed as the resistance of a column of purified mercury 1.063 meters long, 1 mm^2 in cross section, at a temperature of 0°C. To give some idea of the size of the ohm, ordinary 18-gauge copper, two-conductor, extension cord wire has a resistance of about 1 ohm for 75 feet of cord (150 feet of wire).

Voltage

Since the current flow depends partly upon the driving force, we should describe this effect as it affects the electric circuit. This driving force may be compared to the potential energy possessed by water in an elevated tank. If a pipe at a lower elevation than the bottom of the tank is opened, water will flow. In a similar manner, a source of electric energy, such as a battery or generator producing a potential difference in a circuit, will cause a current to flow if the circuit conditions are favorable. The unit of electric potential is the *volt*, so called in honor of Alessandro Volta who performed early experiments with electric batteries.

A *volt* is the potential difference between two points that will cause 1 ampere of current to flow through a resistance of 1 ohm. Potential difference or voltage may be measured by using a type of meter called a *voltmeter*.

Ohm's Law

In the course of Ohm's experiments he discovered that the electric current in a circuit would vary directly with the voltage of the source and inversely with the circuit resistance. This relation may be shown by the equation

$$I = \frac{E}{R}$$

where I is the current in amperes flowing in the circuit, E is the potential difference or voltage of the source in volts, and R is the circuit resistance in ohms.

Like all generalizations, Ohm's law possesses many implications not apparent in the equation. A study of these variations is beyond the scope of this text because they involve circuits of a complex nature. However, the basic applications of Ohm's law can be shown readily.

Example: A battery having a voltage of 6.71 volts is connected to a circuit having a resistance of 1.51 ohms. What current will flow? Ω is the symbol for ohms.

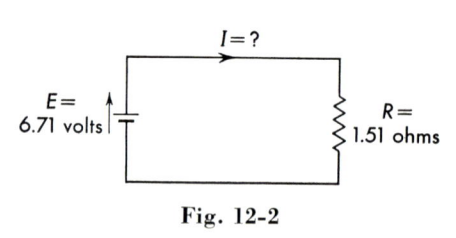

Analysis: In electrical problems, draw a circuit diagram* using conventional symbols, and label the parts. In this case, for convenience in solving, we shall assume all the circuit resistance to be lumped at one point. The current will be the quotient of voltage and resistance.

Fig. 12-2

Solution:
$$I = \frac{E}{R}$$
$$I = \frac{6.71 \text{ volts}}{1.51 \text{ ohms}}$$
$$I = 4.45 \text{ amperes}$$

*An electric circuit diagram is one type of an *idealized model system*. See page 240.

Problem Analysis

Example: Two resistances of 2.81 ohms and 7.06 ohms are connected in series in a circuit and 0.330 amp flows in the circuit. What voltage is applied to the circuit?

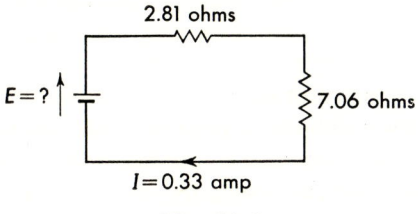

2.81 ohms

E = ?   7.06 ohms

I = 0.33 amp

Fig. 12-3

Analysis: Since two resistances are connected in series, the total resistance is the sum of the two. Using Ohm's law, solve for the voltage.

Solution: Total resistance = 2.81 + 7.06 = 9.87 ohms
$$E = IR$$
$$E = (0.330)(9.87)$$
$$E = 3.26 \text{ volts}$$

Example: Two resistances of 50.7 ohms and 38.1 ohms, respectively, are connected in parallel across a power source of 115.4 volts. What current will flow in each resistance? What will be the total resistance of the two resistances in parallel?

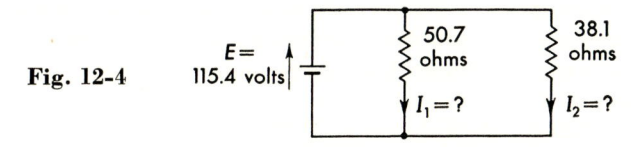

Fig. 12-4   E = 115.4 volts   50.7 ohms   38.1 ohms $I_1 = ?$ $I_2 = ?$

Analysis: Since each resistance has the full voltage applied to it, solve for the currents individually. Total values of current and voltage will then permit computing total resistance.

Solution:
$$I = \frac{E}{R}$$
$$I_1 = \frac{115.4 \text{ volts}}{50.7 \text{ ohms}}$$
$$I_1 = 2.275 \text{ amp}$$
$$I_2 = \frac{115.4 \text{ volts}}{38.1 \text{ ohms}}$$
$$I_2 = 3.03 \text{ amp}$$
$$\text{Total current} = I_1 + I_2$$
$$I_t = 2.275 + 3.03$$
$$I_t = 5.31 \text{ amp}$$

$$\text{Total resistance} = \frac{E}{I}$$

$$R_t = \frac{115.4 \text{ volts}}{5.31 \text{ amp}}$$

$$R_t = 21.75 \text{ ohms}$$

This shows that as resistances are placed in parallel, the total resistance of the combination is less than the resistance of the smaller in the group.

Another method of obtaining the total resistance of two parallel resistances is to divide the product of the resistances by their sum. For example:

$$R_t = \frac{(R_1)(R_2)}{R_1 + R_2}$$

$$R_t = \frac{(50.7)(38.1)}{50.7 + 38.1}$$

$$R_t = 21.75 \text{ ohms}$$

ECONOMICS OF ENGINEERING

The engineer must be concerned not only with performing a given task but also with completing it at a reasonable cost. This economic factor is of extreme importance because in our modern economy if a process, a project, or a whole industry does not show a profit, it cannot long continue to be in operation. It is the responsibility of the engineer to see that part of his evaluation of an operation or construction includes information on relative costs. Technical know-how must be used to adapt the most effective means at hand to accomplish the work at the lowest possible cost.

An example of these principles may be illustrated by the following situation: A laboratory acceptance test of fifty small pressure gauges is to be made. The engineer in charge of the testing is asked to determine the kind of test equipment that should be set up. He reasons that several methods may be used, some of which follow:

1. Purchase a test bench with a suitable mercury manometer to provide accurate standard pressure references.

2. Use a compressed air tank and a laboratory-type gauge. The tank is available in the laboratory, but a suitable range of test gauge will have to be purchased.

3. Send the gauges to a commercial testing laboratory which has a dead-weight tester.

4. Purchase a dead-weight tester for the laboratory with the idea of possible future use after using it on this batch of fifty gauges.

The engineer knows that this is the first time in the three years he has been in this laboratory that a requirement for testing gauges has arisen. He cannot foresee any repetition of this test in the near future. He deter-

Problem Analysis

mines by questions concerning the use of the gauges that an extremely accurate calibration of the gauges is not necessary except for two gauges whose calibrations must be determined as closely as the scales can be read. He reasons that an investment in testing equipment (in Method 1) of $1100 probably is not justified. The tester (in Method 4) will cost $250 which also is not feasible.

The engineer finds that if he uses Method 2, a test gauge, if purchased, will cost $44.50. Using other available laboratory equipment, the test of each gauge will involve about 85 cents in materials and labor costs.

However, this method is not accurate enough for two of the gauges. From a telephone call, he finds that a commercial laboratory will test and certify the two gauges for $5.00 each.

Using a combination of Method 2 and Method 3, he figures the approximate cost as follows:

Laboratory test gauge.	$44.50
Testing 48 gauges @ 85 cents each.	$40.80
Testing of two gauges by another lab.	$10.00
	$95.30

The engineer recommends that Method 2 and Method 3 be employed to acceptance-test the fifty gauges, considering the other information he was able to determine.

It should be pointed out that if all fifty of the gauges had needed extremely accurate calibrations and if there would be a continuing need for testing other gauges at a later time, the engineer most certainly would have explored more extensively the costs of equipment and labor involved in Method 1 or Method 4.

In many cases engineering work may involve the use of money over an extended period of time. This may be money that must be borrowed and on which interest must be paid; or it may be money already on hand that will be tied up in equipment where otherwise the money could have been invested to earn interest.

Interest is basically rent which a borrower pays for the use of money from a lender. Interest charges include not only a return to the borrower for the use of the money but also a fee as insurance against possible loss plus, in some cases, a service charge for clerical work in handling the loan. The item of a fee as insurance against loss frequently accounts for the difference between governmental obligations which pay only a low percentage of interest and a highly speculative stock which may pay 20 per cent or more.

Interest may be computed either as simple or compound interest. Simple interest pays a fixed percentage of the principal amount each year for the use of the money. Compound interest pays not only on the original principal sum but also on interest which has accrued prior to the time of computing the current interest payment.

As an example, simple interest on $5000 at 5 per cent would be $250 per year regardless of the number of years the loan ran. However, if at the end of the first year, the $250 in interest were added to the $5000 principal, interest would be paid during the second year on $5250. This interest would be $262.50, which would make a total amount owed of $5512.50.

Expressing this as an equation:

$$S = P(1 + i)^n$$

where S is the amount owed at the end of n periods of payment, P is the original amount of the principal, and i is the interest rate.

Using the above example, the amount owed at the end of two years would be

$$S = 5000(1 + 0.05)^2$$
$$S = \$5512.50$$

Tables of compound interest factors have been prepared to give values of $(1 + i)^n$ and are available in books on investments and economics.

It is frequently desirable to determine the present worth of money which will be paid sometime in the future. For example, a note for $700 carrying 5 per cent interest rate is to be paid in three years. What is the present worth of the money? To determine this we make use of the expression:

$$P = \frac{S}{(1 + i)^n}$$
$$P = \frac{700}{(1 + 0.05)^3}$$
$$P = \$604.49$$

The above example illustrates one simple application of basic economic principles concerning the worth of money. The student will encounter more complex situations involving depreciation, tax savings, and amortization of indebtedness in later courses in economics.

Problems

12-1. A river has a flow of 3,000,000 gal per 24-hr day. Compute the flow in cubic feet per minute.

12-2. Compute the weight in lb_f of 1982 ft of copper wire 1/4 in. in diameter.

12-3. A round iron rod is 0.125 in. in diameter. How long will a piece have to be to weigh 1 lb_f?

12-4. A cylindrical tank 2.7 ft high has a volume of 380 ft³. What is its diameter?

Problem Analysis

12-5. Find the weight of water contained in a cylindrical tank 6 ft in diameter when the water is 8.5 ft deep.

12-6. A piece of flat steel 3/8 in. thick is cut in the shape of a right triangle. The hypotenuse is 4.6 ft long and a side is 2.09 ft long. How much will the piece weigh?

12-7. Find the weight of a lead ball 3/4 in. in diameter.

12-8. Find the area of a circular sector with a central angle of 0.805 radian which has been cut from a circle having a diameter of 23.4 in.

12-9. Find the weight of a common brick that is 2.6 in. by 4 in. by 8.75 in.

12-10. An open-top cylindrical tank is 12 ft inside diameter, 16 ft high, and is made of steel plate 3/16 in. thick. Water is 3.8 ft deep in the tank. What is the volume of water in the tank in ft^3.

12-11. A white oak beam is 18 ft long and 8 in. by 10 in. in cross section. What is its weight?

12-12. What will be the diameter of a tank 22.5 ft high that holds 1620 ft^3 of water?

12-13. A cylindrical tank is 20.6 ft in diameter, 8 ft high, and contains 15,300 gal of water. What weight of water is contained in the tank?

12-14. A cylindrical tank is 20.8 ft in diameter, 8 ft high, and is made of steel 3/16 in. thick. What is the area of the side and bottom of the tank? What is the weight of the tank?

12-15. A storage vat is 100 yd long, 12 ft deep, and its width is 10 ft at the bottom and 15 ft at the top (trapezoidal cross section). The ends of the vat are vertical. Oil flows into the vat at a rate of 500 gpm. Find the time in hours that is required to fill the vat to a depth of 10 ft.

12-16. Find the weight of a lead ball 1 7/8 in. in diameter.

12-17. How many gallons of water will be contained in a horizontal pipe 10 in. in diameter and 15 ft long, if the water is 6 in. deep in the pipe?

12-18. Find the cost of 23 pieces of 2-in. by 10-in. yellow pine boards 12 ft long at $100 per 1000 fbm.

12-19. A white pine board is 14 ft long and 2 in. by 8 in. in cross section. How much will the board weigh? At $120 per 1000 fbm, what is its value?

12-20. A cast iron cone used in a machine shop is 10 in. in diameter at the bottom and 34 in. high. What is the weight of the cone?

12-21. How many cubic yards of soil will it take to fill a lot 63 ft wide by 100 ft deep if it is to be raised 3 ft in the rear end and gradually sloped to the front where it is to be 1 1/2 ft deep?

12-22. A sphere whose radius is 1.42 in. is cut out of a solid cylinder 8.8 in. high and 7.8 in. in diameter. Find the volume cut away, in cubic inches. If the ball is steel, what does it weigh?

12-23. A piece of Styrene base foam is cylindrical in shape and weighs 30 lb_f. It is 18 in. in diameter and 5 in. high. If a sector is cut from it that has a 30° angle at the center, find the cost of the sector of foam at $2.50 per pound. Find the number of cubic inches in the sector.

12-24. A container is 12 in. high, 10 in. in diameter at the top, and 6 in. in diameter at the bottom. What is the volume of this container in cubic inches? What is the weight of mercury that would fill this pail?

12-25. A canal on level land is 19 miles long, 22 ft deep, and has a trapezoidal cross section. The distance across the canal at the top is 36 ft and across the bottom is 15 ft. Find: (a) the number of cubic yards of dirt that were removed to complete the canal; (b) the time in hours required to pump the canal dry of water if the pump discharges 600 gpm and gates at either end are closed.

12-26. A cylindrical tank 7.50 ft in diameter and 15.9 ft long is lying with its axis horizontal. Compute the weight of kerosene when it is one-third full.

12-27. A container which is in the form of a right rectangular pyramid has the following dimensions: base 26 in. by 39 in., height 16 ft. This container has one-half of its volume filled with ice water. Neglect the weight of the container. Find the weight of the contents.

12-28. A hemispherical container 3 ft in diameter has half of its volume filled with lubricating oil. Neglecting the weight of the container, how much would the contents weigh if kerosene were added to fill the container to the brim?

12-29. A concrete water trough is 18 in. deep, 24 in. wide and 8 ft long inside measurements. If the sides and end are 3.5 in. thick and the bottom 4 in. thick, what will the total weight of tank and contents be if two-thirds of its volume is filled with water?

12-30. What must be the diameter of a conical tank 16 in. deep that holds 1.25 gal of water?

12-31. A certain city lot 50 ft wide by 120 ft deep has a difference in elevation of 1 ft from front to rear. It is to be filled until it is level. How many cubic yards of dirt will be required?

12-32. A pipe 7.8 in. inside diameter and 13 ft long is lying horizontally. Water is 5 in. deep in the pipe. How many gallons of water are in the pipe?

12-33. An eight-sided wrought iron bar weighs 3.83 lb_f per linear foot. What will be its dimension across diagonally opposite corners?

12-34. A solid cylinder of steel has a diameter of 2.4 in. and is 10 in. long. The outside shape of the cylinder is machined, and the cross section is changed from a circle to a hexagon inscribed in the original circle. What is the change in the total outside area of the piece of steel? How much does it weigh after being machined?

12-35. A piece of cast iron has a very irregular shape and its volume is to be determined. It is submerged in water in a cylindrical tank having a diameter of 16 in. The water level is raised 3.4 in. above its original level.

Problem Analysis

How many cubic feet are in the piece of cast iron? How much does it weigh?

12-36. A water pipe 19 ft long and 9.2 in. in diameter is lying with its axis horizontal. If the water in the pipe is 3.2 in. deep, how many gallons of water are there in the pipe?

12-37. A certain kind of structural steel weighs 151,900 lb_f per mile. What is the cross-sectional area of a piece of this material if its length is 13 yd?

12-38. A round helical spring has a mean diameter of 2 7/8 in. and stands 7 1/2 in. high. If there are 1.02 coils per inch of height, find the total length of wire in the spring.

12-39. A hemisphere and cone are carved out of the same material and their weights are equal. The height of the cone is 3 ft, 10 1/2 in., while the radius of the hemisphere is 13 in. If a flat, round cover were to be made for the cone, what would be its area in square inches?

12-40. An aircraft fuel tank has been constructed in the form of a frustum of a right pyramid. The bottom and top are square with the bottom, being 10 in. on a side. If the tank is filled to a depth of 11 in. with JP-4 fuel and the surface area of the JP-4 fuel is 233 in.^{2}, how many gallons of JP-4 are in the tank?

12-41. A conical cup has been cut from a circular sheet of paper. If the diameter of the cup is 4 in. and it is 5 in. deep, what is the minimum size piece of paper from which this cup has been cut?

12-42. Two objects are made of the same material and have the same weights and diameters. One of the objects is a sphere 16 in. in diameter. If the other object is a right cylinder, what is its length?

12-43. A rectangle is 4 in. wide and 8 in. long. What is the area of the smallest circle that will circumscribe the rectangle? Which is longer and by how much—the perimeter of the rectangle or the circumference of the circle?

12-44. A rectangular area 11 in. high and 13 in. long has the corners designated as A, B, C, D; A being the upper left-hand corner, B the upper right-hand corner, C the lower right-hand corner, and D the lower left-hand corner. (a) Determine the area of the circle that can be inscribed within the rectangle and the area of the circle that will circumscribe the rectangle. (b) What distance is the longer and how much: the perimeter of the circumscribed circle or the rectangle? (c) If a line were drawn from D to a point 3 in. to the right of A, what would be the length of the longest line of the triangle formed? What would be the area of each of the two areas so formed?

12-45. A string is wrapped around an iron ball 3 in. in diameter. (a) If 2 in. are added to the length of the string, and the string is then stretched in the form of a circle around the ball, how much distance is there between the ball and string? (b) Same data as above except use a ball 12 in. in diameter.

264   *Engineering: Elementary Problem Analysis*

(c) What would this show about the distance between the earth and a string if the length of the string is equal to the circumference of the earth plus 2 in.?

12-46. A certain distance between two fixed points was measured to be 1025 ft. It was later found that the 100-ft tape used was actually 100.10 ft long. What is the corrected length?

12-47. A distance of 3255.20 ft is to be laid out on the ground, using a tape which is marked to be 50 ft long but which is actually 50.2 ft long. What tape distance should be used?

12-48. A measuring stick for an underground gasoline tank is to be prepared. The tank is a cylinder 7.0 ft in diameter and 8.5 ft long and is lying with its axis horizontal. How many gallons of gasoline will be in the tank for each foot of depth?

12-49. A belt is to connect two pulleys which are 7 ft 3 in. apart, center to center. The driving pulley is 3 ft 6 in. in diameter and the driven pulley is 1 ft 2 in. in diameter. (a) What length of belt is needed to connect the pulleys if they are to rotate in the same direction? (b) What length of belt is needed if the pulleys rotate in opposite directions? (c) If the driving pulley is rotating 320 rpm, what speed will the driven pulley rotate?

12-50. A vertical pole which extends 61 ft above the ground is to be braced with guy wires attached at the top and extending to the ground. One guy wire passes over a roadway and must clear the roadway by 12 ft at a point 26 ft from the pole. (a) How far from the base of the pole will the guy wire touch the ground? (b) Allowing 2 ft 3 in. for tying, how long will the guy wire need to be?

12-51. A flagpole and the center of the rotunda of a building are 215 ft apart. An observer inside the dome of the building finds that he is on a level with the top of the pole and 15 ft directly underneath the light on the dome. He sights to the bottom of the pole and finds the angle from the horizontal to be 63°21′. How far is the light on the dome above the ground?

12-52. At what time between eight o'clock and nine o'clock will the hands of a clock coincide?

12-53. The minute hand of a clock is 3.20 in. long and the hour hand is 2.80 in. long. At what time between two o'clock and two-fifteen will the line between the tip of the hands be perpendicular to the hour hand?

12-54. In order to determine the height of a building, an observer measures the angle between the horizontal and the line of sight to the top of the building and finds it to be 58°15′. The horizontal distance from the observer to the building is 55.6 ft. The observer's eye is 5.2 ft from the ground. How high is the building?

12-55. It is desired to determine the height of a tower at a rocket-launching site. The base of the tower is not accessible, so to measure the height, a sight is taken from point *A* to the top of the tower and the angle with the horizontal is found to be 31°20′. After moving in a horizontal line

Problem Analysis 265

directly toward the tower a distance of 268 ft, the angle of sight to the top of the tower is found to be 59°30′. How tall is the tower?

12-56. A truck at a missile site climbs a ramp that rises 1.0 ft vertically for each 3.6 ft horizontally. The platform at the top of the ramp is 28.5 ft high. If the outside diameter of the tires is 26.4 in., how many revolutions will a wheel make in climbing the ramp? Through how many radians will it turn?

12-57. A stairway in a chemical plant is 25.2 ft long and makes an angle of 50°30′ with the horizontal. If the rise of each step is 8.2 in., what will be the height of the upper landing above the level of the foot of the stairway?

12-58. An 8-ft chain link fence along a railroad right of way is built in a circular arc of 825-ft radius. The angle between the radii at the ends of the arc is 73°40′. What is the length of the fence along the arc?

12-59. A helicopter pilot is 1260 ft above a large body of water. He looks downward at an angle of 60°0′ with the horizontal and turns the helicopter through 360°. What is the area on the water surface enclosed by the circle the line of his sight generates? How high will he have to be if he keeps his line of sight at 60° with the horizontal, turns through 360°, and generates a circle having twice the area of the first?

12-60. A spring used in the control system of a jet airplane is to be made of steel piano wire 0.075 in. in diameter. The finished spring is to be 4.75 in. long, have an average diameter of 1.22 in., and have a pitch (distance between adjacent turns) of 1.25 in. How much wire is required to make the spring?

12-61. In a plant making nonferrous castings, a 42.5-in. diameter pulley on a blower is connected with a 20.0-in. driving pulley by a belt in such manner that the pulleys rotate in opposite directions. The pulleys are mounted on shafts whose centers are 5.5 ft apart. Compute the length of the belt.

12-62. A V-belt drive for a tumbler in a foundry passes around a 2.8-ft diameter pulley. If the driving pulley is 0.94 ft in diameter and the angle between the sides of the belt is 41°30′, what will be the length of belt in contact with the tumbler pulley?

12-63. The construction of a winding staircase in an oil refinery necessitates a rise of 7.0 ft per revolution. If a man walking up the stairs travels in a 2.0-ft radius, how far will he actually walk in climbing to a height of 103 ft?

12-64. The outlet of an air-conditioning duct has a wire grille placed over it consisting of No. 22 round iron wires horizontally and vertically on 1/4-inch centers. What percentage of the duct outlet is obstructed by the wire grille?

*12-65. To conserve space in shipping, a 5-in. diameter steel bar and a 2 3/4-in. diameter steel bar are placed inside an 8-in. inside diameter steel pipe. What is the largest diameter bar that can be placed in the pipe which is holding the above two bars?

*12-66. At a surplus sale, a packing box made of 1-in. pine boards is 4.5 ft long, 2.5 ft wide, and 2.0 ft high and is supposed to be full of rubber heels for men's shoes. Sale rules will not permit opening the box and examining the merchandise, but it is warranted to be new and in good condition. (a) If the contents are as warranted, approximately how many shoe heels are in the box? (b) What will be the approximate weight of the box and contents?

*12-67. Assuming equal conditions of air pressure in a tire, what will be the percentage change in the speedometer reading of a car if the tread on 6.70 by 15 tires wears off an average depth of 0.30 in?

*12-68. A jewelry chain is to be made by cutting 0.012-in. diameter, 10-carat gold wire into pieces each 0.205 in. long and forming each piece into a circular link. How many inches of wire will be needed to make a chain 18 in. long? How much will the chain weigh in troy ounces?

*12-69. An American-made car in the medium price range turns a corner at a 90° street intersection. The inside front wheel follows a path forming a quarter-circle whose average radius is 22.5 ft. (a) How much farther does the outside front wheel travel than the inside wheel? (b) If the tires are standard 8.00 by 15 tires, how many more revolutions will the outside wheel make than the inside wheel makes in traversing the quarter-circle?

*12-70. If a clock keeps perfect time, how many minutes elapse between each time that the minute and hour hand coincide?

*12-71. A steel tube 0.250 in. outside diameter is to be threaded with a 1/4—28 thread. Will a wall thickness of 0.035 in. be sufficient to carry a maximum static tension load of 55 lb_f? Assume that the tensile strength of the steel is 125,000 psi.

*12-72. A pair of step cone pulleys are to be machined so that a 30 in. long V-belt may be used to drive a small drill press from a 1/3-hp motor. Desired ratios of speeds are 4:1; 2:1; 1:1; 1:2; 1:4, and the minimum pulley diameter is 1.50 in. What will be the diameters of each step so that the same length of belt can be used without changing center-to-center distances between the pulleys?

*12-73. A 1200-ft capacity 16-mm reel has 1100 ft of developed movie film on it. Using fourth class parcel post rates, how much will it cost to mail it to Postal Zone 6?

12-74. A steel shaft 6.0 ft long and 4.0 in. in diameter is to be turned in a lathe. The lathe is capable of carrying a longitudinal feed of 1/32 in. per revolution when the depth of cut is 0.020 in. (a) How many revolutions per minute must the shaft turn to give a cutting speed of 50.0 fpm? (b) How many minutes will be required to take a maximum cut the full length of the shaft? (c) How many pounds of metal will be removed in one cut?

Problem Analysis

12-75. A taper plug is 2.00 in. in diameter at one end and 1.75 in. in diameter at the other end. It is 4.00 in. long. What is the taper expressed in inches per foot?

*12-76. At a convention it is suddenly discovered that insufficient seating has been provided for the unexpectedly large crowd. In order to provide additional seating, it is proposed to construct backless benches, using 12 ft long 2-in. by 12-in. fir lumber. (a) Make a freehand sketch of a bench, showing enough detail for a carpenter to use to make benches. (b) Prepare a bill of material for enough material to make benches to seat 3500 people.

*12-77. A simple overhand knot is tied tightly by hand in a manilla rope which has an average diameter of 1.25 in. By approximately how many inches will the rope be shortened?

12-78. Concrete steps are to be built on an incline which is approximately 114 ft long from bottom to top, measured along the incline. The steps will be built with an 8-in. rise and a 12-in. tread and will be 8.5 ft wide. The thickness of the concrete at the back corner of the step is to be not less than 3.0 in., measured perpendicular to the incline. (a) How many steps should be provided for in building forms for the concrete? (b) How many cubic yards of concrete should be needed for the construction?

12-79. A section of titanium sheet for the skin of a jet plane is to be laid out as shown. Determine the size of the angle β.

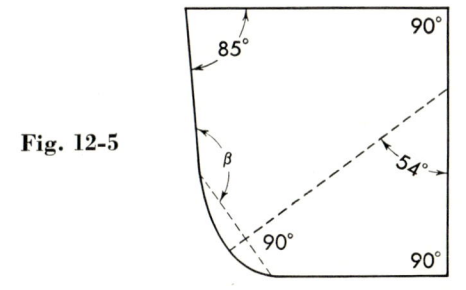

Fig. 12-5

*12-80. A sheet of aluminum 0.030 in. thick is to be cut to form part of the skin of a missile. The dimensions are shown on the sketch. Compute the area of the section shown.

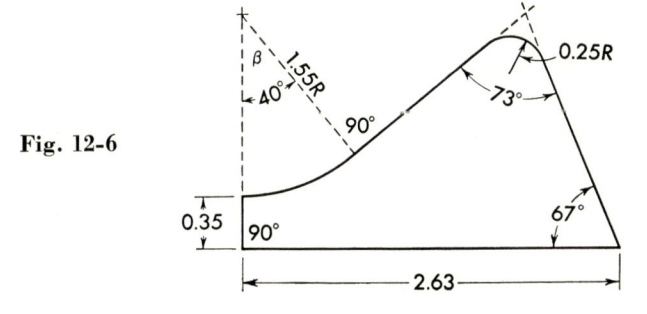

Fig. 12-6

*12-81. Two hardened steel cylinders are to be ground so that when laid in a notch in a tooling block, as shown in Fig. 12-7, they just touch the sides of the notch and touch each other. Using dimensions shown on the sketch, what will be the diameters of the cylinders?

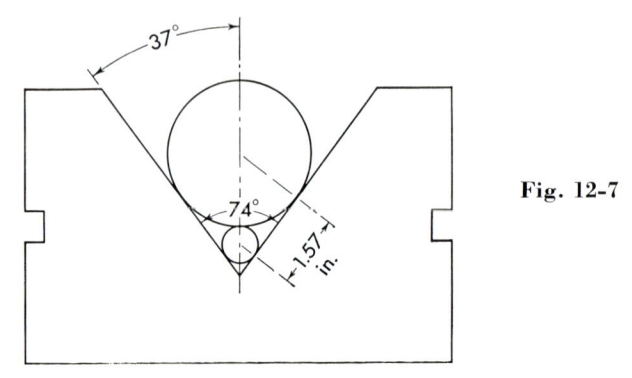

Fig. 12-7

12-82. Convert the following Fahrenheit temperatures to centigrade temperatures. (a) 68°, (b) 98.6°, (c) 156°, (d) 359°, (e) 711°, (f) 2880°, (g) 4.7 (10^4)°, (h) −5°, (i) −40°, (j) −255°.

12-83. Convert the following centigrade temperatures to Fahrenheit temperatures. (a) 20°, (b) 37°, (c) 155°, (d) 580°, (e) 8800°, (f) 1.22 (10^5)°, (g) −2°, (h) −40°, (i) −273°.

12-84. The temperature of liquid oxygen used as missile fuel is about −183°C. What is its temperature in degrees Fahrenheit?

12-85. The temperature of dry ice (solid carbon dioxide), used in shrinking metal parts to fit them together, is −78.5°C. What is the corresponding temperature in degrees Fahrenheit?

12-86. An air-storage tank used in wind-tunnel research has a volume of 138 ft³. How many cubic feet of air at atmospheric pressure will have to be pumped into it to raise the pressure to 185 psig?

12-87. A tight-fitting piston 3.77 in. in diameter in a closed cylinder compresses air from an initial pressure of 35 psig to 68 psig. If the final volume of the air is 14.58 in.³, what will be the distance the piston moves?

12-88. Natural gas in an underground pipe line 24 in. inside diameter is under a pressure of 375 psig. If this gas is allowed to expand to a pressure of 3.0 psig, what volume would the gas in a mile of high-pressure pipe occupy?

12-89. An open-end cylinder with the open end down is lowered into a lake. If the pressure due to water is 0.434 psi for each foot depth of water, how deep would the cylinder be lowered to reduce the volume of trapped air by one-fifth its original volume?

12-90. The normal pressure of the atmosphere at sea level (14.7 psi) will support a column of mercury 29.92 in. high in a barometer. The

Problem Analysis

atmospheric pressure changes approximately 0.1 in. of mercury for each 90 ft of elevation change at low elevations. What will be the approximate normal atmospheric pressure in psi at an elevation of 3050 ft above sea level?

12-91. An automobile tire is inflated to a pressure of 28 psig when the temperature is 51°F. After a period of driving, the temperature of the air in the tire has been raised to 125°F. What will be the gauge pressure of the air?

12-92. Air which has been confined under a pressure of 5.0 psig in the cylinder of an air compressor is further compressed by a tight fitting piston which decreases the volume from 0.89 ft³ to 0.27 ft³. At the same time the temperature of the air is raised from 43°F to 138°F. What will be the final gauge pressure of the confined air?

*12-93. A balloon used for meteorological research has a volume of 137 ft³. At the time it leaves the ground the pressure of the gas inside the balloon is 3.0 ounces per in.² gauge and the temperature is 88°F. It rises to a height where the temperature is −40°F and the pressure in the balloon is 6.88 psia. If the balloon expands freely, what will be the new volume?

12-94. A steel drum of oxygen shows a gauge pressure of 2100 psig at a temperature of 95°F. What will be the gauge pressure at a temperature of −12°F?

*12-95. An open end cylinder 10 ft long is lowered into a tank of water with the open end down so that the lower end is at a depth of 9.65 ft. The temperature of the trapped air is 43°F. At what air temperature would the trapped air have expanded until it had displaced all the water which had risen inside the cylinder? The pressure due to water is 0.433 psi per ft of depth.

12-96. A battery having a voltage of 28.75 volts is connected to a closed circuit having a resistance of 8.08 ohms. What current will flow?

12-97. An ammeter indicates a current of 0.055 amp in an instrumentation circuit of 384-ohm resistance. What is the applied voltage?

12-98. An automobile storage battery having a voltage of 12.81 volts delivers a current of 183.5 amp during an engine start. What is the circuit resistance at this time?

12-99. A power unit which has a voltage of 30.5 volts will deliver 875 amp to operate the starter of an airplane jet engine. What is the circuit resistance?

12-100. A resistance of 75.3 ohms is connected to a battery having a voltage of 45.4 volts during a test of a missile guidance system. (a) What current will flow in the circuit? (b) If the circuit has a resistance of 12.9 ohms added in series, what will be the current through the two resistances?

12-101. A warning lamp in an aircraft instrument panel requires 0.31 amp and has a resistance of 46.5 ohms. If it is to be connected to a voltage source of 27.5 volts, what resistance must be placed in series with it to limit the current to the proper value?

12-102. An electrically operated camera which takes motion pictures of a missile launching requires 5.45 amp from a 29.4-volt line. If a temperature recorder which requires 2.80 amp at the same voltage is placed in parallel with the camera, what will be the total resistance of the circuit containing the two instruments?

12-103. A note is made for $1200 at 6 per cent interest to enable a shop to purchase a small lathe. Compute the simple interest that will be paid in five years.

12-104. The proprietor of a small shop borrows $120 at 5 per cent interest for one year to pay for some tools. He repays the loan in twelve equal monthly payments on the principal and interest. What is the actual interest rate paid?

12-105. A deposit of $4500 is made in a savings account at a bank which pays 2 1/2 per cent interest compounded semiannually. (a) If no withdrawals are made, what will be the amount in the account in ten years? (b) To what rate of simple interest would this compounded interest correspond?

12-106. A United States Savings Bond that costs $37.50 is worth $50.00 in eight years, eleven months. What is the average interest rate?

12-107. It is proposed to install an automatic lathe in a manufacturing plant. In order to purchase the lathe, a note for $13,500 at 6 per cent interest will have to be made. If the note is to run for ten years, what annual return must be expected from the lathe to justify the investment?

chapter thirteen

Analysis in Static Mechanics

Courtesy Bethlehem Steel Company

Rainbow Bridge, Niagara Falls. Principles of static mechanics were used in the design of the structural members of this bridge.

chapter thirteen

Analysis in Static Mechanics

Mechanics is the physical science which describes and predicts the effects of forces acting on material bodies. The condition under study may be one of rest or one of motion. There are three specialized branches into which the general field of mechanics may be divided for more specific studies. These are:

1. Mechanics of rigid bodies
    a. Statics
    b. Dynamics
2. Mechanics of deformable bodies
3. Mechanics of fluids
    a. Compressible flow
    b. Incompressible flow

Our study here is concerned with an introduction to 1.a., Static Mechanics, as a vehicle for the application of the engineering method of problem solution.

FUNDAMENTAL CONCEPTS AND DEFINITIONS

Concepts used in our study of static mechanics are *force*, *space*, and *matter*. These concepts are basic and, as a frame of reference, should be accepted on the basis of our general experience. A *force* is the result of the interaction of two or more bodies and in our study here will be considered to be a localized vector quantity. A force may be evolved as the result of physical contact, or it may be developed at some distance—as is the case with magnetic and gravitational forces. *Space* is a region extending in all directions. It is associated with the location or position of a particle or of particles with respect to one another. *Matter* is substance that occupies space.

A *particle* may be said to be a negligible amount of matter that occupies a single point in space. A *rigid* body is a body that is constructed entirely of particles which do not change their position in space with respect to each other. No real body is rigid. However, in many situations the deformation, or change in position of the particles, is very small and therefore would have a negligible effect upon the analysis. Such is the assumption in this chapter.

A *scalar* quantity is one that can be completely defined by giving its magnitude. Examples of scalar quantities are temperature, work, volume, time, speed, and energy. A *vector* quantity is one that must be described by direction, as well as magnitude, to define it completely. Vectors may be free in space, with no specific line of action, or localized to a unique point of application or fixed position in space. Examples of vector quantities are force, velocity, acceleration, displacement, and momentum. Scalars may

Analysis in Static Mechanics 273

be added, subtracted, etc., according to the ordinary laws of algebra. Vectors, on the other hand, must be handled according to principles of vector mathematics, which will be discussed later in this chapter. Force systems are said to be:

1. *Coplanar*, when all of the force vectors lie in the same plane.

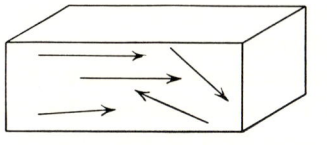

Coplanar Force System

Fig. 13-1

2. *Collinear*, when all forces act along the same line.

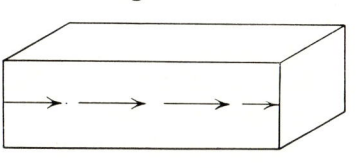

Collinear Force System

Fig. 13-2

3. *Concurrent*, when all the forces originate or intersect at a single point.

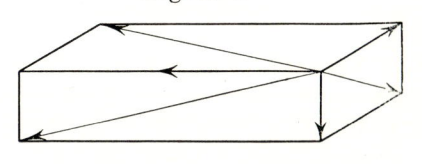

Fig. 13-3   Concurrent Force System

All force vectors should plainly show the sense or direction of force. This can best be done by the use of arrowheads on the point of the force. Space co-ordinate axes are frequently used to aid in positioning vector systems.

Example: A force of 150 lb$_f$ is pulling upward from a point at an angle of 30° with the horizontal.

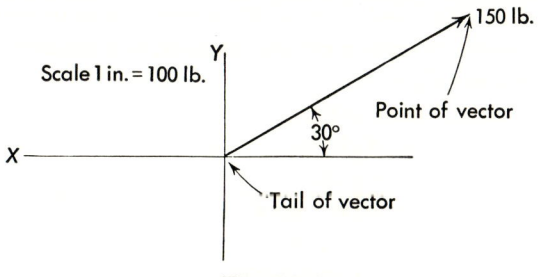

Fig. 13-4

The length of the arrow in the above example was scaled (using an engineer's scale) to 1 in. equals 100 lb$_f$ and is 1 1/2 in. long acting upward at an angle of 30° with the horizontal. In graphical work the arrow point should not extend completely to the end of the vector, since it is very easy to "over-run" the exact length of the measured line in the drawing of the arrowhead.

In rigid-body mechanics the external effect of a force on a rigid body is independent of the point of application of the force along its line of action. Thus it would be considered immaterial whether a tractor pushed or pulled a box from a given position. The total effect on the box would be the same in either case. This is called the *Principle of Transmissibility* and will be used extensively in this chapter. This may be illustrated as shown in Fig. 13-5.

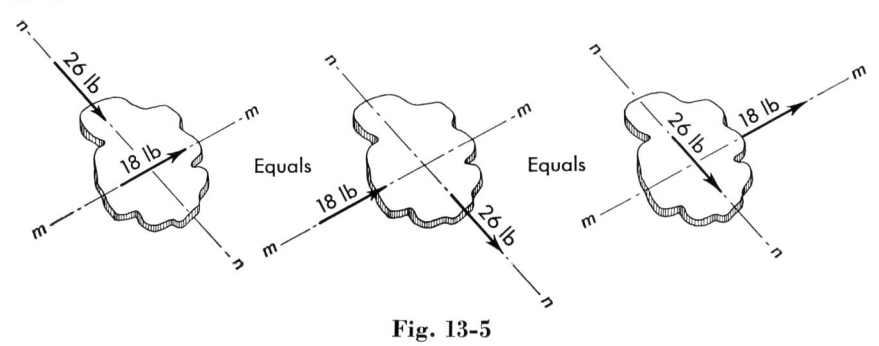

Fig. 13-5

Example: In each case the body is being acted upon by forces of 26 lb$_f$ and 18 lb$_f$. The total effect on the body is assumed to be the same for each example, since it is the line of action of a force which is significant, rather than its point of application.

Resolutions of Forces

In this initial study of static mechanics we shall deal mainly with concurrent, coplanar force systems. It is sometimes advantageous to combine two such forces into a single equivalent force which we shall call a *resultant*. The original forces are called *components*.

Example: What single force R pulling at point O will have the same effect as components F_1 and F_2?

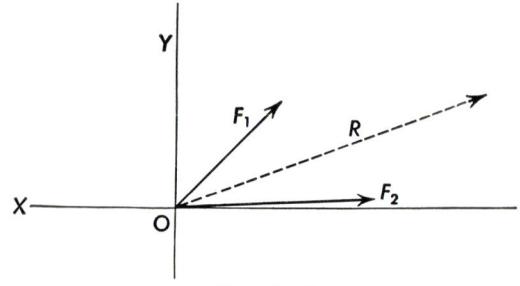

Fig. 13-6

Analysis in Static Mechanics 275

There are several methods of combining these two components into a single resultant. Let us examine the *parallelogram method*, the *polygon of forces*, and the *rectangular component method*.

PARALLELOGRAM METHOD

1. Choose a suitable scale.
2. Lay out the two coplanar components to scale, pointing away from the point of intersection.
3. Using these two components as sides, construct a parallelogram.
4. Draw the diagonal through the point of intersection.
5. Measure the diagonal (which is the resultant of the two components) for magnitude (with engineer's scale) and direction (with protractor).

Example: Solve for the resultant of components F_1 and F_2 if they are separated by angle θ.

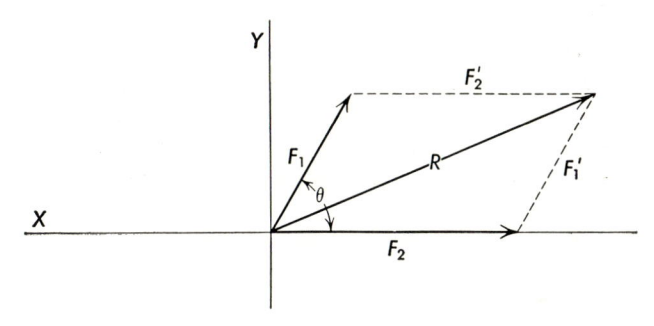

Fig. 13-7

Example: Two coplanar forces of 30 lb$_f$ and 40 lb$_f$, respectively, are at right angles to each other. Determine the magnitude of the resultant and the angle between the resultant and the 40-lb$_f$ force.

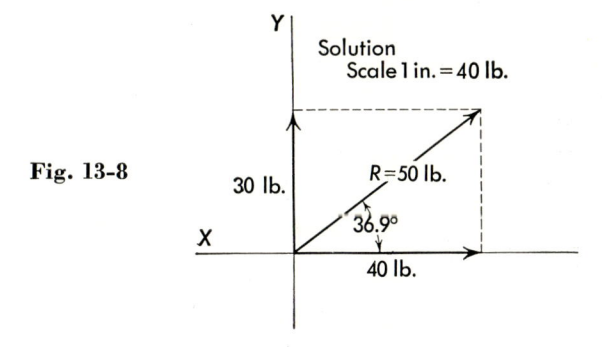

Fig. 13-8

Lay out the two forces to scale as outlined above. The diagonal is measured to be 50 lb$_f$ and is located at an angle of 36.9° with the 40-lb$_f$ force.

Problems

Solve, using the parallelogram method.

13-1. Find the resultant of two concurrent forces of 1939 lb$_f$ and 1220 lb$_f$, respectively, if the angle between them is 20°; if the angle is 130°.

13-2. Find the resultant of two concurrent forces, one 320 lb$_f$ due east and the other 550 lb$_f$ S 30° E.

13-3. Force A is 450 lb$_f$. Force B is 325 lb$_f$ and acts at an angle of 54° with A. The forces are concurrent. What is the amount of the resultant and what angle does it make with force A?

13-4. Find the resultant of two concurrent components, one of 1225 lb$_f$ due west and the other of 1450 lb$_f$ S 30° E.

13-5. A heavy piece of machinery is being moved along a floor with two cables making an angle of 28°30′ with each other. If the pulls are 45,000 and 25,000 lb$_f$, respectively, by what single force could they be replaced, and at what angle would the force act?

13-6. Find the resultant of a velocity of 150 mph due east and a velocity of 280 mph S 70° E. Use a scale of 1 in. equals 20 mph.

13-7. Three ropes are attached to a heavy body. If the first is pulled east by a force of 159 lb$_f$, the second by a force of 75 lb$_f$ 30° east of north, and the third north by a force of 108 lb$_f$, what is the resultant pull exerted on the body?

13-8. Find the resultant in amount and direction of the following concurrent coplanar force system: 1275 lb$_f$ N; 1350 lb$_f$ N 16° E; 1407 lb$_f$ N 60° E; 1450 lb$_f$ due south.

13-9. Find the resultant of the following concurrent coplanar force system: 350 lb$_f$ S; 680 lb$_f$ N 75° W; 670 lb$_f$ N 15° E; and 480 lb$_f$ S 45° W. Use a scale of 1 inch equals 30 lb$_f$.

13-10. The resultant of two components is 763 lb$_f$ acting east. If one of the forces acts N 36° E and has a magnitude of 600 lb$_f$, what is the amount and direction of the other force?

13-11. A wind velocity of 560 mph is blowing toward the east. Find its components along two lines, one N 40° E and the other S 15° E.

13-12. Find the resultant of a 650-lb$_f$ and a 900-lb$_f$ force if they act at an angle of 97° to each other. If the 900-lb$_f$ force acts horizontally, what angle does the resultant make with the vertical?

13-13. The resultant of two components is 150 lb$_f$, 40° east of north. If one of the components is 135 lb$_f$ acting east, what is the amount, direction, and position of the second force?

13-14. A radar support has three lines attached to it, one line runs due north and exerts a pull of 78 lb$_f$, one line runs 65° east of south with a tension of 228 lb$_f$ in the wire, and one line runs 50° west of north with a pull of

Analysis in Static Mechanics

185 lb$_f$. Compute the resultant pull on the support. Use a scale of 1 inch equals 40 lb$_f$.

13-15. Three lines are connected to a missile. One line, having a tension of 1500 lb$_f$, runs due north; a second line, with a tension of 870 lb$_f$, runs S 75° W; a third line, with a tension of 1240 lb$_f$, runs N 58° E. Find the position and direction of a properly placed guy wire to brace the missile.

13-16. A man pulls straight ahead on a test sled with a force of 148 lb$_f$. If this man is replaced by two men, one pulling 36° to his left and the other pulling 20° to his right, what force must each of the new men exert if the sled is to move in the same direction?

*13-17. A weight is held up by two cables which make angles of 50° and 25°, respectively, with the horizontal. Their resultant is vertical and equal to the weight which is 260 lb$_f$. Find the tension in each cable.

*13-18. Two men are raising a 100 lb$_f$ container from a reactor by means of two ropes. Find the force each man is exerting on his rope if one rope makes a 15° angle with the vertical and the other makes a 25° angle with the vertical.

*13-19. Vectors representing two accelerations have been plotted as 4.36g (a resultant) and 8.21g acting vertically downward. If the other component is 6.86g, determine the direction of all vectors.

*13-20. Rocket velocities of Mach 3.61 and Mach 4.09 must be added in such manner as to produce a desired resultant of Mach 2.66 vertically upward. In what directions must the components act to produce this effect?

POLYGON OF FORCES

If two or more forces (or components) are concurrent and coplanar, their resultant can be determined by a faster and more convenient method known as the *polygon of forces*. In order to apply this method, proceed as follows:

1. Select a suitable scale.
2. Lay out one of the components with its correct magnitude and direction. At the tip of this component construct very lightly a small space co-ordinate system.
3. From the origin of this new space co-ordinate system lay out another component, placing the tail of the second component against the point of the first component.
4. Proceed in like manner until all components are used once (and only once).
5. Draw a vector from the original origin to the tip of the last component. This vector represents the *resultant* of the force system in both magnitude and direction.

Example: Solve for the resultant of the vector system shown below:

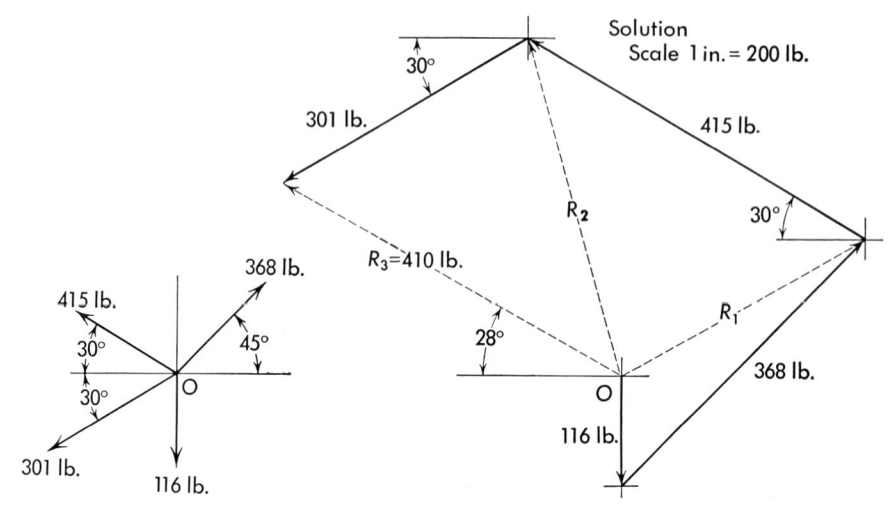

Fig. 13-9

Observe that R_1 is the resultant of the 116-lb$_f$ component and the 368-lb$_f$ component, R_2 is the resultant of R_1 and the 415-lb$_f$ component, and R_3 is the resultant of R_2 and the 301-lb$_f$ component. We see that R_3 (410-lb$_f$ at $\theta = 28°$), then, is the resultant of all the components.

It makes no difference in what sequence the components are placed in series. The resultant will be the same in magnitude and direction. In some cases the vectors cross one another, but this, too, is nothing to cause concern.

Example: Solve for R, and the angle it makes with the X-axis.

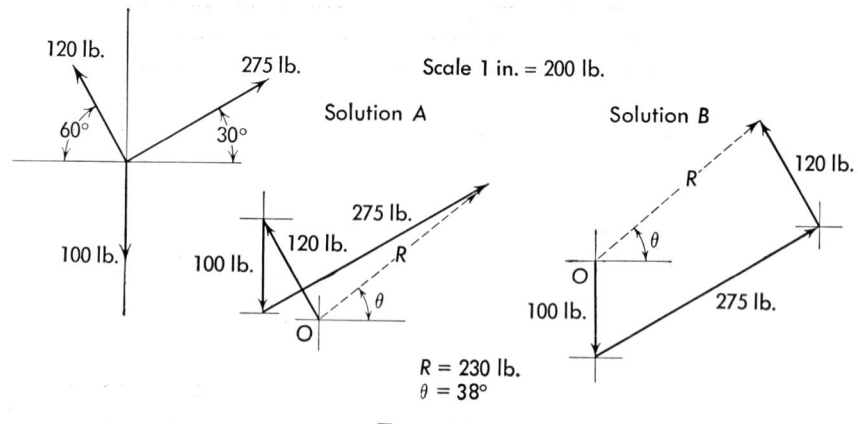

Fig. 13-10

Note that in Solution A in Fig. 13-10 we began with the 120-lb$_f$ component and used components in a counterclockwise direction, while in solution B

Analysis in Static Mechanics

we began with the 100-lb$_f$ component and worked in a counterclockwise direction.

Problems

Solve, using the polygon of forces. Find the resultant of each of the following force systems and the angle the resultant makes with force A.

13-21. Forces A and B act 136° apart. $A = 180$ lb$_f$, $B = 325$ lb$_f$.

13-22. Forces A and B act 21° apart. $A = 39.3$ lb$_f$, $B = 41.6$ lb$_f$.

13-23. Forces A and B act 320° apart. $A = 5960$ lb$_f$, $B = 4976$ lb$_f$.

13-24. Forces A, B, and C act 36° apart, with B acting between A and C. $A = 516$ lb$_f$, $B = 430$ lb$_f$, $C = 771$ lb$_f$.

13-25. Forces A, B, and C act 49° apart, with B acting between A and C. $A = 49.3$ lb$_f$, $B = 66.7$ lb$_f$, $C = 35.8$ lb$_f$.

13-26. Find the resultant force which would replace the three forces in Fig. 13-11.

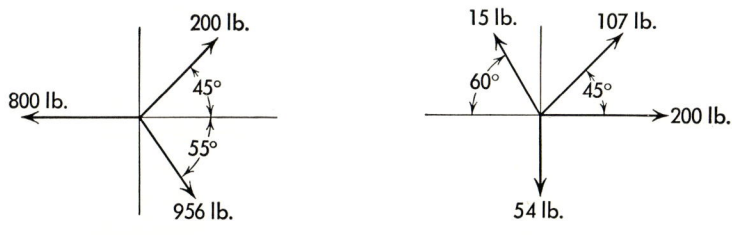

Fig. 13-11

Fig. 13-12

13-27. A man weighing 210 lb$_f$ stands at the middle of a wire supported at points 60 ft apart and depresses it 12 ft below the level of the ends. Solve for the tension in the wire due to the man's weight.

13-28. Solve for the magnitude and direction of the resultant of the forces shown in Fig. 13-12.

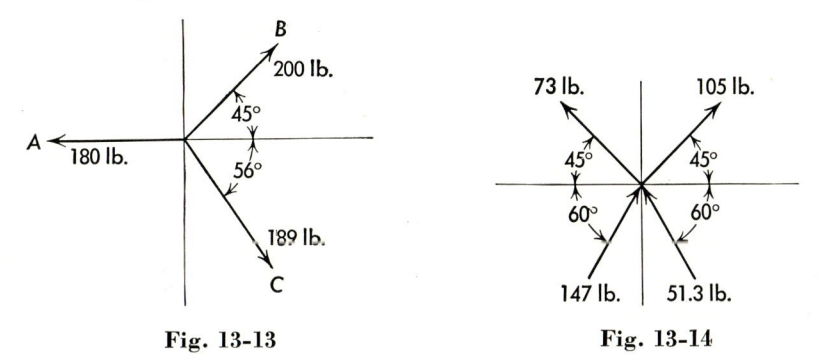

Fig. 13-13

Fig. 13-14

13-29. Find the resultant force that would replace the three forces A, B, and C in Fig. 13-13.

13-30. Find the resultant of the four forces shown in Fig. 13-14.

13-31. Solve for the resultant of the force systems shown in Fig. 13-15.

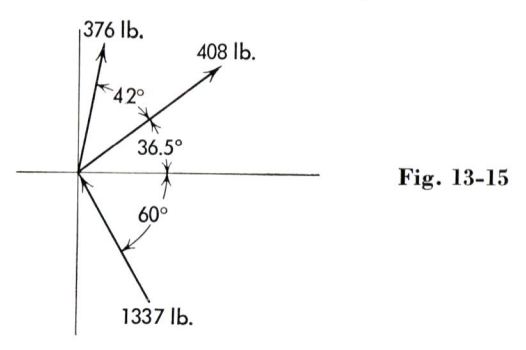

Fig. 13-15

*13-32. Graphically resolve the force, shown in Fig. 13-16 into three components, one of which is 10 lb$_f$ acting vertically upward and another 30 lb$_f$ acting horizontally to the left.

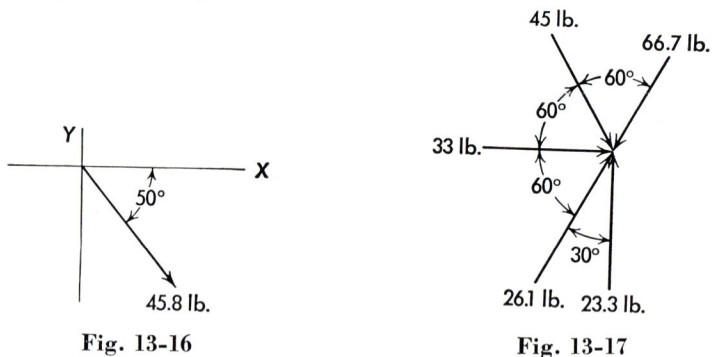

Fig. 13-16

Fig. 13-17

*13-33. Given the following force system (force A; north, 100 lb$_f$, force B; N 43° E 350 lb$_f$, force C; S 30° E 75 lb$_f$, force D; N 15° W 105 lb$_f$); find the amount and direction of the resultant.

*13-34. Find the resultant of the force system shown in Fig. 13-17, using a scale of 1 in. equals 10 lb$_f$.

*13-35. Find the resultant of the velocity vectors: 33 mph south, 75 fps 20° west of north, and 2530 fpm north.

RECTANGULAR COMPONENTS

Graphical solutions, such as the *parallelogram method* and the *polygon of forces*, are useful for estimations where time is a factor. However, where exactitude is important, a numerical technique is needed. The method most frequently used by engineers is the *rectangular component method*, which will be discussed here.

As we have seen in the previous methods, vector components can be added together or subtracted—always leaving some resultant value. (This resultant value, of course, may be zero.) Also, any vector or resultant

Analysis in Static Mechanics

value can be replaced by two or more other vectors which are usually called *components*. If the components are two in number and perpendicular to each other, they are called *rectangular components*. Although it is common practice to use space co-ordinate axes which are horizontal and vertical, it is by no means necessary to do so. Any orientation of the axes will produce equivalent results.

The example below shows a vector quantity F and its rectangular components F_x and F_y. Note that the lengths of the components F_x and F_y can be determined numerically by trigonometry.

$$F_y = F \sin \theta$$
$$F_x = F \cos \theta$$

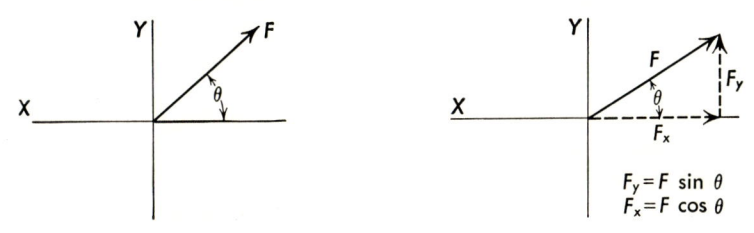

Fig. 13-18

Example: The components F_x and F_y also can be resolved into the force F by the polygon of forces. Hence, they may replace the force F in any computation.

Let us examine a concurrent coplanar force system and resolve each force into its rectangular components.

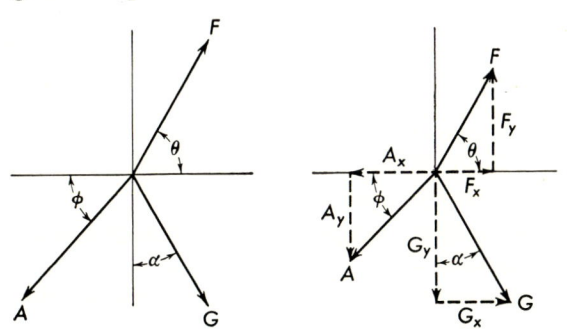

Fig. 13-19

Example: By trigonometry, F_x can be found, using F and the cosine of the angle θ, or $F_x = F \cos \theta°$. In the same manner $F_y = F \sin \theta°$.

In order to keep the directions of the vectors better in mind, let us assume that horizontal forces acting to the right are positive and those acting to the left are negative. Also, the forces acting upward may be considered positive and those acting downward negative.

In working such force systems by solving for the rectangular components, the following table may be used.

282 Engineering: Elementary Problem Analysis

FORCES	HORIZONTAL COMPONENT	HORIZONTAL VALUE	VERTICAL COMPONENT	VERTICAL VALUE
		=		=
		=		=
		=		=
Total Value	Positive		Positive	
Total Value	Negative		Negative	
Sum	Horizontal		Vertical	

When the sums of the horizontal and vertical components have been determined, lay off these values on a new pair of axes to prevent confusion.

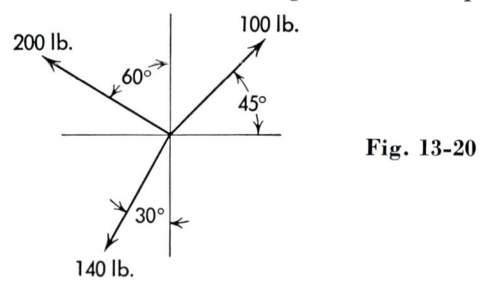

Fig. 13-20

Solve for the resultant in both magnitude and direction, using the method explained on page 275.

Example: Solve for R, using the method of rectangular components.

FORCES	HORIZONTAL COMPONENTS	HORIZONTAL VALUE	VERTICAL COMPONENT	VERTICAL VALUE
100 lb$_f$	100 cos 45° =	+70.7 lb$_f$	100 sin 45° =	+70.7 lb$_f$
200 lb$_f$	200 sin 60° =	−173.2 lb$_f$	200 cos 60° =	+100 lb$_f$
140 lb$_f$	140 sin 30° =	−70.0 lb$_f$	140 cos 30° =	−121 lb$_f$
Total value	Positive	+70.7 lb$_f$	Positive	+170.7 lb$_f$
Total value	Negative	−243.2 lb$_f$	Negative	−121 lb$_f$
Sum	Horizontal	−172.5 lb$_f$	Vertical	+49.7 lb$_f$

Analysis in Static Mechanics

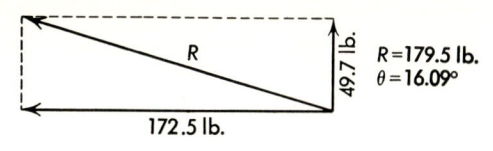

Fig. 13-21

Problems

Solve, using rectangular components (analytical method).

13-36. Find the resultant, in amount and direction, of the following concurrent coplanar force system: force A, 180 lb$_f$ acts S 60° W; and force B, 158 lb$_f$, acts S 80° W. Check graphically, using a scale of 1 in. equals 50 lb$_f$.

13-37. Find the resultant of the following concurrent coplanar force system: $A = 30$ lb$_f$ due north; $B = 25$ lb$_f$ N 30° E; $C = 35$ lb$_f$ S 45° E; $D = 55$ lb$_f$ S 30° W.

13-38. Four men are pulling a box. A pulls with a force of 115 lb$_f$, N 20°40′ E; B pulls with a force of 95 lb$_f$ S 64°35′ E; C pulls with a force of 140 lb$_f$ N 40°20′ E; and D pulls with a force of 68 lb$_f$ east. In what direction will the box tend to move?

13-39. Determine the amount and direction of the resultant of the concurrent coplanar force system as follows: force A, 10 lb$_f$, acting N 55° E; force B, 16 lb$_f$, acting due east; force C, 12 lb$_f$, acting S 22° W; force D, 15 lb$_f$, acting due west; force E, 17 lb$_f$, acting N 10° W.

13-40. Find the resultant and the angle the resultant makes with the vertical, using the following data: 10 lb$_f$, N 18° W; 5 lb$_f$, N 75° E; 3 lb$_f$, S 64° E; 7 lb$_f$, S 0° W; 10 lb$_f$, S 50° W.

13-41. Five forces act on an object. The forces are as follows: 130 lb$_f$, 0°; 170 lb$_f$, 90°; 70 lb$_f$, 180°; 20 lb$_f$, 270°; 300 lb$_f$, 150°. The angles are measured counterclockwise with reference to the horizontal through the origin. Determine graphically the amount and direction of the resultant by means of the polygon of forces. Check analytically, using horizontal and vertical components. Calculate the angle that R makes with the horizontal.

13-42. (a) In the sketch in Fig. 13-22, using rectangular components, find the resultant of these four forces: $A = 100$ lb$_f$, $B = 130$ lb$_f$, $C = 195$ lb$_f$, $D = 138$ lb$_f$. (b) Find a resultant force that would replace forces A and B. (c) By the polygon of forces, break force A into two components, one of which acts N 10° E and has a magnitude of 65 lb$_f$. Give the magnitude and direction of the second component.

13-43. Find the resultant of the forces A, B, C, and D in Fig. 13-23.

13-44. Three forces of 1780 lb$_f$, 9800 lb$_f$, and 3848 lb$_f$ are acting on a ship. The first acts 16° east of north, the second acts 8° east of south, and the third acts 43° west of north. Find the resultant, in amount and direction, of the three forces on the ship.

284   *Engineering: Elementary Problem Analysis*

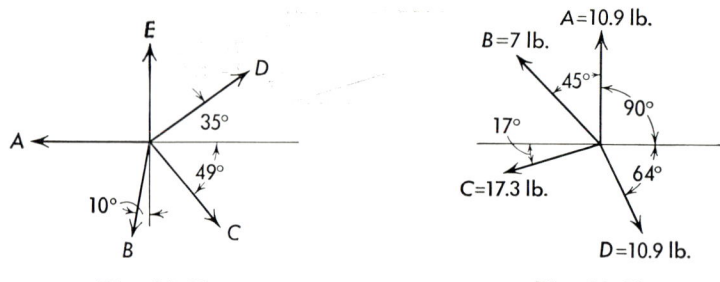

Fig. 13-22

Fig. 13-23

13-45. Determine the amount and direction of the resultant of the concurrent coplanar force systems: force A, 100 lb$_f$ acting upward to the right 30° with horizontal; force B, 175 lb$_f$ acting to the left horizontally; force C, 125 lb$_f$ acting downward to the right 60° with horizontal; force D, 200 lb$_f$ acting to the right horizontally.

13-46. Determine the amount and direction of the resultant of the five forces listed here. Calculate the angle that R makes with the horizontal. The angles are measured counterclockwise with reference to the horizontal through the origin. Five forces: 230 lb$_f$, 0°; 180 lb$_f$, 90°; 70 lb$_f$, 180°; 20 lb$_f$, 270°; 300 lb$_f$, 150°.

13-47. Given the force system shown in Fig. 13-24, find the resultant of the forces.

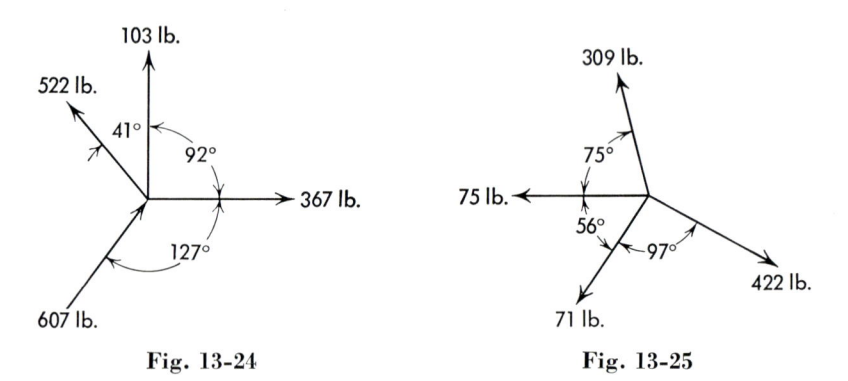

Fig. 13-24

Fig. 13-25

13-48. Find the resultant of the forces shown in Fig. 13-25.

13-49. Solve for the resultant in magnitude and direction: $A = 196$ lb$_f$, N 40° E; $B = 403$ lb$_f$, west; $C = 551$ lb$_f$, N 10° W, $D = 231$ lb$_f$, S 27° W, $E = 347$ lb$_f$, N 21° W.

*13-50. A man weighing 225 lb$_f$ stands at the middle of a wire supported at points 60 ft apart, and he depresses it 10 ft below the level of the ends. Solve for the tension in the wire due to the man's weight.

Analysis in Static Mechanics

*13-51. Two inclined posts, making angles of 45° and 60° with the horizontal, are pinned together 8 ft above the ground. If a load of 1800 lb$_f$ is hung from the pin, solve for the compression forces in the posts.

*13-52. A weight of 1200 lb$_f$ is hung by a cable 23 ft long. What horizontal pull will be necessary to hold the weight 8 ft from a vertical line through the point of support? What will be the tension in the cable?

*13-53. A weight of 80 lb$_f$ is suspended by two cords, the tension in AC being 70 lb$_f$ and in BC being 25 lb$_f$. Find the angles α and θ.

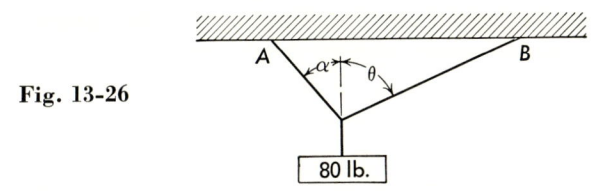

Fig. 13-26

*13-54. Solve for the force necessary to balance the system shown in Fig. 13-27. $A = 196$ lb$_f$, $B = 405$ lb$_f$, $C = 227$ lb$_f$, $D = 501$ lb$_f$, $E = 425$ lb$_f$

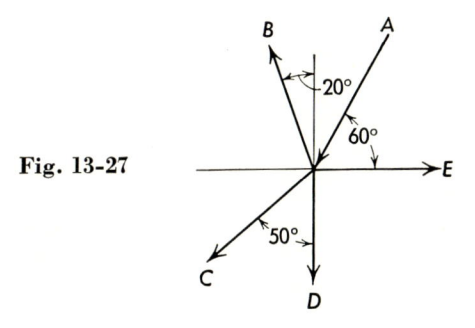

Fig. 13-27

*13-55. A weight of 1906 lb$_f$ is supported at the midpoint of a wire 8.3 ft long. If the safe tension in the wire is 1000 lb$_f$, what is the greatest distance allowable between the ends A and C? See Fig. 13-28.

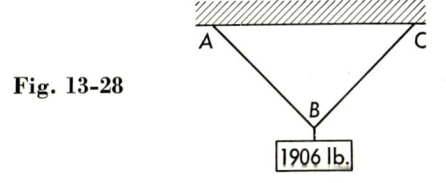

Fig. 13-28

Moments

If a force is applied perpendicular to a pivoted beam at some distance away from the pivot point, there will be a tendency to cause the beam to turn in either a clockwise or counterclockwise direction. The direction of

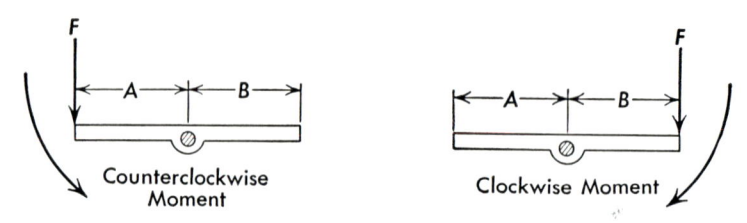

Fig. 13-29

the tendency will depend on the direction of the applied force. This tendency of a force to cause rotation about a given center is called *moment*.

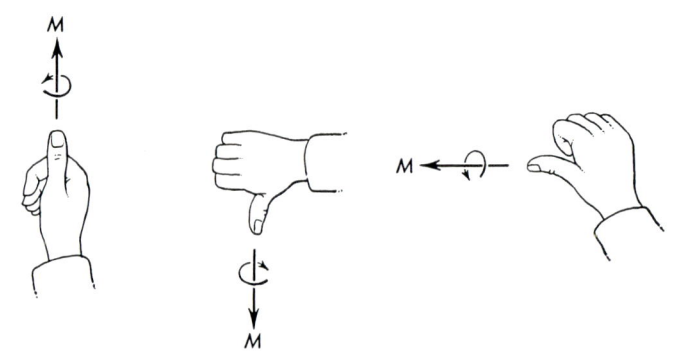

Fig. 13-30. *Moment* is a vector quantity and, as such, may be represented vectorially. The direction, or sense, of the vector representing a *moment* is found by applying the right hand rule as shown above. The fingers of the right hand are curled in the direction of the tendency of rotation. The right thumb will then point in the direction of the vector which may represent this *moment*. Note that moment vectors usually are shown with a small "curl," in order to distinguish them from the more common force vectors.

The amount of *moment* will depend upon the magnitude of the applied force as well as upon the length of the moment arm. The moment arm is the perpendicular distance from the point of rotation to the applied force. The magnitude of the moment is calculated by multiplying the force by the moment arm.

The sign convention being used in a given problem analysis should be placed on the calculation sheet adjacent to the problem sketch. In this way no confusion will arise in the mind of the reader concerning the sign convention being used. We shall assume that vectors acting to the right have a positive sign, vectors acting upward have a positive sign, and moments directed counterclockwise have a positive sign. To aid in establishing a system of positive senses, the sketch shown in Fig. 13-31 will serve as a basis for problem analysis in this text.

Analysis in Static Mechanics 287

Example:

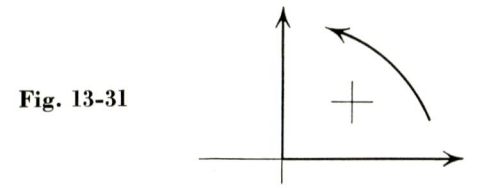

Fig. 13-31

Example: Solve for the moments in Fig. 13-32 that tend to cause turning of the beam about the axle.

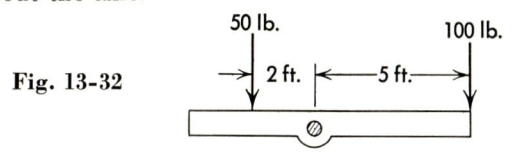

Fig. 13-32

Counterclockwise moment = (50 lb)(2 ft) = +100 lb-ft
Clockwise moment = (100 lb)(5 ft) = −500 lb-ft

Since *moment* is the product of a force and a distance, its units will be the product of force and length units. By convention, moments are usually expressed with the force unit being shown first, as lb_f-ft, lb_f-in., kip-ft (a kip is 1000 lb_f), etc. This is done because *work* and *energy* also involve the product of distance and force, and the units ft-lb_f, in.-lb_f, etc., are commonly used for this purpose.

The moment of a force about some given center is identical to the sum of the moments of the components of the force about the same center. This principle is commonly called *Varignon's theorem*. In problem analysis it is sometimes more convenient to solve for the sum of the moments of the components of a force rather than the moment of the force itself. However, the problem solutions will be identical.

Example: Solve for the total moment of the 1000-lb_f force about point A (Fig. 13-33).

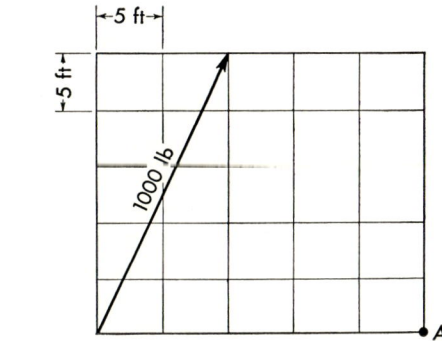

Fig. 13-33

288 Engineering: Elementary Problem Analysis

Solution A: Moment of a force (Fig. 13-34).

$$\theta = \arctan 25/10 = 68.2°$$
$$\text{Moment arm} = 25 \sin 68.2°$$
$$\text{Total moment} = (1000)(25 \sin 68.2°)$$
$$= 23{,}200 \text{ lb}_f\text{-ft}$$

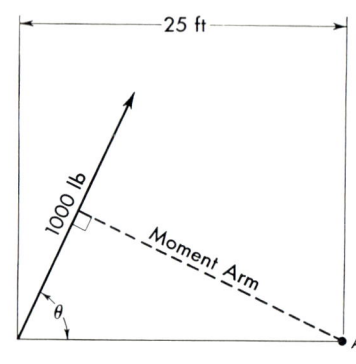

Fig. 13-34

Fig. 13-35. Moments of components of a force.

Solution B: Moments of components of a force (Fig. 13-35).

$$\text{Vertical component} = 1000 \sin 68.2°$$
and
$$\text{Moment arm} = 25 \text{ ft}$$
$$\text{Horizontal component} = 1000 \cos 68.2°$$
and
$$\text{Moment arm} = 0$$

(Note that the horizontal component passes through the center A.)

$$\text{Total moment} = (1000 \sin 68.2°)(25) = 23{,}200 \text{ lb}_f\text{-ft}$$

Problems

13-56. Solve for the algebraic sum of the moments in pound-feet about A when h is 20 in. (Fig. 13-36).

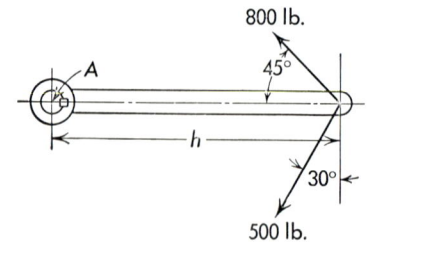

Fig. 13-36

Analysis in Static Mechanics

13-57. Solve for the algebraic sum of the moments of forces about A (Fig. 13-37).

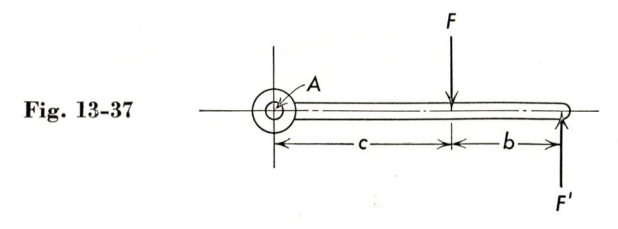

Fig. 13-37

13-58. Solve for the algebraic sum of the moments about the center of the axle (Fig. 13-38).

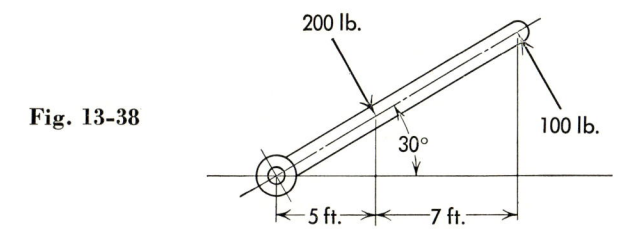

Fig. 13-38

13-59. (a) Write an equation for the clockwise moments about the point of application of force R in Fig. 13-39. (b) Write an equation for the counterclockwise moments about the point of application of force Y.

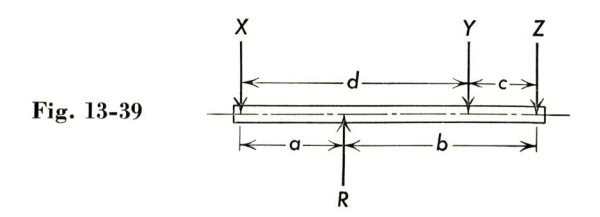

Fig. 13-39

13-60. (a) Solve for the clockwise moments about A, B, C, D, and E in Fig. 13-40. (b) Solve for the counterclockwise moments about A, B, C, D, and E. (c) Solve for the algebraic sum of the moments about A, B, C, D, and E.

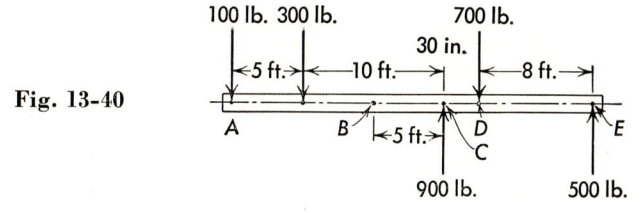

Fig. 13-40

290   *Engineering: Elementary Problem Analysis*

13-61. Find the summation of the moments of the forces shown around A in Fig. 13-41. Find the moment sum around D.

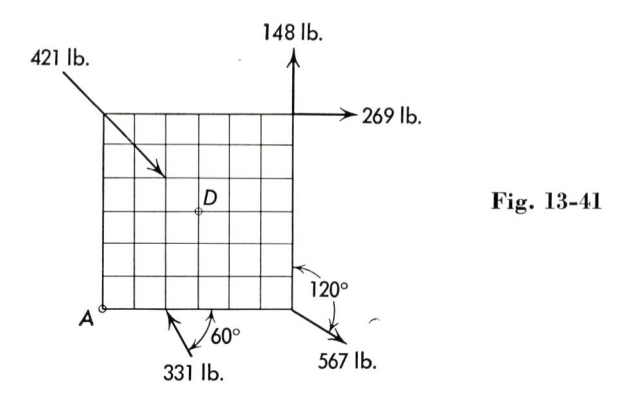

Fig. 13-41

13-62. Find the moment of each of the forces shown about O (Fig. 13-42).

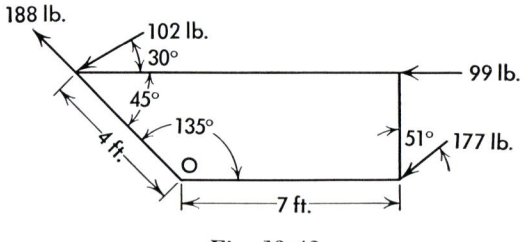

Fig. 13-42

13-63. The trapezoidal body shown in Fig. 13-43 is acted on by three forces. (a) Find the resultant of these three forces. (b) What additional force could be added that would cause this body to be in equilibrium? Describe it fully.

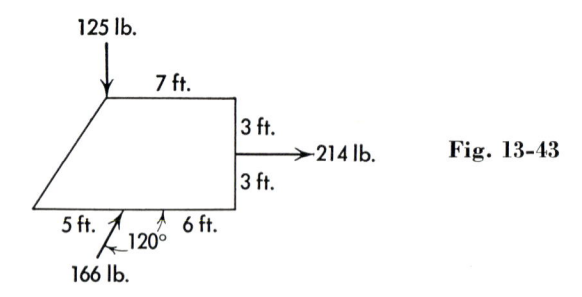

Fig. 13-43

13-64. On the trapezoidal body shown in Fig. 13-44, find the moment of each of the forces about point O.

Analysis in Static Mechanics

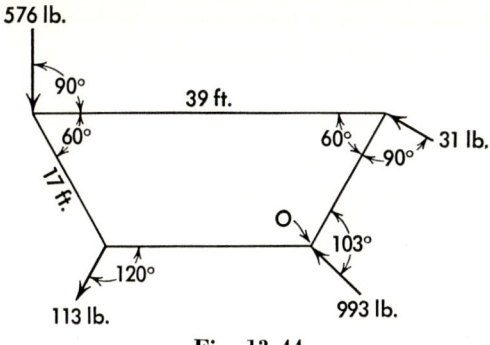

Fig. 13-44

13-65. Find the moment of each of the forces shown in Fig. 13-45, about the point A.

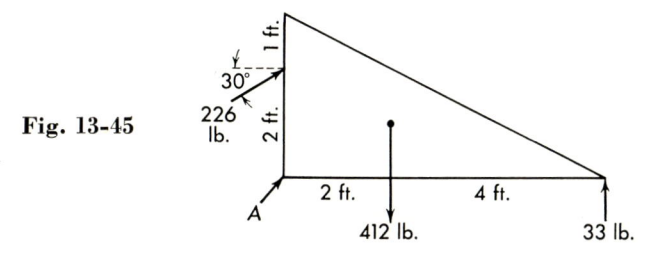

Fig. 13-45

*__13-66.__ A frame structure is pivoted at point A and is acted on by five forces as shown in Fig. 13-46. (a) Find the moment of each force about point A. (b) What vertical force applied through point B would cause the structure to balance, neglecting the weight of the structure?

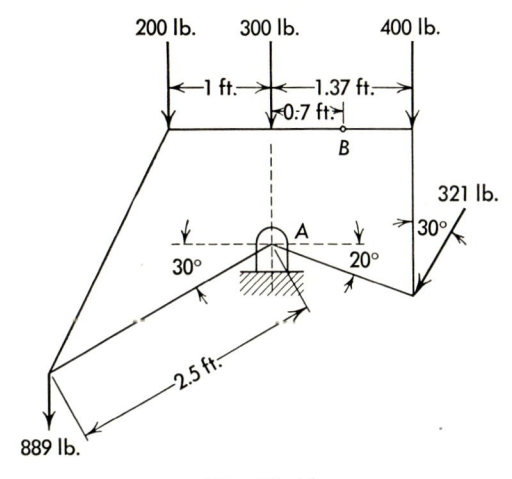

Fig. 13-46

292   Engineering: Elementary Problem Analysis

*13-67. Three forces act on a body as shown in Fig. 13-47. Find the amount, direction, and position of the resultant of these forces.

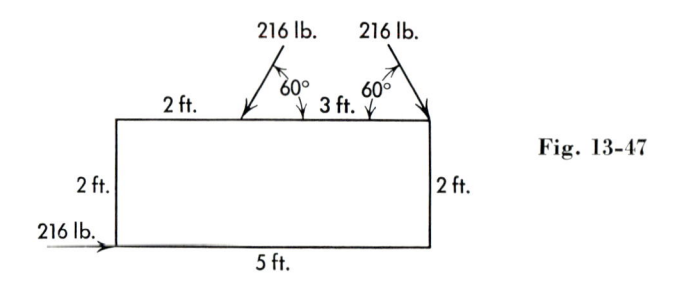

Fig. 13-47

*13-68. A rigid triangular body is acted on by the force of gravity and three other forces as shown in Fig. 13-48. (a) Find all the characteristics of the resultant of the three other forces in relation to point A. (b) What single force would create a state of equilibrium for the body?

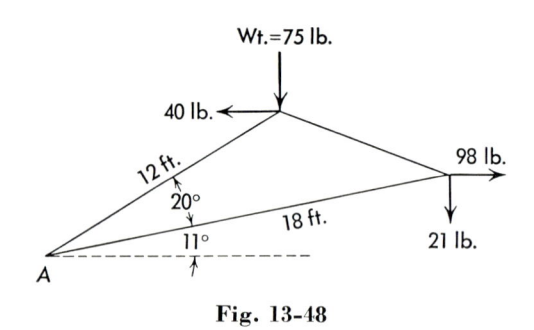

Fig. 13-48

13-69. In order for the moments of this system to balance, what must be the force P shown in Fig. 13-49?

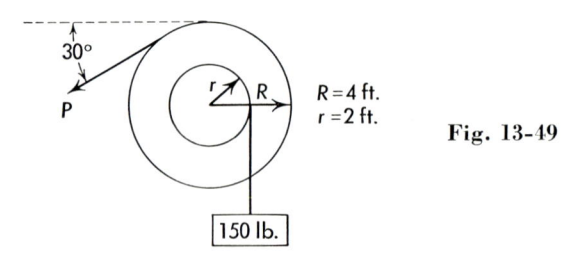

Fig. 13-49

*13-70. Solve for the total moment effect of the two forces about the shaft axis in Fig. 13-50.

Analysis in Static Mechanics

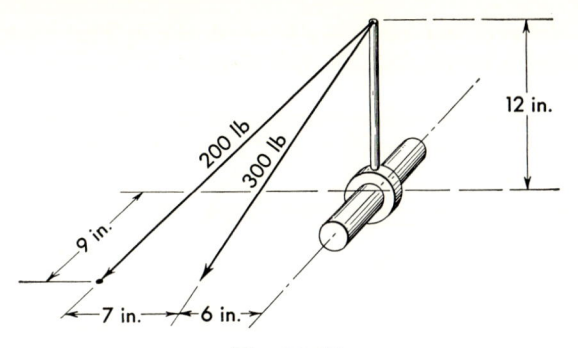

Fig. 13-50

13-71. What pull P is required on the handle of a claw hammer to exert a vertical force of 750 lb$_f$ on a nail. Dimensions are shown on Fig. 13-51.

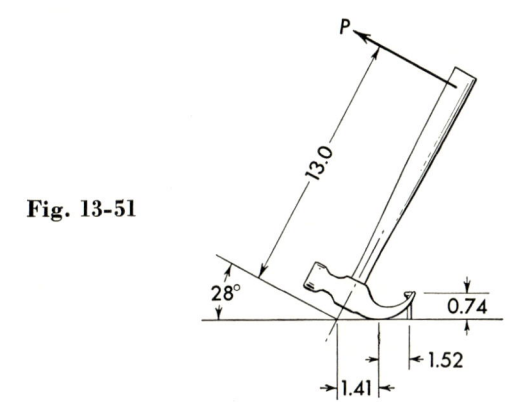

Fig. 13-51

Equilibrium

The term *equilibrium* is used to describe the condition of any body when the resultant of all forces acting on the body equals zero. For example, the forces acting upward on a body in equilibrium must be balanced by other forces acting downward on the body. Also, the forces acting horizontally to the right are counteracted by equal forces acting horizontally to the left. Since no unbalance in moment or turning effect can be present when a body is in equilibrium, the sum of the moments of all forces acting on the body must also be zero. The moment center may be located at any convenient place on the body or at any place in space. We may sum up these conditions of equilibrium by the following equations:

$\Sigma F_x = 0$ (the sum of all horizontal forces acting on the body equals zero)
$\Sigma F_y = 0$ (the sum of all vertical forces acting on the body equals zero)
$\Sigma M_o = 0$ (the sum of the moments of all forces acting on the body equals zero)

294   *Engineering: Elementary Problem Analysis*

These equilibrium equations may be used to good advantage in working problems involving beams, trusses, and levers.

Example: A beam of negligible weight is supported at each end by a knife-edge. The beam carries a concentrated load of 500 lb$_f$ and one uniformly distributed load weighing 100 lb$_f$ per linear foot, as shown in Fig. 13-52. Determine the scale readings under the knife-edges.

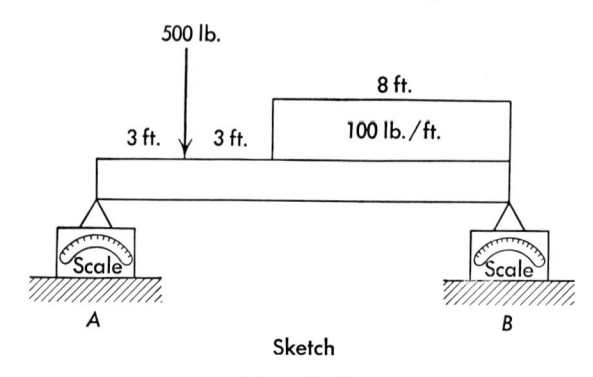

Sketch

Fig. 13-52

Solution: The uniformly distributed load is equivalent to a resultant of $8 \text{ ft} \times 100 \frac{\text{lb}_f}{\text{ft}} = 800 \text{ lb}_f$ acting at the center of gravity of the uniform-load diagram. Therefore the entire distribution load can be replaced by a concentrated load of 800 lb$_f$ acting at a distance of 10 ft from the left end.

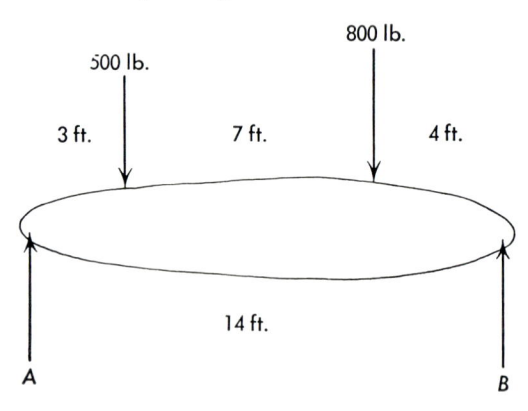

Fig. 13-53

1. Draw a free-body diagram of the beam.
2. Since there are no horizontal forces acting on the free body, $\Sigma F_x = 0$ is satisfied.

Analysis in Static Mechanics

3. From $\Sigma F_y = 0$, we know that

$$A + B = 500 \text{ lb}_f + 800 \text{ lb}_f$$
$$A + B = 1300 \text{ lb}_f$$

4. From $\Sigma M_o = 0$, we know that the moments about any point must equal zero. Let us take moments about point A.

$$\Sigma M_A = 0$$
$$(B \text{ lb}_f)(14 \text{ ft}) - (500 \text{ lb}_f)(3 \text{ ft}) - (800 \text{ lb}_f)(10 \text{ ft}) = 0$$
$$B \text{ lb}_f = \frac{1500 \text{ lb}_f\text{-ft} + 8000 \text{ lb}_f\text{-ft}}{14 \text{ ft}}$$
$$B \text{ lb}_f = \frac{9500 \text{ lb}_f\text{-ft}}{14 \text{ ft}}$$
$$B = 679 \text{ lb}_f$$

5. From the third step we saw that $A + B = 1300 \text{ lb}_f$. We can now subtract and obtain

$$A = 1300 \text{ lb}_f - 679 \text{ lb}_f = 621 \text{ lb}_f$$

NOTE: The same answer for A could have been obtained by taking moments about B as a moment center.

Example: Solve for the pin reaction and the roller reaction. Neglect the weight of the beam.

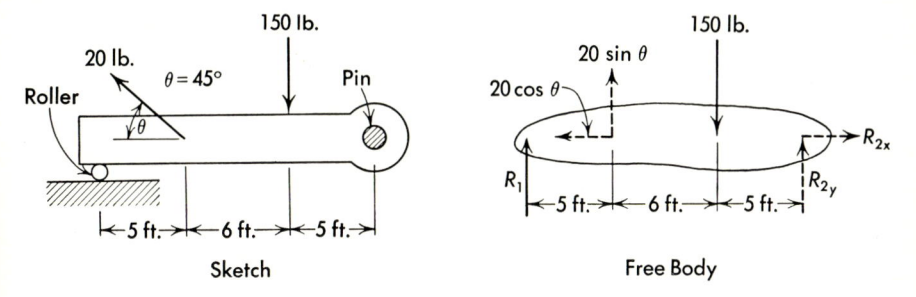

Fig. 13-54

Since all moments and forces acting on a body in equilibrium must be equal to zero, we can say:

1. Σ (summation) of all horizontal forces = 0, or $\Sigma F_x = 0$.
2. Σ of all vertical forces = 0, or $\Sigma F_y = 0$.
3. Σ of all moments = 0, or $\Sigma M_o = 0$.

The reaction R_1 is known to act vertically and is assumed to point in a positive direction. The components of R_2 are assumed to act in a positive direction. Since the horizontal component of the 20-lb_f force acts in a

negative direction, we see immediately that R_{2x} must act in a positive direction because
$$\Sigma F_x = 0$$

We can solve for the reaction R_1 by taking moments about the pin connection. $\Sigma M_{R2} = 0$ must exist if the system is to be in equilibrium. Note that the component *20 cos 45°* has no moment arm, and hence its moment about the pin is zero.

$$\Sigma M_{R2} = 0 = (150 \text{ lb}_f)(5 \text{ ft}) - (20 \sin 45°)(11 \text{ ft}) - (R_1 \text{ lb}_f)(16 \text{ ft})$$
$$= 750 \text{ lb}_f\text{-ft} - 155.5 \text{ lb}_f\text{-ft} - 16R_1 \text{ lb}_f\text{-ft}$$
$$R_1 = \frac{750 - 155.5}{16}$$
$$= \frac{594.5 \text{ lb}_f\text{-ft}}{16 \text{ ft}}$$
$$= 37.1 \text{ lb}_f$$

Since R_1 is determined as a positive quantity, we know that our original assumption as to its direction was correct. Also

$$\Sigma F_x = 0 \text{ for the entire beam}$$
$$\Sigma F_x = 0 = R_{2x} - 20 \cos 45°$$
$$R_{2x} = 14.14 \text{ lb}_f$$
$$\Sigma F_y = 0$$
$$\Sigma F_y = 0 = 20 \sin 45° + R_1 + R_{2y} - 150 \text{ lb}_f$$
$$R_{2y} = -14.14 \text{ lb}_f - 37.1 \text{ lb}_f + 150 \text{ lb}_f$$
$$R_{2y} = 98.76 \text{ lb}_f$$

which indicates that R_{2y} acts upward as we originally assumed. Thus R_2 is solved as follows:

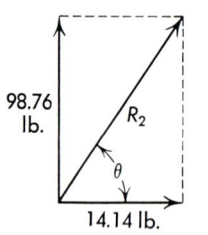

Fig. 13-55

Using the slide rule we find
$$R_2 = 99.8 \text{ lb}_f$$
$$\theta = 81.86°$$

In this book problems involving trusses, cranes, linkages, bridges, etc., should be considered to be *pin-connected*, which means that the member is free to rotate about the joint. For simplicity, members also are usually considered to be weightless.

Problem 3	GIVEN: Smith, Bob

SKETCH

(Sketch: Wall on left with cable AB at 30° from wall, length 12 ft, member BC horizontal from wall to point B, with 100 lb load hanging at B.)

FIND:
a. Solve for tension in cable AB
b. Solve for compression in member BC

SOLUTION:

(Free body diagram of point B showing AB at 30°, ABy vertical component, ABx horizontal component, BC to the right, 100 lb down)

$\Sigma Fx = 0$
$\Sigma Fy = 0$
$\Sigma Mo = 0$

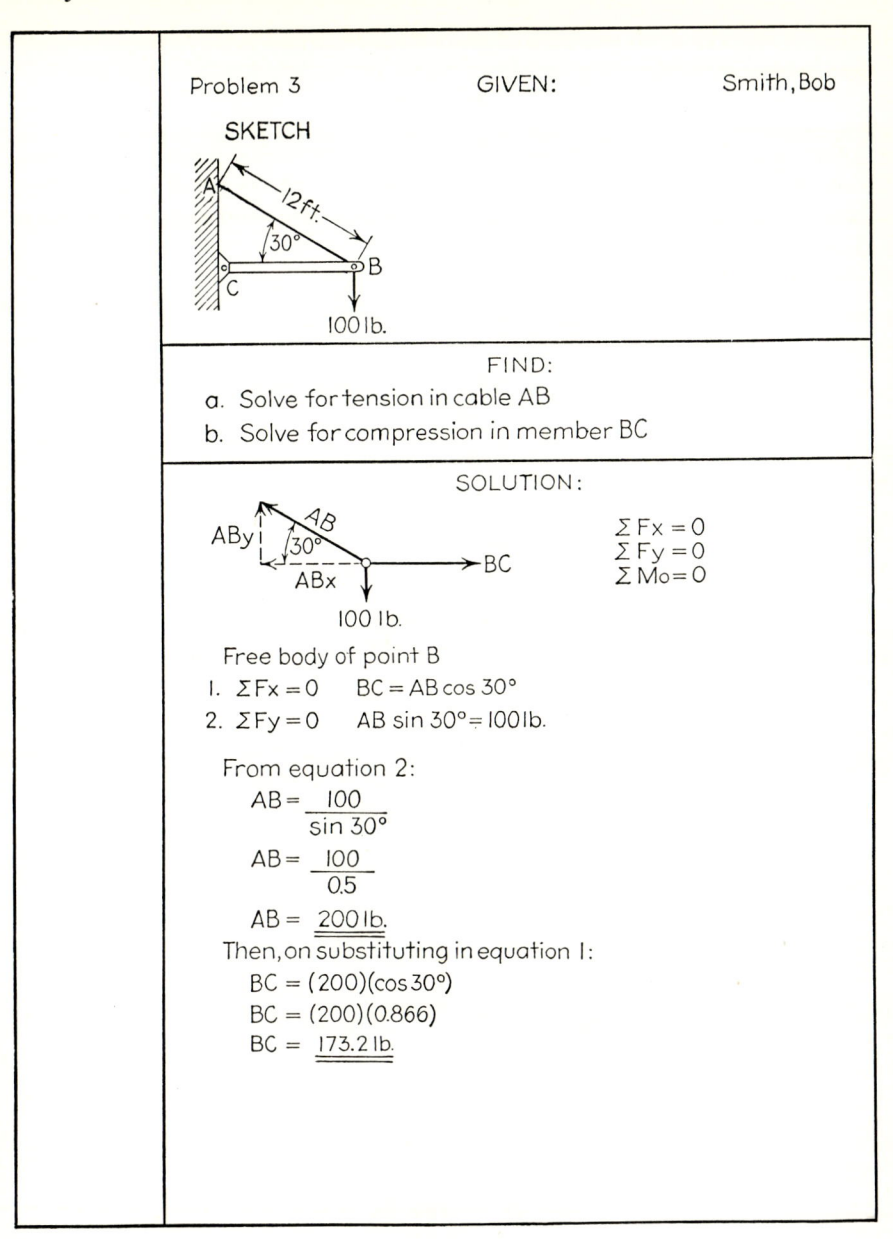

Free body of point B
1. $\Sigma Fx = 0$ $BC = AB \cos 30°$
2. $\Sigma Fy = 0$ $AB \sin 30° = 100$ lb.

From equation 2:
$$AB = \frac{100}{\sin 30°}$$
$$AB = \frac{100}{0.5}$$
$$AB = \underline{\underline{200 \text{ lb.}}}$$

Then, on substituting in equation 1:
$BC = (200)(\cos 30°)$
$BC = (200)(0.866)$
$BC = \underline{\underline{173.2 \text{ lb.}}}$

Fig. 13-56. Model problem sheet showing a method of analysis and presentation of a system in equilibrium.

298   *Engineering: Elementary Problem Analysis*

By examining each member of the structure separately, internal forces in the various members may be obtained by the conditions of equilibrium.

Example: Solve for the tensions in cables AF and ED and for the reactions at C and R in Fig. 13-57.

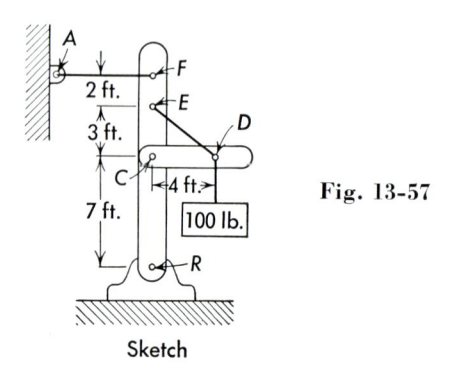

Fig. 13-57

Sketch

Equilibrium Equations
$$\Sigma F_x = 0$$
$$\Sigma F_y = 0$$
$$\Sigma M_o = 0$$

Solution

1. Take moments about point R in free body No. 1, Fig. 13-58.

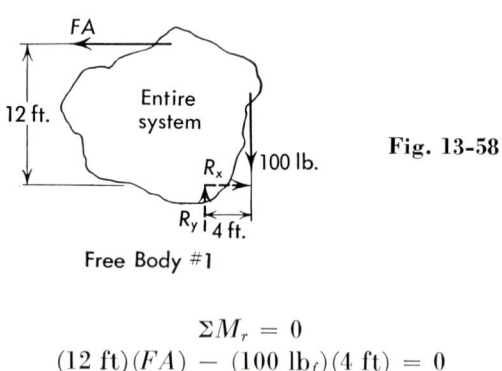

Fig. 13-58

Free Body #1

$$\Sigma M_r = 0$$
$$(12 \text{ ft})(FA) - (100 \text{ lb}_f)(4 \text{ ft}) = 0$$
$$FA = \frac{400 \text{ lb}_f\text{-ft}}{12 \text{ ft}} = 33.3 \text{ lb}_f$$
$$\Sigma F_x = 0$$
$$R_x - FA = 0$$
$$R_x = FA = 33.3 \text{ lb}_f \rightarrow$$

Analysis in Static Mechanics

2. Take moments about point C in free body No. 2, Fig. 13-59.

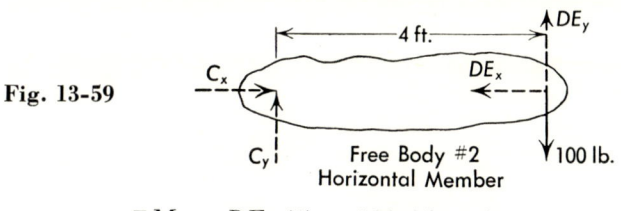

Fig. 13-59

Free Body #2 — Horizontal Member

$$\Sigma M_c = DE_y(4) - 100(4) = 0$$
$$DE_y = 100 \text{ lb}_f$$

Therefore
$$DE = \frac{100 \text{ lb}_f}{\sin 36.9°} = 166.8 \text{ lb}_f$$

And free body No. 2
$$\Sigma F_y = 0$$
$$C_y = 100 \text{ lb}_f - 100 \text{ lb}_f$$
$$C_y = 0$$

Also free body No. 2
$$\Sigma F_x = 0$$
$$C_x = DE_x = \frac{100 \text{ lb}_f}{\tan 36.9°}$$
$$C_x = 133.1 \text{ lb}_f \rightarrow$$

3. Consider $\Sigma F_y = 0$, using the third free body (vertical member). Remember that in two force members, such as cable DE, the reactions at

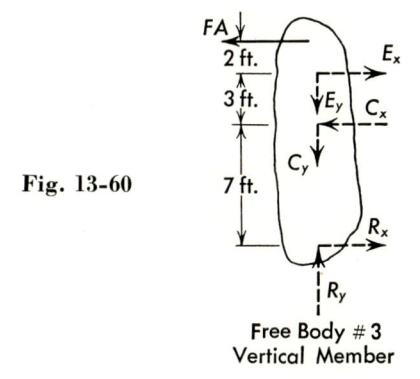

Fig. 13-60

Free Body #3 — Vertical Member

each end will be equal in magnitude but opposite in direction; that is, E_x and E_y are equal to DE_x and DE_y.

$$\Sigma F_y = 0$$
$$R_y - DE_y = 0$$
$$R_y = 100.0 \text{ lb}_f \uparrow$$

The resultant is indicated as before and solved by using the slide rule.

Fig. 13-61

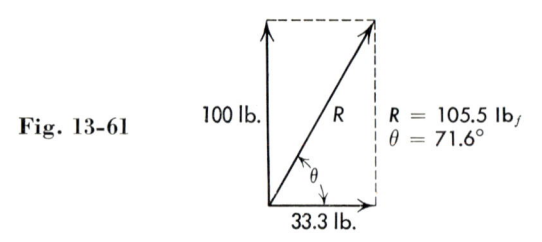

100 lb.   R   R = 105.5 lb$_f$
              θ = 71.6°
          θ
       33.3 lb.

Equilibrium Problems

13-72. A horizontal beam 20 ft long weighs 150 lb$_f$. It is supported at the left end and 4 ft from the right end. It has the following concentrated loads: at the left end, 200 lb$_f$; 8 ft from the left end, 300 lb$_f$; at the right end, 400 lb$_f$. Calculate the reactions at the supports.

13-73. A horizontal beam 8 ft long and weighing 30 lb$_f$ is supported at the left end and 2 ft from the right end. It has the following loads: at the left end, 18 lb$_f$; 3 ft from the left end, 22 lb$_f$; at the right end, 15 lb$_f$. Compute the reactions at the supports.

13-74. A beam 22 ft long weighing 300 lb$_f$ is supporting loads of 700 lb$_f$ 3 ft from the left end and 250 lb$_f$ 7 ft from the right end. One support is at the left end. How far from the right end should the right support be placed so that the reactions at the two supports will be equal?

13-75. A horizontal rod 8 ft long and weighing 12 lb$_f$ has a weight of 15 lb$_f$ hung from the right end, and a weight of 4 lb$_f$ hung from the left end. Where should a single support be located so the rod will balance?

13-76. A uniform board 22 ft long will balance 4.2 ft from one end when a weight of 61 lb$_f$ is hung from this end. How much does the board weigh?

13-77. An iron beam 12.7 ft long weighing 855 lb$_f$ has a load of 229 lb$_f$ at the right end. A support is located 7.2 ft from the load end. (a) How much force is required at the opposite end to balance it? (b) Disregarding the balancing force, calculate the reactions on the supports if one support is located 7 ft from the left end and the other support is located 4 ft from the right end.

13-78. A horizontal rod 8 ft long and weighing 1.2 lb$_f$ per linear foot has a weight of 15 lb$_f$ hung from the right end, and a weight of 4 lb$_f$ hung from the left end. Where should a single support be located so the rod will balance?

13-79. A beam 20 ft long has the following loads: a load of 60 lb$_f$ located 4 ft from the right end; a load of 85 lb$_f$ 14 ft from the right end; and a uniform load of 50 lb$_f$ per foot beginning at the left end and extending to the right for a distance of 10 ft. Calculate the reactions on the supports if one support is located 7 ft from the left end and the other support is located 4 ft from the right end.

13-80. A beam 18 ft long is supported at the right end and at a point 5 ft from the left end. It is loaded with a concentrated load of 250 lb$_f$ located 2 ft from the right end and a concentrated load of 450 lb$_f$ located 9 ft from the right end. In addition, it has a uniform load of 20 lb$_f$ per linear foot for its entire length. Find the reactions at the supports.

13-81. A 12-ft beam which weighs 10 lb$_f$ per foot is resting horizontally. The left end of the beam is pinned to a vertical wall. The right end of the beam is supported by a cable which is attached to the vertical wall 6 ft above the left end of the beam. There is a 200-lb$_f$ concentrated load acting vertically downward 3 ft from the right end of the beam. Determine the tension in the cable and the amount and direction of the reaction at the left end of the beam.

13-82. A steel I-beam, weighing 75 lb$_f$ per linear foot and 20 ft long, is supported at its left end and at a point 4 ft from its right end. It carries loads of 10 tons and 6 tons at distances of 5 ft and 17 ft, respectively, from the left end. Find the reactions at the supports.

13-83. A factory door 4 ft wide and 8 ft high weighing 50 lb$_f$ hangs from two hinges, each 1 ft from the ends. The door swings horizontally. If the hinges carry equal weights, find the reaction at each hinge.

13-84. A rope runs over a single pulley and is holding a weight of 79 lb$_f$. The angle between the two sides of the rope is 35°. Calculate the amount and direction of the reaction at the pulley support.

13-85. A 2-ft diameter sphere weighs 56 lb$_f$ and is suspended by a cable and rests against a vertical wall. If the cable AB is 2 ft long, (a) calculate the angle the cable will make with the smooth wall, (b) solve for the tension in the cable and the reaction at C in Fig. 13-62. Check results graphically.

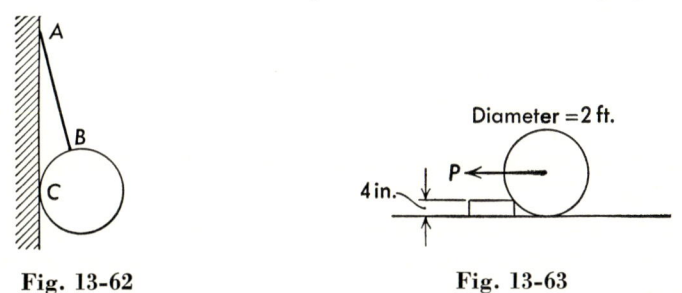

Fig. 13-62   **Fig. 13-63**

13-86. What horizontal pull P will be necessary just to start the wheel weighing 1400 lb$_f$ over the 4-in. block in Fig. 13-63?

13-87. A vertical pole 12 ft long is pinned to the ground at A and is stayed by a guy wire running from the top of the pole, B, to a point C, 8 ft to the left of A. If a horizontal force of 1900 lb$_f$ is applied to the pole at D, 6 ft above A, determine the tension in the guy wire BC, and the amount and direction of the pin reaction at A.

13-88. Find the tension in AB and the angle θ that AB makes with the vertical in Problem 13-87.

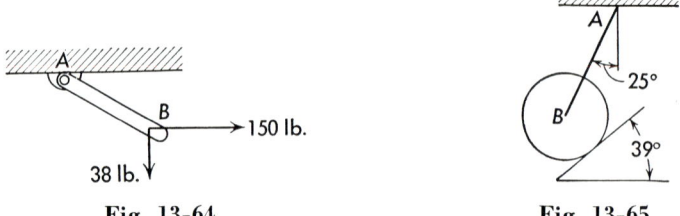

Fig. 13-64

Fig. 13-65

13-89. If the tension in the cable AB in Fig. 13-65, is 196 lb_f, how much does the sphere B weigh? How much is the reaction of the inclined plane on the sphere?

13-90. The wheel B in Fig. 13-66 weighs 175 lb_f. Solve for the force in member AB, the reaction at C, and the horizontal and vertical force components at A.

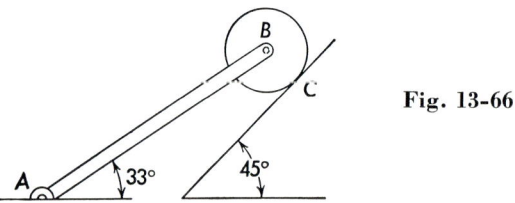

Fig. 13-66

13-91. A cylinder weighing 206 lb_f is placed in a smooth trough as shown in Fig. 13-67. Find the two supporting forces.

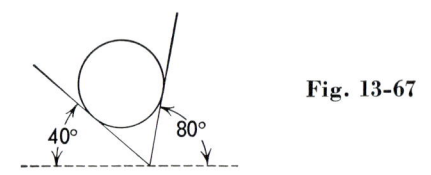

Fig. 13-67

13-92. A 796-lb_f load is supported as shown in Fig. 13-68. AB equals 8 ft, θ equals 25°. (a) Neglecting the weight of the beam AB, solve analytically for the tension in the cable and the reaction at A. (b) If beam AB is uniform and weighs 12 lb_f per foot, solve for the tension in the cable and the reaction at A.

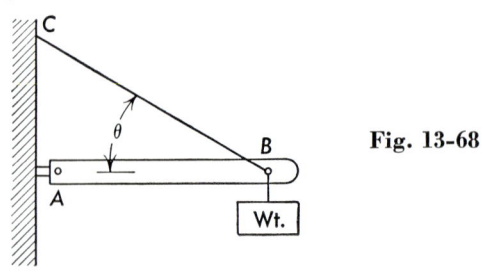

Fig. 13-68

Analysis in Static Mechanics 303

13-93. Solve for the compression in BD and the reaction at D in Fig. 13-69.

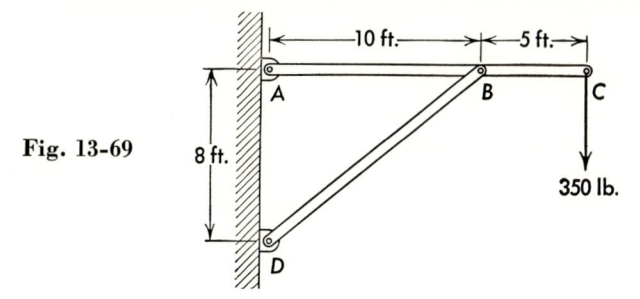

Fig. 13-69

13-94. Find the tension in AB and the compression in BC in Fig. 13-70.

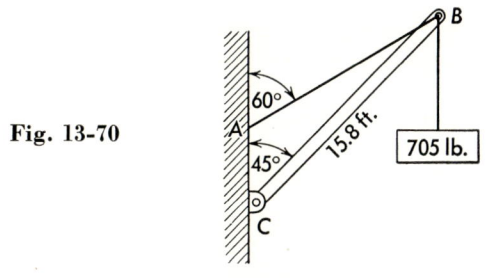

Fig. 13-70

13-95. A weight of 5280 lb_f is hung from a crane boom as shown in Fig. 13-71. Calculate the compression or tension in members A and B.

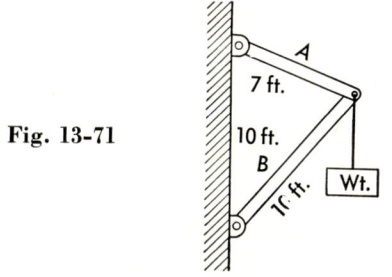

Fig. 13-71

13-96. A car that is stuck in a mudhole has one end of a 35-ft cable tied to the bumper and the other end of the cable tied to a nearby tree. A pull of 75 lb_f is applied perpendicular to the cable at its midpoint and moves the midpoint of the cable 5 ft to one side. How much force is exerted on the car?

13-97. A weight of 1135 lb_f is hung by a cable 23 ft long. What horizontal pull will be necessary to hold the weight 8 ft from the vertical line through the point of support? What will be the tension in the cable?

13-98. A weight of 1355 lb_f is supported by two ropes making angles of 30° and 45° on opposite sides of the vertical. What is the tension in each rope?

13-99. A weight of 1368 lb$_f$ is supported from the ceiling by a rope 15 ft long. It is pulled aside 6 ft by another rope which is horizontal. Find the tension in the horizontal rope and in the supporting rope.

13-100. A rope 20 ft long is fastened to supports 18 ft apart on the same level. What will be the tension in the rope when a weight of 100 lb$_f$ is hung from the middle of the rope?

*13-101. Each sphere in Fig. 13-72 is 5 ft in diameter. Each sphere weighs 157 lb$_f$. (a) Find the force between ball B and the trough. (b) Find the force between balls A and C.

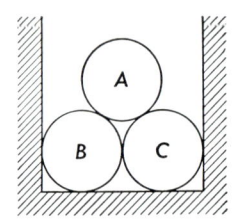

Fig. 13-72

*13-102. A weight is hung from a crane as shown in Fig. 13-73. Determine the forces in members A and B.

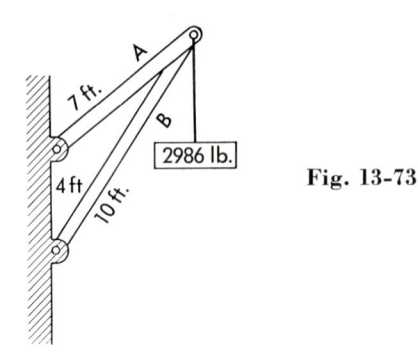

Fig. 13-73

*13-103. Cylinder No. 1 in Fig. 13-74 has a 10-in. diameter and weighs 84 lb$_f$. Cylinder No. 2 has a 6-in. diameter and weighs 27 lb$_f$. Find the reactions at A, B, and C. All surfaces are smooth.

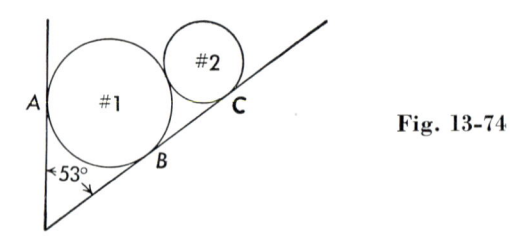

Fig. 13-74

Analysis in Static Mechanics 305

*13-104. Forces are applied on a rigid frame as shown in Fig. 13-75. Find the reactions at A and B.

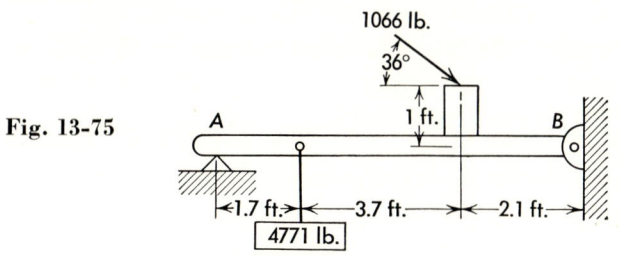

Fig. 13-75

*13-105. (a) What is the tension in BC in Fig. 13-76? (b) What is the amount and direction of the reaction at A?

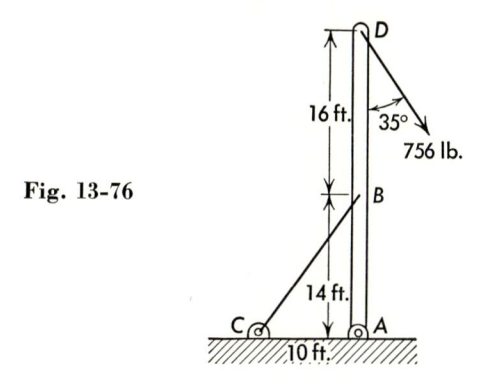

Fig. 13-76

*13-106. (a) Find the tension in AC in Fig. 13-77. (b) Find the amount and direction of the reaction at B. $BC = 10$ ft, $BD = 25$ ft.

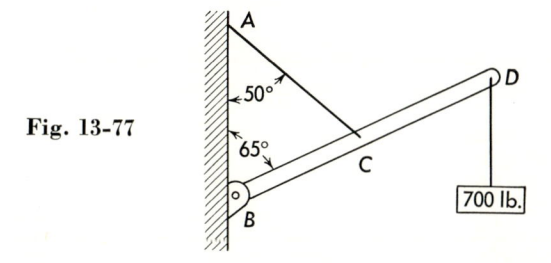

Fig. 13-77

*13-107. (a) Find the force in member AB in Fig. 13-78 and the reaction at point E. (b) Find the force in member CG and the horizontal and vertical components of the reaction at pin D.

Fig. 13-78

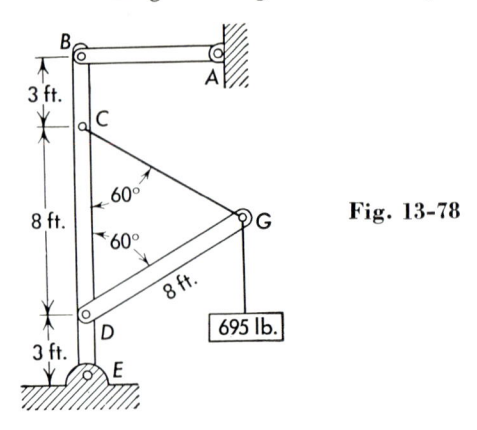

*13-108. A 436-lb$_f$ load is supported as shown in Fig. 13-79. Neglect the weight of the members and find the forces in members AD, BE, and the reaction at C.

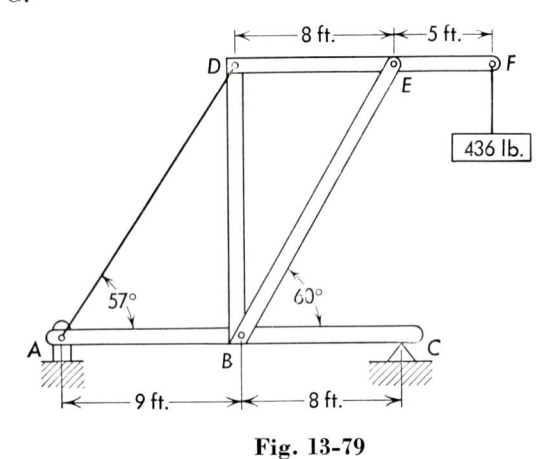

Fig. 13-79

*13-109. Find the tension T_1 in cable EF in Fig. 13-80, the tension T_2 in cable AD, and the reaction at C on the horizontal member CG.

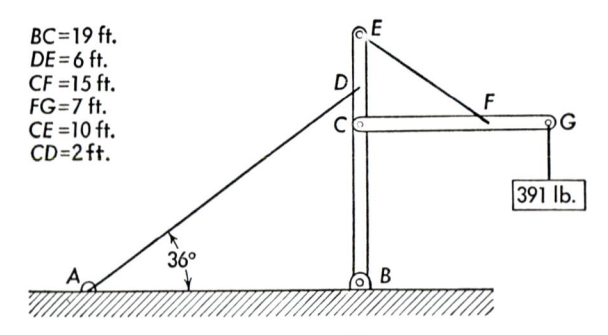

BC = 19 ft.
DE = 6 ft.
CF = 15 ft.
FG = 7 ft.
CE = 10 ft.
CD = 2 ft.

Fig. 13-80

Analysis in Static Mechanics

*13-110. A 15-ft ladder leans against the side of a smooth building in such a position that it makes an angle of 60° with the ground (horizontal). A man weighing 190 lb$_f$ stands on the ladder three-fourths of the way up the ladder. The bottom of the ladder is prevented from sliding by the ground. Find the horizontal and vertical components of the reaction at the foot of the ladder and the force between the ladder and the wall.

*13-111. Solve for the reactions at 1, 2, 3, 4, and 5 in Fig. 13-81. Weights: $A = 150$ lb$_f$, $B = 100$ lb$_f$, $C = 70$ lb$_f$, $D = 35$ lb$_f$. Diameters: $A = 26$ in., $B = 20$ in., $C = 15$ in., $D = 9$ in., and $\theta = 30°$.

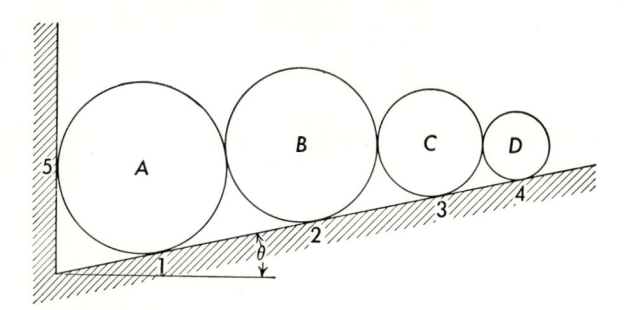

Fig. 13-81

Friction

When two bodies are in contact and one moves or tends to move with respect to another, there is always a force which opposes the relative motion between the surfaces. This force is called *friction*. The two principal kinds we shall consider are static and kinetic friction. The friction that appears between surfaces which tend to move with respect to each other but which actually have no motion is called *static friction*. The friction that is present between surfaces which are moving relative to each other is called *kinetic friction*. In many cases friction is essential for power transfer, for transportation, and even for such things as dams. Often, however, friction is not desirable, as in bearings, and we go to great trouble and expense to make friction as small as possible.

Friction always tends to equalize the motion between two surfaces and will therefore always be in a direction opposite to a force producing a sliding motion. From experiments it has been shown that as an applied force is gradually increased, the friction force increases up to some maximum determined by the nature of the surfaces in contact, and then falls slightly when motion between the surfaces begins.

The general behavior of frictional forces may be stated as follows:

Static friction is slightly greater than kinetic friction.

For non-lubricated surfaces the frictional forces are substantially independent of the area in contact.

308   *Engineering: Elementary Problem Analysis*

Courtesy The Black and Decker Manufacturing Company

Fig. 13-82. The evidence of friction is a common experience of everyday life. Here heat produced by friction of the grinding wheel against metal is shown by the shower of incandescent particles.

Friction will vary in proportion to the pressure between the surfaces and will depend upon the nature of the surfaces in contact.

The relation between the force pressing the surfaces together (normal force) and the corresponding frictional forces may be expressed as a ratio:

$$\frac{\text{Maximum frictional force } (F)}{\text{Normal force } (N)} = \text{coefficient of friction } (f)$$

To determine the value of the coefficient of friction f for two surfaces, we may perform a simple experiment as shown in Fig. 13-83.

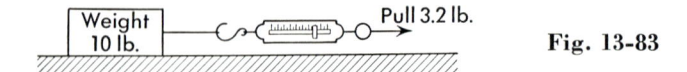

Fig. 13-83

Analysis in Static Mechanics

As we increase the pull on the spring balance we may observe that the block just tends to slip when we are pulling 3.2 lb$_f$, as shown on the spring balance. The coefficient of static friction will be

$$f_s = \frac{F}{N} = \frac{3.2}{10}$$
$$= 0.32$$

If we pull enough to start the block and move it at a constant velocity we may find the spring balance reads 2.9 lb$_f$. The coefficient of kinetic friction will be

$$f_k = \frac{F}{N} = \frac{2.9}{10}$$
$$= 0.29$$

The coefficient of friction as calculated in this form has no units. However, the coefficient may sometimes be expressed in pounds per ton-weight when applied to traction resistance of trains and vehicles.

Another way of determining the coefficient of friction is by using an inclined plane. If we set a block on a plane and then tilt the plane until the block starts sliding, the component of weight parallel to the plane will equal the frictional force, and the component of weight perpendicular to the plane will equal the normal resistance of the plane. A ratio can be set up to determine the value of the coefficient of friction.

Example: When a block of wood weighing 2 lb$_f$ (Fig. 13-84) is set on an inclined board and the angle the board makes with the horizontal is increased to 18°, the block is observed just to begin to slide. What is the coefficient of static friction between the block and the board?

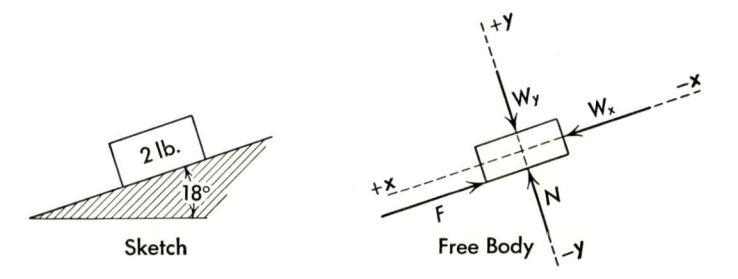

Sketch   Free Body

Fig. 13-84

In these problems the body is considered to be small enough so that the tendency of the forces to cause rotation may be disregarded. First calculate the components of the weight:

$$W_x = W \sin 18°$$
$$= (2)(0.309)$$
$$= 0.618 \text{ lb}_f$$
$$W_y = W \cos 18°$$
$$= (2)(0.95)$$
$$= 1.90 \text{ lb}_f$$

Just before slipping occurs, the block is in equilibrium.

$$\Sigma F_x = 0$$
$$\Sigma F_x = -F + W_x = 0$$
$$F = 0.618 \text{ lb}_f$$

and

$$\Sigma F_y = 0$$
$$\Sigma F_y = N - W_y = 0$$
$$N = 1.90 \text{ lb}_f$$
$$f_s = \frac{F}{N} = \frac{0.618}{1.90}$$
$$f_s = 0.325$$

It may be observed that if we take the resultant of the frictional force F and the normal force N at this time, their resultant will be a vertical force equal to the weight of the block.

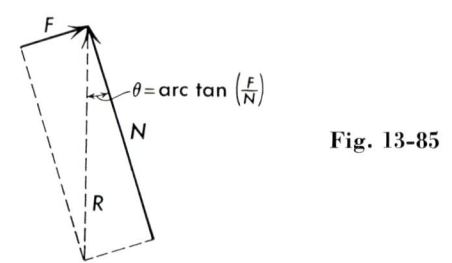

Fig. 13-85

Further we can show (Fig. 13-85) that the angle this resultant makes with the normal vector is an angle whose tangent is F/N. When an object is on an inclined plane and slipping is impending, an equilibrium condition exists such that the tangent of the angle of incline of the plane is equal to the coefficient of friction. This limiting angle is called the *angle of repose*. We may see then that if the angle of the plane is less than the angle of repose, the block will not slip of its own accord, and if the angle of the plane is greater than the angle of repose, the block will slip unless it is held by an outside force. In symbol form:

Analysis in Static Mechanics

$$f_s = \frac{F}{N} > \tan (\angle \text{ of incline}) \quad \text{(Body will not slip.)}$$

$$f_s = \frac{F}{N} < \tan (\angle \text{ of incline}) \quad \text{(Body will slip.)}$$

$$f_s = \frac{F}{N} = \tan (\angle \text{ of incline}) \quad \text{(Slipping impends: angle of repose.)}$$

Example: A crated machine weighing 3400 lb$_f$ (Fig. 13-86) is resting on wood skids and is being pulled up a wood ramp having a slope of 14 per cent by a cable parallel to the ramp. The coefficient of wood on wood may be

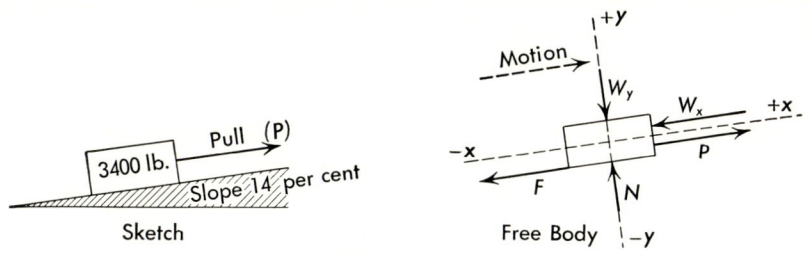

Fig. 13-86

taken as 0.4. What force is necessary in the cable to move the crated machine?

$$\text{Angle of plane } \theta = \arctan 0.14 = 8°$$
$$W_x = W \sin 8° = (3400)(0.1392)$$
$$= 474 \text{ lb}_f$$
$$W_y = W \cos 8° = (3400)(0.99)$$
$$= 3370 \text{ lb}_f$$
$$\Sigma F_y = 0$$

(This is true because there will be no motion in a direction perpendicular to the surface of the ramp.)

$$\Sigma F_y = N - W_y = 0$$
$$N = 3370 \text{ lb}_f$$
$$f = \frac{F}{N}$$
$$F = fN = (0.4)(3370)$$
$$= 1345 \text{ lb}_f$$
$$\Sigma F_x = 0$$

(This is true even if the object is moving, as long as there is no acceleration of the object.)

$$\Sigma F_x = P - W_x - F = 0$$
$$P = 474 + 1345$$
$$= 1819 \text{ lb}_f \quad \text{(tension in the cable)}$$

Problems on Friction

13-112. By experiment it is found that it requires 15 lb_f of force applied horizontally to slide a 300-lb_f cake of ice across a floor. What is the coefficient of friction between the ice and the floor?

13-113. A wooden box weighing 26.8 lb_f is moved at uniform speed across a level floor. If the coefficient of friction between the box and the floor is 0.31, how much horizontal force is applied?

13-114. A box weighing 208 lb_f is dragged across a level floor by a cable that makes an angle of 25° above the horizontal. The tension in the rope is 81 lb_f. What is the coefficient of sliding friction?

13-115. A box weighing 78 lb_f is sitting on an inclined plane having a slope of 37 per cent. What horizontal force will be necessary to prevent slipping down the plane when (a) friction is zero, (b) friction is 12.5 lb_f.

13-116. Find the horizontal force P required to keep a 134-lb_f box moving up a 23° incline at a constant velocity? Coefficient of friction is 0.22.

13-117. The coefficient of static friction between the driving wheels of a 350-ton locomotive and the rails is 0.24. What is the maximum drawbar pull that the locomotive can exert on the train before the wheels begin to spin?

13-118. A plane is inclined 21° to the horizontal and has a 42.0-lb_f weight resting on it. If the weight is on the verge of slipping, find the friction force and the coefficient of friction.

13-119. What force pulling at an angle of 28° above the floor will be needed to move a 22-ton engine base made of cast iron across a concrete floor at a uniform speed? ($f_k = 0.4$.) Would this force be more or less than the force required just to start the base to move? Give reasons for your answer.

13-120. A block weighing 530 lb_f is held on an inclined plane by a horizontal brace. Friction is 65 lb_f and the slope of the plane is 55 per cent. What force must the brace withstand?

13-121. A block weighing 58 lb_f is sitting on an inclined plane having a slope of 37 per cent. If a horizontal force of 8 lb_f will just prevent the block from slipping down the plane, what is the coefficient of friction between the block and the plane?

13-122. A pull of 60 lb_f acting 40° above the horizontal has a 159-lb_f weight on the verge of sliding along a horizontal plane. Find f_s between the weight and the plane.

13-123. A 55-lb_f box is sitting on an inclined chute which makes an angle of 38° with the horizontal. A force of 12 lb_f is acting parallel to the plane and keeps the 55-lb_f body from slipping. What must be the coefficient of friction to keep the body from slipping?

13-124. A 300-lb_f weight is being drawn along a plane at a uniform speed, and the coefficient of friction is 0.2. What pull P, 25° above the plane, is needed to maintain this speed?

Analysis in Static Mechanics

13-125. A pull of 185 lb_f on a rope that makes an angle of 25° above the horizontal puts a box on the verge of moving. The coefficient of friction between the box and the horizontal floor is 0.30. Find the weight of the box.

13-126. A 188-lb_f weight rests on an inclined plane where $f_s = 0.40$. What will be the angle between the plane and the horizontal that will cause the weight to be on the verge of slipping? What will be the angle if the weight is doubled and the coefficient of friction remains 0.40?

13-127. A box weighing 425 lb_f is pushed up a 21° plane, for which the coefficient of sliding friction is 0.35, by a force which makes an angle of 12° with the plane. What is the amount of force to produce uniform motion?

13-128. An 88-lb_f block is pulled 35 ft up a 17° inclined plane by a force acting at 15° above the plane. The coefficient of friction is 0.2. Solve for the force causing motion.

13-129. An automobile weighing 2900 lb_f is moving over wet pavement where the coefficient of friction between the tires and the pavement is 0.12. What is the greatest frictional force that may develop between the tires and the pavement when the brakes are applied, assuming that the weight is equally distributed on the four wheels?

*13-130. (a) In a certain experiment a wooden block weighing 1.35 lb_f has a string attached to it which passes over a pulley so that the string attached to the block is horizontal. When a weight of 6.4 oz is hung from the end of the string, the block is observed just to begin slipping. What is the coefficient of friction between the block and the surface?

(b) In the experiment described, a weight of 2 lb_f is placed on the block, and it is found that 15.88 oz hung from the end of the string is needed to cause the block just to start slipping. What is the coefficient of friction? What conclusion could you draw about the variation of the coefficient of friction with a change of weight from the results of these data?

*13-131. What tensile strength is required for a horizontal cable to drag a 3200-lb_f log over horizontal ground where the average coefficient of friction is 0.40? Assuming that the working load on the cable is one-eighth of the breaking strength, find from handbook data what size cable is required.

*13-132. The coefficient of friction between a tire and concrete pavement is 0.60. What is the greatest angle at which an inclined roadway could be built so that the tires would not slip? Why would this much grade not be practical?

*13-133. Two weights of 25.5 lb_f and 31.8 lb_f are fastened together by a string and placed on two inclined planes in the shape of an inverted V. The string passes over a frictionless pulley at the top of the planes, which make an angle of 60° with the horizontal. The coefficient of friction between the 25.5-lb_f weight and the plane is 0.22, and between the 31.8-lb_f weight and the plane it is 0.31. If the weights are released will they move? How much is the unbalanced force tending to move the weights?

*13-134. (a) A block weighing 383 lb$_f$ is sitting on an inclined plane having a slope of 41 per cent. What horizontal force will just prevent slipping down the plane when the coefficient of friction is 0.3?

(b) From data in (a): If it takes a horizontal force of 189 lb$_f$ to cause the block to begin slipping up the plane, what will be the new value of the coefficient of friction between the block and the plane?

chapter fourteen

Analysis in Motion

Courtesy Allis-Chalmers Manufacturing Company

The principles of angular motion must be used in the design of rotating machines such as this crushing roll which produces sand for use in building construction.

chapter fourteen

Analysis in Motion

Today one of our most important studies is the theory of motion and moving things. Moving people, animals, fast-moving trains, automobiles, jet airplanes, missiles, and space vehicles are all a part of our daily life. Moving pictures have replaced still pictures, and even our wars are most decidedly wars of motion.

Force is a push or pull that tends to change the shape or motion of a body. For our study, bodies will be considered to be rigid. Motion means *change of position* with reference to some other object or datum plane. An airplane passenger may be sitting still in relation to other passengers, but he is in rapid motion with reference to a farmer plowing in the field below him. The motion of the airplane may be uniform, if it has balanced forces acting on it, or accelerated if jet thrust, air resistance, and gravity do not balance each other.

Sometimes we speak of the motion of a body as *speed*, which refers to its rate of motion. The scientific term *velocity*, which refers *to rate of motion in a given direction*, is sometimes used incorrectly as a synonym for speed. Speed is the term used to designate the magnitude of velocity. Thus speed equals distance divided by time.

Examples: $\dfrac{\text{ft}}{\text{sec}}$, $\dfrac{\text{mile}}{\text{hr}}$, $\dfrac{\text{cm}}{\text{sec}}$, $\dfrac{\text{yd}}{\text{hr}}$. etc.

Velocity equals distance divided by time, all expressed in a given direction.

Examples: $\dfrac{\text{mile}}{\text{hr}}$ north, $\dfrac{\text{ft}}{\text{sec}}$ 30° east of north

Sir Isaac Newton, an English scientist, was the first to generalize the laws of forces and motions. His findings have been set forth in three laws as follows:

NEWTON'S FIRST LAW

A body at rest or in motion will continue either at rest or in motion in the same line and at the same speed unless acted on by some external unbalanced force.

Automobile wrecks result from this tendency of bodies to continue in the same line. The engine and brakes can act against this tendency and slow the car.

NEWTON'S SECOND LAW

When an external, unbalanced force F acts on a rigid particle of mass, the motion of the particle will be changed. The particle will be accelerated. Its

Analysis in Motion

rate of change in motion will be in the direction of the unbalanced force and proportional to it.

Acceleration is the *rate of change of velocity*. This is a measurement of how much slower (or faster) a body is traveling now than it was 1 sec ago. For example: An automobile may start from rest and accelerate to a velocity of 48 mph during an 8-sec period. This means that for every second that the engine acts on the car, there will be an increase in velocity of 6 mph per second, or 8.8 fps per second. The rate at which a body slows down is sometimes called *negative acceleration* or *deceleration*. Acceleration is measured as

$$\frac{\text{distance}}{(\text{time})^2}; \quad \text{i.e.;} \quad \frac{\text{ft}}{(\text{sec})^2}, \frac{\text{mile}}{(\text{hr})^2}, \frac{\text{ft}}{(\text{min})^2}, \text{etc.}$$

NEWTON'S THIRD LAW

When any force acts on a body, there is created an equal and opposite reaction.

The study of motion may become confusing if all situations are represented as mathematical expressions. For this reason our discussion here will be presented in diagram form. In this way the problems are pictorially represented, and the amount of memory work normally associated with the various relations is reduced.

THE SPEED-TIME DIAGRAM

In motion problems the total distance traveled is represented by the area which lies under the travel line of a speed-time diagram. For example, if an automobile travels at a uniform velocity of 30 mph for 30 min, it will cover a distance of 15 miles.

$$30\,\frac{\text{mile}}{\text{hr}} \times 30\,\text{min} \times \frac{1\,\text{hr}}{60\,\text{min}} = 15\,\text{miles}$$

This is shown graphically in Fig. 14-1.

If the speed is constant, then the distance traveled may be found by multiplying the ordinate value by the abscissa value. In this case the acceleration is zero, as indicated by the straight line *A-B* in Fig. 14-1.

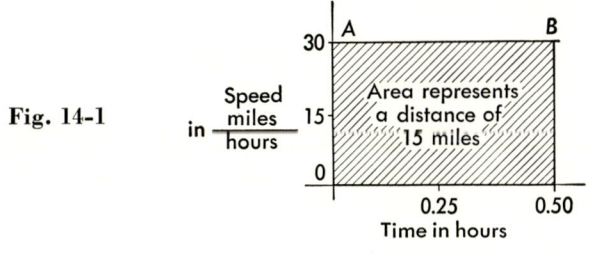

Fig. 14-1

Therefore, in order to work the above problem, the student need only to draw the speed-time diagram and then find the area under the travel line *A-B* by simple arithmetic.

Speed-time diagram principles may be summarized as follows:
1. The ordinate of the travel line at any instant will give the speed at that instant.
2. Abscissa values give the time consumed during travel.
3. The *area* under the travel line of the speed-time diagram gives the distance traveled during the time interval under consideration.
4. The slope of the travel line at any point gives the acceleration of the body at that point.

Slope may be defined as the *steepness* of a line and can be calculated by dividing the vertical rise by the corresponding horizontal distance.

Example: An automobile accelerates uniformly from a speed V_1 to a speed V_2 in time t (Fig. 14-2).

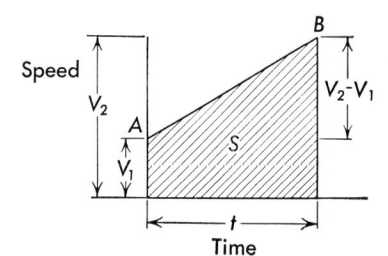

Fig. 14-2

A speed-time diagram of the stated problem is drawn. The total distance traveled during time t can be calculated by solving for the area under the line *A-B*. This area is a trapezoid, and by simple arithmetic:

$$\text{Area} = \tfrac{1}{2}h\,(b_1 + b_2) \quad \text{(see page 365)}$$

or

$$S = \tfrac{1}{2}t\,(V_1 + V_2) \quad \text{(from speed-time diagram)}$$

The acceleration has been defined as the slope of the travel line. An examination of Fig. 14-2 shows that this is also the change in velocity $(V_2 - V_1)$ divided by the time (t) that it took to make the change.

Stated algebraically we have

$$a = \frac{V_2 - V_1}{t} \quad \text{(slope of travel line)}$$

Example: An automobile starts from rest (Fig. 14-3) and accelerates uniformly to 30 mph in 11 sec. What is its acceleration? What distance was covered during the change in velocity?

$$\left(30\,\frac{\text{mile}}{\text{hr}}\right)\left(5280\,\frac{\text{ft}}{\text{mile}}\right)\left(\frac{1\text{ hr}}{3600\text{ sec}}\right) = 44\text{ ft/sec}$$

Analysis in Motion

(a) $$a = \frac{V_2 - V_1}{t} = \frac{44 \text{ ft/sec} - 0}{11 \text{ sec}}$$

$$a = 4 \frac{\text{ft}}{\text{sec} \times \text{sec}} \quad \text{or} \quad 4 \frac{\text{ft}}{(\text{sec})^2}$$

(b) $S = \frac{1}{2} Vt$ (Area of cross-hatched triangle)
$S = \frac{1}{2}(44 \text{ ft/sec})(11 \text{ sec}) = 242 \text{ ft}$

In some instances the term *average velocity* or *average speed* is used. Average velocity is not necessarily an average of the initial and final velocities.

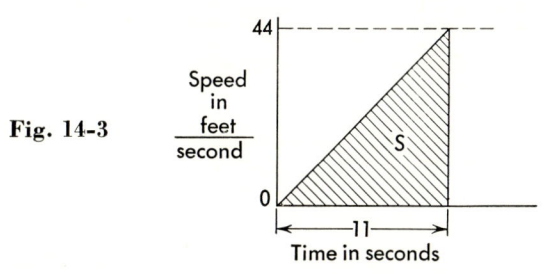

Fig. 14-3

It may be expressed as

$$\text{Average velocity} = \frac{\text{total distance traveled}}{\text{total time during travel}}$$

Example: An automobile traveled a total distance of 100 miles at an average speed of 50 mph. During the first 50 miles, the average speed of the automobile was 60 mph. What was the average speed for the last 50 miles?

$$\text{Average speed for trip} = \frac{\text{total distance}}{\text{total time}}$$

$$\text{Total time } (t) = \frac{100 \text{ mile}}{50 \text{ mile/hr}} = 2 \text{ hr}$$

For the first 50 miles:

$$\text{Time} = \frac{50 \text{ mile}}{60 \text{ mile/hr}} = 0.833 \text{ hr}$$

Time remaining = 2 hr − 0.833 hr = 1.167 hr

For the last 50 miles:

$$\text{Average speed} = \frac{50 \text{ mile}}{1.167 \text{ hr}} = 42.8 \text{ mile/hr}$$

Many of the situations encountered in linear motion can be solved readily by the use of the speed-time diagram. Some problems involve varied speeds and accelerations during any period under consideration. These changes should be clearly indicated on the speed-time diagram.

Example: A train (Fig. 14-4) travels 10 miles at a speed of 50 mph and then uniformly increases its speed to 65 mph during a 30-min period. The train continues at this speed for 1 hr before being uniformly slowed to a stop with a deceleration of 650 mph per hour. Find (a) stopping time, (b) distance traveled during acceleration, (c) total time, (d) total distance traveled.

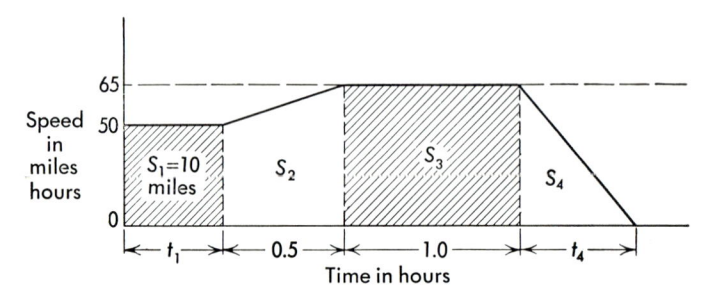

Fig. 14-4

Solution

(a)
$$(a) = \frac{V_2 - V_1}{t} \text{ (slope of travel line as train stops)}$$

$$-650 \text{ mile/(hr)}^2 = \frac{0 - 65 \text{ mile/hr}}{t_4 \text{ hr}}$$

$$t_4 = 0.10 \text{ hr}$$

(b)
$$S = \left(\frac{V_1 + V_2}{2}\right) t$$

$$S_2 = \tfrac{1}{2} \times 0.5 \text{ hr } (50 \text{ miles/hr} + 65 \text{ miles/hr})$$
$$S_2 = 28.75 \text{ miles}$$

(c)
$$t = \frac{S}{V_{avg}}$$

$$t_1 = \frac{10 \text{ miles}}{50 \text{ miles/hr}} = 0.20 \text{ hr}$$

$$\text{Total time} = t_1 + t_2 + t_3 + t_4$$
$$= 0.20 + 0.50 + 1.0 + 0.10$$
$$= 1.8 \text{ hr}$$

(d)
$$S = (V_{avg})(t)$$
$$S_3 = 65 \text{ miles/hr} \times 1 \text{ hr} = 65 \text{ miles}$$

$$S = \left(\frac{V_1 + V_2}{2}\right) t$$

$$S_4 = \tfrac{1}{2}(65 \text{ miles/hr} + 0) \, 0.10 \text{ hr}$$
$$S_4 = \frac{6.5 \text{ miles}}{2} = 3.25 \text{ miles}$$

$$\text{Total distance} = S_1 + S_2 + S_3 + S_4$$
$$= 10 + 28.78 + 65 + 3.25$$
$$= 107.03 \text{ miles}$$

Analysis in Motion 321

Problems on Linear Velocities and Accelerations

14-1. A ball is thrown vertically upward, and in due course of time it falls back to the place of beginning. Starting from the time the ball leaves the hand, sketch a speed time diagram which shows the motion involved. Add such explanation as you deem necessary.

*14-2. An airplane travels from point A to point B and returns, all at an air speed of 200 mph. If a 50-mph wind blows from point A to B during the entire trip, what was the average ground speed?

14-3. A body moving with a constant acceleration of 16 fps per second passes an observation post with a velocity of 25 fps. (a) What will be its speed in inches per second after 1 min? (b) How far will it have gone in 1 min?

14-4. A train moves out from a dead stop at the station and in 12 min has uniformly increased its speed to 60 mph. It travels at this speed for 15 min and then uniformly decelerates to a stop in 1.5 miles. (a) Draw a speed-time diagram to show the entire movement. (b) Find the acceleration in the first 12-min period. (c) Find the total distance traveled. (d) Find the total time consumed.

14-5. A truck passes station A with a speed of 10 mph and increases its speed to 45 mph in 1.8 min. At this time its speed becomes constant and remains so for 8 min. The speed is then decreased to zero in 2 min. (a) Draw a speed-time diagram for the truck. (b) What total distance does the truck travel? (c) What is the acceleration in the first 1.8 min? (d) What is the deceleration in the last 2 min?

14-6. An electric train running at 60 mph is brought to a stop in 321 yd. Find (a) average speed of the train in stopping, (b) time in minutes required to stop the train.

14-7. An airplane accelerates uniformly to a speed of 126 fps, using 903 ft of runway. If the airplane started from rest, find (a) acceleration, (b) time in seconds to travel the 903 ft.

14-8. Solve for the acceleration in feet per second per second of an automobile that is uniformly accelerated from rest to 52 mph in ¼ mile. How long did it require in seconds to gain this speed? If the acceleration is constant, how much longer will it be before the automobile is traveling 65 mph?

*14-9. A car having an initial speed of 15 mph increases its speed uniformly at the rate of 5.5 fps per second for a distance of 295 ft. (a) What will be its final speed? (b) How long will it require to cover this distance?

14-10. A car traveling at 45 mph meets a train which is moving 33 mph. The time required for the car to pass the train is 18 sec. What is the length of the train in feet?

322   *Engineering: Elementary Problem Analysis*

14-11. A mail plane travels 10.3 miles at a speed of 151 mph, then accelerates uniformly for 5 min to a speed of 229 mph and travels at this speed for 37 miles. Find (a) acceleration in feet per second per second, (b) total time, (c) total distance.

*14-12. An airplane starting from rest travels 600 ft before the wheels leave the ground. Its acceleration is 7.7 ft/sec per second. What was its speed at the time the wheels left the ground? How many seconds were required for it to take off?

14-13. An automobile is climbing a 20 per cent grade and has an initial speed of 27 mph and a final speed of 60 mph. If the time is 38 sec, find (a) acceleration in feet per second per second up the grade, (b) distance it moves up the grade.

14-14. An automobile which has a speed of 80 mph is decelerated at the rate of 20 ft/sec² for 5 sec. What is the speed at the end of the 5 sec, and how far did the car travel in this time?

14-15. A factory cart traveling at a speed of 16 mph is given a constant acceleration of 90 fps per minute. (a) What will be its speed at the end of 10 sec? (b) How far will the automobile travel in the 10 sec?

*14-16. A 3300-lb automobile is traveling up a steep hill, whose grade is 22 per cent, at a rate of 31 mph when the power is shut off and the car is allowed to coast. Because of the loose gravel on the hill, the car comes to a stop in a distance of 125 ft. After traveling 75 ft, what will be the speed of the car?

14-17. A ball is dropped from the top of a tower 86 ft high. If its acceleration is 32.2 ft/sec², (a) how long does it take it to reach the ground, (b) with what speed does it strike the ground?

14-18. An elevator goes down at the rate of 9 mph. If the elevator starts from rest, and the maximum permissible acceleration is 22 fps per second, how many feet are required for the elevator to attain maximum speed? Find the time in seconds required to attain this speed.

14-19. As a train reaches the city limits, it reduces its speed uniformly from 60 mph to 18 mph in a distance of 1/4 mile. It continues at 18 mph for 6 min and as it leaves the city limits, it again increases its speed to 40 mph in 2½ min. Find (a) the deceleration while train is slowing down, (b) the acceleration during the last 2½ min, (c) the total distance traveled.

*14-20. An automobile is traveling at 35 mph when the driver sees a cow crossing the highway ahead. If 0.9 sec is allowed for reaction time before the brakes take effect, how far away was the cow when the driver first saw her if the car stopped just as it touched the cow, and the time in decelerating was 4 sec?

*14-21. A train running on a straight level track at 60 mph suddenly detaches its caboose, which decelerates uniformly to a stop. After traveling

Analysis in Motion

2 miles, the brakeman notices the accident, and he stops the train uniformly in 50 sec. At the instant the train stops, the caboose stops. What distance in feet did the train have to back up in order to hook on to the caboose?

*14-22. An automobile crashes into a building. The driver contends that he was not exceeding a 30-mph speed limit when he applied the brakes. If the skid marks of the tires extend for 176 ft and the stopping time was 3 sec, would you agree that the driver was telling the truth?

*14-23. The speed of a ship traveling at the rate of 16 knots is uniformly retarded to 5 knots in a distance of 1 statute mile. If the rate of retardation continues constant, (a) what remaining time in minutes will be required to bring the ship to rest? (b) How many feet will it have traveled from the point where the speed is 16 knots?

*14-24. A train and an automobile are passing in opposite directions. When the automobile passes the front of the train, the automobile has a speed of 33 mph and the train has a speed of 26 mph. When the automobile passes the rear of the train, the speed of the train is 45 mph and that of the automobile is 20 mph. If the train is 4000 ft long, find the time in seconds for the two to pass.

*14-25. A man in a car travels a certain distance at an average speed of 19 mph. After he arrives, he turns around and returns over the same route at an average speed of 13 mph. What was the man's average speed for the round trip?

*14-26. An airplane travels from Stephenville to Fort Worth (65 miles) and returns with an over-all average ground speed of 196 mph. If there were a 20-mph tailwind on the trip out and a 20-mph headwind on the return trip, what was the air speed of the airplane during the trip? (Assume that the air speed for the trip was constant.)

*14-27. An airplane flies from Fort Worth to Amarillo and returns (325 miles each way) at an air speed of 276 mph. If a wind from the northwest (i.e., from Amarillo to Fort Worth) is blowing at 29.6 mph, what is the average ground speed for the return trip? What is the average ground speed for the round trip?

*14-28. A rock is dropped into a well. The sound of impact is heard 3 sec after the rock is dropped. Sound travels 1100 ft/sec. What was the depth of the well?

*14-29. Several small steel balls fall from a tall building at a uniform rate of three every second. After the second ball has fallen for 3 1/2 sec, what distance in inches separates it and the ball following it? What distance separates it and the ball preceding it?

*14-30. A 152-lb_f rocket sled at the China Lake Naval Ordnance Test Station achieved a maximum speed of 2575.1 miles/hr in 1.90 sec during a test on the 4 mile long monorail track. (a) Assuming a uniform change in speed, what was the average acceleration? (b) What was the distance traveled in 1.90 sec? During this test, recording instruments showed that the top speed was attained in a distance of 3050 ft. (c) Show by a simple freehand graph how the computed speed varied with distance and how the actual speed probably varied with distance. (Let the X co-ordinate represent distance.)

ANGULAR MOTION

The motion we have just studied was linear motion and concerned the movement of a body or particle in straight-line travel. Many of our machines, however, have parts that do not travel in straight-line motion. For example, flywheels, fan blades, turbine rotors, and motor armatures all travel in curved paths or with angular motion. For purposes of study here, all bodies having angular motion will be considered to be rotating about a fixed center. While rotating about this fixed center, there may be a *speeding up* or *slowing down* of the body.

Angular distance (usually designated by some Greek letter such as θ, ϕ, β, etc.) can be measured in degrees, radians, or revolutions. A radian is defined as a central angle subtended by an arc whose length is equal to the radius of the circle.

$$1 \text{ revolution} = 360°$$
$$1 \text{ revolution} = 2\pi \text{ radians}$$
$$1 \text{ radian} = 57.3° \text{ (approximately)}$$

Example: Point A in Fig. 14-5 travels through an angular distance θ while moving to position B. $\theta = 120°$, $\theta = 0.333$ revolutions, $\theta = 2.095$ radians

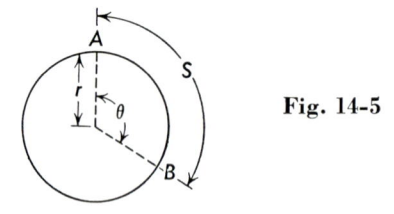

Fig. 14-5

Time is measured in the same units as before, i.e., seconds, hours, days, etc. Thus angular velocity, which is an angular distance divided by time, may have such units as radian per second; revolution per minute, degrees per second, etc. Angular velocity is usually designated by the Greek letter ω (omega).

Analysis in Motion

Angular acceleration can be found by solving for the slope of the travel line as in linear motion. As in linear motion we must divide the change in angular speed by the time it took to make the change. Problems are worked as before, using the speed-time diagram where applicable. In addition to angular distance being represented by the symbol θ, angular speed, which is θ/t, is usually represented by the symbol ω (omega). Also angular acceleration, represented by α (alpha), is ω/t.

There is a definite relation between angular motion and linear motion. Let us consider a point on the rim of a flywheel. In one revolution the point will travel through an angular distance of 2π radians or a linear distance of $2\pi r$ linear units. All points on a body will travel through the same angular distance during a period of time, but their linear speeds will depend on the radii to the points under consideration. Therefore linear distance is equal to angular distance in radians multiplied by the radius. Linear speed is found by multiplying the angular speed by the radius.

Length of arc:
$$S = r\theta$$

where θ is measured in radians.

Linear speed:
$$V = r\omega$$

where ω is measured in radians per unit of time.

Linear acceleration:
$$a = r\alpha$$

where α is measured in radians per unit of (time)^2

Example: Point A in Fig. 14-6 is located on the outside of a flywheel 6 ft in diameter. Point B is located on the inside of the rim 1 ft from point A.

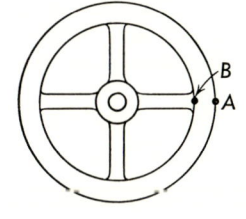

Fig. 14-6

If the flywheel travels at 300 rpm for 10 min, find (a) total angular distance traveled by point B in radians, (b) linear speed of point B in ft/min, (c) linear distance traveled by point A in miles.

326 Engineering: Elementary Problem Analysis

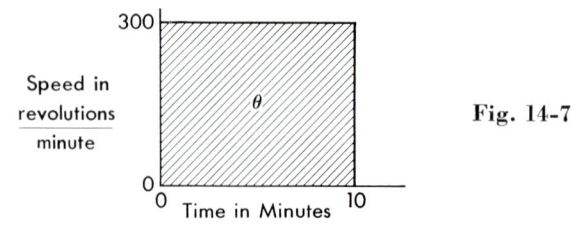

Fig. 14-7

Solution: Refer to Fig. 14-7.

a. $\theta = (300 \text{ rev/min})(10 \text{ min}) = 3000 \text{ rev}$
   $\theta = (3000 \text{ rev})(2\pi \text{ rad*/rev}) = \underline{\underline{18,900 \text{ rad}}}$

b. $V = r\omega$
   $V = (2 \text{ ft/rad})[300 \text{ rev/min}(2\pi \text{ rad/rev})] = \underline{\underline{3780 \text{ ft/min}}}$

c. $S = r\theta$
   $S = (3 \text{ ft/rad})(18,900 \text{ rad})$
   $S = \underline{\underline{56,700 \text{ ft, or } 10.75 \text{ miles}}}$

Example: The flywheel of a gasoline engine (Fig. 14-8) changes its angular velocity from 150 rpm to 300 rpm during a 5-min period. Solve (a) for the total distance traveled by a point on the rim of the flywheel, and (b) the angular acceleration of the point during this change.

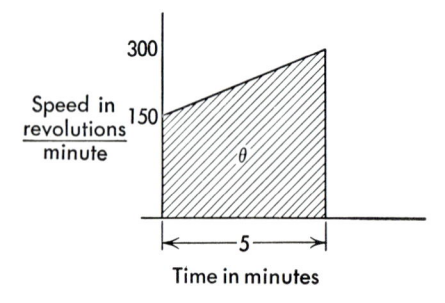

Fig. 14-8

Solution

(a) θ = travel during the change
θ = area of the speed-time diagram under the travel line
$\theta = \left(\dfrac{\omega_1 + \omega_2}{2}\right) t$
$\theta = 5 \text{ min} \left[\dfrac{150 \text{ rev/min} + 300 \text{ rev/min}}{2}\right]$
$\theta = (5 \text{ min})(225 \text{ rev/min})$
$\theta = \underline{\underline{1125 \text{ revolution}}}$

---

* *Radian* is a name that is given to a ratio, and it is a sterile value. However, in order to be able to show the name in the answer, it has been carried through this analysis as a name rather than as a unit.

Analysis in Motion

(b) α = angular acceleration
        α = slope of the travel line

$$\alpha = \frac{\omega_2 - \omega_1}{t}$$

$$\alpha = \frac{300 \text{ rev/min} - 150 \text{ rev/min}}{5 \text{ min}}$$

$$\alpha = \underline{\underline{30 \text{ rev/min}^2}}$$

Problems on Angular Velocities and Accelerations

14-31. While going around a circular curve of 3000-ft radius, a train slows down from 36 to 13 mph in a distance of 850 ft. Find the angular distance covered in degrees.

14-32. Two pulleys, 8 in. and 17 in. in diameter, are 10 ft apart on centers, and the 17-in. pulley runs 400 rev/min. How many radians per second does the small pulley turn?

14-33. Given $t = 5$ sec; $\omega_1 = 50$ rev/sec; and $\omega_2 = 15$ radian per second. Draw a speed-time diagram for the motion involved, calibrating both ordinate and abscissa. Is the angular acceleration positive or negative? Why?

14-34. If an automobile engine is accelerated from 1090 to 4600 rpm in 3.98 sec, what is the angular acceleration of the crankshaft? What is the distance traversed in feet by a point on the circumference of the 10-in. flywheel?

14-35. A locomotive, having drive wheels 6 ft in diameter, is traveling at the rate of 58 mph. What are the revolutions per minute of the drive wheels?

14-36. Two wheels rolling together without slipping have a velocity ratio of 3 to 1. The driver, which is the smaller of the two, is 9 in. in diameter, and turns at 50 rpm. (a) What is the speed in feet per second at a point on the surface of the wheels? (b) What is the angular speed of the larger wheel? (c) What is the diameter of the larger wheel?

14-37. A belt passes around a 15-in. pulley and a 3-ft pulley. If the 15-in. pulley revolves at the rate of 200 rpm, (a) what is the angular speed of the 15-in. pulley in radians per second? (b) What is the angular speed of the 3-ft pulley in radians per second? (c) What is the speed of the belt in feet per second?

14-38. A 2-ft diameter motor armature has an initial rotational speed of 186 rpm and increases this to 1500 rpm over an angular distance of 519 radians. Find (a) time in seconds, (b) angular acceleration in radians per second per second.

14-39. A belt passes around an 18-in. shaft and a 4-ft pulley. If the shaft revolves at the rate of 300 rpm, find (a) angular speed of shaft in radians per second, (b) angular speed of pulley in radians per second, (c) speed of belt in feet per second.

14-40. An elevator hoisting drum is decelerating at the rate of 15 rpm per minute. If the drum is brought to rest in 9 min, find (a) total number of revolutions, (b) the initial speed in radians per second.

*14-41. A 19-in. diameter pulley is connected with a 3 1/2 ft diameter pulley by an open belt. Their respective shafts are parallel and 7 ft apart. The small pulley rotates at 95 rpm. Find (a) the length of the belt in feet, (b) the speed of the belt in feet per minute, (c) the angular speed of the large pulley in radians per second.

*14-42. A cylindrical drum 2 1/2 ft in diameter is rotated from rest on its axis by pulling a rope wound around it. If the linear acceleration of a point on the rope is 36.9 fps per second, what will be the angular speed in (a) revolutions per minute at the end of 6 sec, (b) radians per second, (c) how many turns will it have made during the 6 sec?

*14-43. The rotor of a steam turbine is 5 ft 4¾ in. in diameter and is turning at the rate of 1850 rpm when the steam supply is cut off. If it takes the rotor 26 min and 47 sec to come to rest, find (a) the angular deceleration of the shaft in revolutions per minute per second, (b) the angular distance in radians passed through by the shaft before stopping, (c) the average linear velocity of a point on the circumference.

*14-44. A locomotive travels in the path of a curve whose radius is 900 ft. The distance traveled in a given time is subtended by a central angle of 37°35'. If the radius of the drivers is 2 ft 4 7/8 in., the speed around the curve is constant, and the time taken on the curve is 12.3 sec. Find (a) the speed of the locomotive in miles per hour, (b) the angular speed of the locomotive around the curve in radians per second.

*14-45. An engine has a flywheel 49 in. in diameter to which a pulley 16 in. in diameter is attached. The speed of the engine flywheel is 180 rpm. The engine pulley is connected by a belt to a pump. Assume that the belt does not slip, and neglect the thickness of the belt. Find (a) the angular speed of the pulley in revolutions per minute, (b) the angular speed in radians per second; (c) what is the linear speed of the belt in feet per minute? (d) What is the linear speed of a point on the rim of the flywheel in feet per minute? (e) If the pump pulley is to turn 105 rpm, what should be its diameter in feet?

*14-46. A 1/40-hp electric motor widely used to power cash registers has a guaranteed average acceleration of 170,000 radians per second per second. How long will it take to reach its rated speed of 3200 rpm? With the X co-ordinate representing time, draw a freehand graph of the variation of computed speed with time and show on the same axes how the actual speed probably varies with time.

chapter fifteen

Analysis in Work, Power, and Energy

Courtesy Allis-Chalmers Manufacturing Company

A 120/160/200-mva, 345,000-volt, single-phase autotransformer. Large power transformers are a necessary part of our modern electrical transmission and distribution system.

chapter fifteen

Analysis in Work, Power, and Energy

Many words used in physics and engineering have meanings which differ from their common, nontechnical meanings in everyday use. A word such as *work* is an example of this confusion of meanings, as reference to any dictionary will show. In the common use of the word *work*, it may mean anything from merely a thinking process to the hardest sort of physical exertion. It has required the efforts of science for over two hundred years to clear up confusion regarding the use of *work* in technical writings, and the handicap of terms loosely used or misused still is a serious factor in concise scientific notations.

Work is defined for our purposes as the product of a force F and a distance S, both measured along the same line. From this definition we can see that a force does work on a body when it acts against a resisting force to produce motion of the body. If there is no motion as a result of an applied force, no work is done.

A person who holds a heavy weight soon gets tired and may feel that he has done hard work. Measured in terms of fatigue, he has done work, but fatigue is not a part of our scientific definition of work. If the distance the weight has moved is zero, the work done is zero. While the ideas advanced regarding work may not agree with the everyday usage of the word *work*, the student is encouraged to accept with an open mind the definition given above, which will be the basis of many definitions of other terms.

The units of work will be the product of a unit of force and a unit of length. For example, in English units, a common measure of work is the foot-pound. One foot-pound of work is done when a force of 1 lb_f is exerted in moving an object through a distance of 1 ft in the direction of the force. In the event that force is not in the same direction that distance is measured, work can be calculated by using the component of force in the same direction as distance is measured.

Example: A constant force of 50 lb_f (Fig. 15-1), acting downward at an angle of 30° with the horizontal, moves a box 10 ft across a floor. How much work is done?

Analysis: In the preceding example, only a portion of the 50-lb_f force was effective in moving the box from position A to position B. This effective portion of the 50-lb_f force was evidently (50) (cos 30°) = 43.3 lb_f.

The vertical component (50)(sin 30°) did not produce any motion but served only to press the box against the floor.

Analysis in Work, Power, and Energy

F = 50 lb.

Position A   Position B

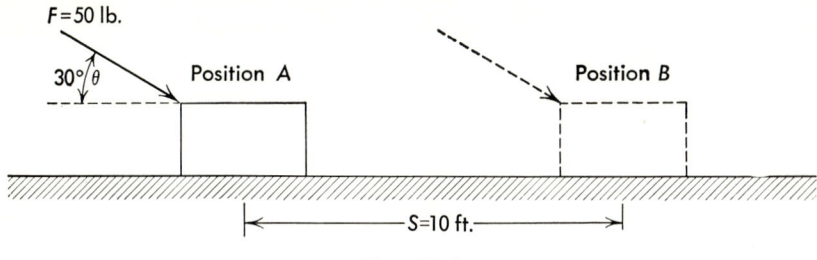

S = 10 ft.

Fig. 15-1

Solution: Work = $(F \cos \theta)(S)$
= $(50 \text{ lb}_f)(\cos 30°)(10 \text{ ft})$
= 433 ft-lb$_f$

Example: A man carries a precision gauge weighing 38.5 lb$_f$ up a flight of stairs that has a rise of 8 in. and a tread of 12 in. He climbs at the rate of two steps per second. How much work is done carrying the gauge up a stairway of thirty-one steps?

Analysis: Since we are attempting to find only the work done on the gauge, we shall ignore the work done in lifting the man's weight. The work done, then, will be the weight lifted times the vertical height. The length of time to move the gauge does not enter into the computation for work.

Solution: Vertical height = $\frac{(8)(31)}{12}$ = 20.65 ft

Work = $(F)(D)$
= $(38.5)(20.65)$
= 795 ft-lb$_f$

Example: A cable (Fig. 15-2) is pulling a wooden crate of electronic computer parts, which weighs 1380 lb$_f$, up a ramp 30.5 ft long that rises to the

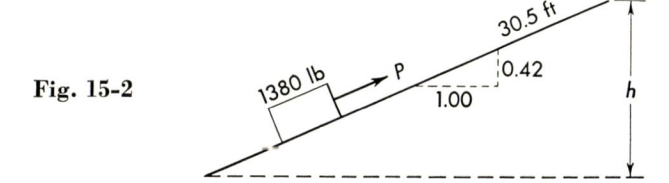

Fig. 15-2

second floor of a building at the rate of 0.42 ft vertically per foot horizontally. (a) If the cable is pulling parallel to the ramp, what work is done on the crate? (b) If the friction force between the crate and the ramp is 120 lb$_f$, what work is done in moving the crate up the ramp?

Analysis: (a) The work done on the crate is its weight times the vertical distance moved.
(b) The work done by the cable is the product of the pull of the cable and the distance through which this pull or force is exerted.

Solution: (a) The ramp makes an angle of arctan 0.42, or 22.8°, with the horizontal (see Fig. 15-2).

$$h = (\sin 22.8°)(30.5)$$
$$= 11.82 \text{ ft}$$
$$\text{Work} = (F)(h)$$
$$= (1380)(11.82)$$
$$= 16{,}310 \text{ ft-lb}_f$$

(b) The pull of the cable is the sum of the friction force and the component of the weight of the crate parallel to the ramp (see Fig. 15-3).

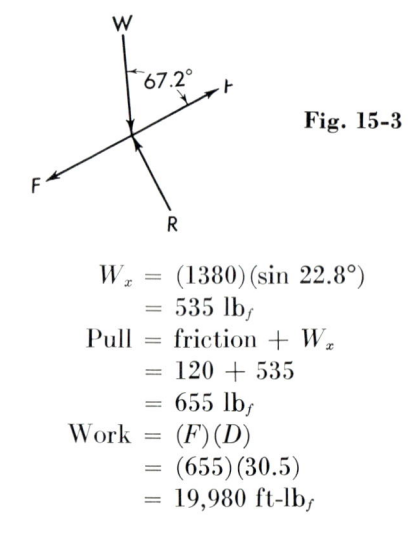

Fig. 15-3

$$W_x = (1380)(\sin 22.8°)$$
$$= 535 \text{ lb}_f$$
$$\text{Pull} = \text{friction} + W_x$$
$$= 120 + 535$$
$$= 655 \text{ lb}_f$$
$$\text{Work} = (F)(D)$$
$$= (655)(30.5)$$
$$= 19{,}980 \text{ ft-lb}_f$$

Problems on Work

15-1. It requires a constant horizontal force of 38 lb$_f$ to move a 450-lb$_f$ layout table across the level floor of a machine shop. How much work is done in moving the table 33 ft?

15-2. An elevator and its load weigh 3.75 tons. How much work is done in lifting the loaded elevator 272 ft vertically?

15-3. A skip hoist lifts a load of bricks to the third floor of a building under construction. The cable exerts an average pull of 2900 lb$_f$ for a distance of 28.8 ft. How much work is done in lifting the loaded hoist?

Analysis in Work, Power, and Energy

15-4. A man exerts an average force of 30 lb$_f$ along the handle of a lawn mower. The handle makes an angle of 44° with the ground. How much work is done in moving the lawn mower 100 ft across the lawn?

15-5. A tractor is towing a loaded wagon weighing 3300 lb$_f$ over level ground, and the average tension in the tow cable is 262 lb$_f$. What work is done by the cable in moving the wagon 1/4 mile?

15-6. (a) A locomotive is pulling a string of 40 box cars, each weighing 46 tons, at a constant speed of 35 mph on a stretch of level track. The frictional resistance of the train is 8 lb$_f$ per ton weight. How much work is done by the drawbar pull of the engine in moving the train 1 mile? (b) If the train is moving up a constant grade of 1½ per cent, how much work is done by the drawbar pull of the engine in moving the train 1 mile?

15-7. A man carries a box weighing 35 lb$_f$ up a stairway of seventeen steps. Each step is 8 in. high and 12 in. wide. How much work does he do in carrying the box up the stairway?

15-8. A hoist and its load weigh 1509 lb$_f$. What total work will be done in lifting the loaded hoist 126 ft if 25 per cent of the total work is used to overcome friction?

15-9. A box weighing 122 lb$_f$ is pulled up an inclined track, which makes an angle of 38° with the horizontal, by a cable parallel to the track. Neglecting friction, how much work is done in pulling the box 19 ft 4 in. up the track at uniform speed?

15-10. A shipping case filled with machined steel gears weighs 188 lb$_f$. It is being dragged across the floor by a rope which makes an angle of 34° with the horizontal. The tension in the rope is 49 lb$_f$ while the box is being moved a distance of 22 ft. How much work is done?

15-11. A flagpole is 72 ft high and has a pulley fixed at the top. A painter pulls himself up in a sling by means of a rope passing over the pulley. The painter and his equipment weigh 160 lb$_f$. How much work will he do in pulling himself to the top of the pole?

15-12. An automobile engine weighing 557 lb$_f$ is lifted from the floor to a bench 31 in. high by means of a block and tackle. How much work is done if 10 per cent of the work is used to overcome friction?

15-13. A car weighs 3200 lb$_f$ and is to be towed ¼ mile up a 5 per cent grade. If the average value of friction is 85 lb$_f$, how much work is done?

15-14. A brick chimney is cylindrical and is 11.5 ft outside diameter with walls 1.5 ft thick and is 78 ft high. If the brick and mortar weigh 110 lb$_f$ per cubic foot what work against gravity is done in lifting the brick and mortar into place during the building of the chimney?

15-15. A hoist and load weighing 3.24 tons is lifted by means of a cable which passes around a 4-ft diameter drum. If the drum makes 37.8 revolutions in lifting the hoist and load, what work is done in raising the hoist?

15-16. An elevated tank at a chemical plant is in the shape of a cylinder. It is 15.6 ft deep and holds 4320 gal. The flat bottom is 30 ft above a ground level reservoir. (a) How much work is done in filling the tank if the water is pumped in at the bottom of the tank? (b) How much work would be done by the pump if the water were pumped in through a pipe entering at the top of the tank?

15-17. A belt passes over a pulley which is 38 in. in diameter. If the difference in tension on the two sides of the belt is 88 lb_f and the pulley is turning 530 rpm, how much work is done per minute by the belt?

15-18. A rope is wrapped around a drum 6 1/2 in. in diameter. A crank handle 14 in. long is connected to the shaft carrying the drum. How much work would be done in lifting a weight of 175 lb_f a vertical distance of 55 ft? If the length of the crank handle is increased to 24 in., what will be the work done in lifting the weight as before?

15-19. The threads on a jack screw have a pitch of 0.75 in. Neglecting friction, what average force is necessary on the end of a rod having an effective length of 16 in. in order to raise a load of 7.4 tons a distance of 6 in.?

15-20. A log is being dragged over level ground by a cable which makes an angle of 19° with the ground. If the average tension in the cable is 775 lb_f, what work is done on the log in moving it 350 yd?

15-21. A locomotive exerts a constant draw bar pull of 37,000 lb_f on a train whose weight is 2000 tons. Rolling frictional resistance is 15 lb_f per ton weight. What work is done in moving the train 1 mile? What work is done per mile in overcoming rolling friction?

15-22. Water is pumped against a constant head of 22 ft at the rate of 510 gal per minute. How much work is done each minute in pumping the water?

15-23. An elevated water storage tank has cylindrical sides and a hemispherical bottom. The tank is 26.8 ft in diameter, and the cylindrical part is 66.3 ft high. A pump is located 57.6 ft below the hemispherical bottom. If the tank is filled from the top, what work is necessary to fill it with water? If the hemispherical part of the tank is already filled, and water is pumped in from the bottom, how much work is done in filling the cylindrical part of the tank?

15-24. A man exerts a force of 26 lb_f along the handle of a lawn mower. If the handle makes an angle of 57° with the ground, what work will he do in moving the lawn mower 100 ft over level ground?

15-25. A man weighing 188 lb_f seated in a sling is lifted up the side of a building. If he lifts himself by pulling down on the rope passing over the pulley, how much work does he do in lifting himself 27 ft above the ground? How much work would be done by a group of men standing on the ground and pulling the rope to lift him 27 ft?

Analysis in Work, Power, and Energy 335

POWER

It is apparent that no interval of time was mentioned in our previous definition of work. In our modern civilization we frequently are as interested in the time of doing work as we are in getting the work done. For this reason the term *power* is introduced, which is the time rate of doing work.

In symbol form:

$$\text{Power} = \frac{\text{work}}{\text{time}}; \quad P = \frac{W}{T}$$

or it may be expressed as

$$\text{Power} = (\text{force})(\text{velocity}); \quad P = FV$$

If a pile of bricks is to be moved from the ground to the third floor of a building, the job may be accomplished by moving one brick at a time, ten bricks at a time, or the whole pile of bricks at once. The work done in any case is the same and is the product of the weight of the pile of bricks and the vertical distance through which the pile is moved. However, the time that will be taken will probably vary in each case, as will the capabilities of the lifting mechanism. In order to obtain an indication of the rate at which work can be done, we use the term *power*, which is a measure of how fast a force can move through a given distance.

The units of power in any system can be found by dividing work units by time units. In the FPS Gravitational system, power may be expressed as *foot-pounds per second*, or *foot-pounds per minute*. Since the days of James Watt and his steam engine, the horsepower is a common unit of power and is numerically equal to 550 ft-lb$_f$ per second or 33,000 ft-lb$_f$ per minute. Another unit of power frequently used is the watt or kilowatt. There are 746 watts in 1 horsepower (hp).

$$\begin{aligned} 1 \text{ hp} &= 550 \text{ ft-lb}_f/\text{sec} \\ &= 33{,}000 \text{ ft-lb}_f/\text{min} \\ &= 746 \text{ watts} \\ &= 0.746 \text{ kw} \end{aligned}$$

Example: A box weighing 1100 lb$_f$ (Fig. 15-4) is lifted 15 ft in 3 sec. How much power is necessary?

Analysis

$$\text{Power} = \frac{\text{work}}{\text{time}}$$

Fig. 15-4

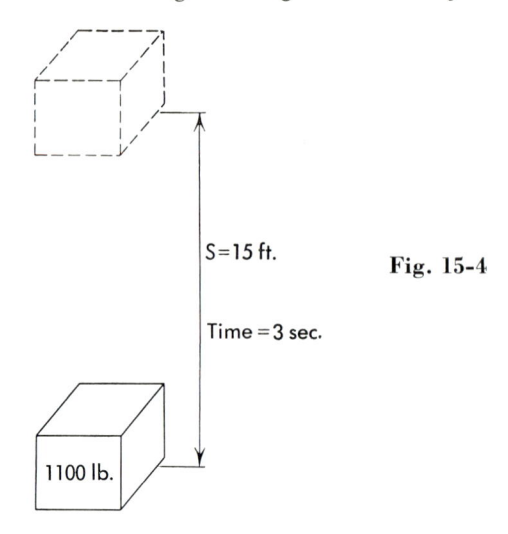

S = 15 ft.

Time = 3 sec.

1100 lb.

Solution:

$$\text{Power} = \frac{(1100) \text{ lb}_f \ (15) \text{ ft}}{3 \text{ sec}}$$

$$P = \underline{\underline{5500 \ \frac{\text{ft-lb}_f}{\text{sec}}}}$$

$$\text{Horsepower} = \frac{\text{work in ft-lb}_f}{(\text{time in sec})(550)}$$

$$\text{hp} = \frac{(1100)(15)}{(3)(550)} = \underline{\underline{10 \text{ hp}}}$$

Electric power usually is expressed in watts or kilowatts. A kilowatt is 1000 watts. When electric rates are prepared by utility companies, they customarily base their rates on the kilowatt-hour. Since the kilowatt-hour is the product of power and time, charges for electric services actually are charges for work or energy. When you pay your electric utility bill, you actually are paying for work performed electrically rather than for electric power.

The kilowatt-hour is simply power consumed at the rate of 1 kw for 1 hr.

Example: How much will it cost to operate a 150-watt electric light for 2.5 hr when the utility company charges are 6.5 cents per kilowatt-hour.

Analysis: Work (or energy) in kwh = (power in kilowatts)(time in hours).

Solution:

$$\text{Energy} = \left(\frac{150}{1000}\right)(2.5)$$

$$E = 0.375 \text{ kwh}$$

$$\text{Cost of electric work (or energy)} = (\text{kwh})(\text{cost per kwh})$$
$$= (0.375)(6.5)$$
$$= \underline{\underline{2.33 \text{ cents}}}$$

Analysis in Work, Power, and Energy

EFFICIENCY

The efficiency of any machine is expressed as the ratio of work output to the work input, or as a ratio of power output to power input. While efficiency has no units, it is usually expressed as a percentage.

$$\text{Efficiency of a machine} = \frac{\text{work output}}{\text{work input}} = \frac{\text{power output}}{\text{power input}}$$

$$\text{Per cent efficiency} = \frac{\text{work output}}{\text{work input}} (100 \text{ per cent})$$

$$= \frac{\text{power output}}{\text{power input}} (100 \text{ per cent})$$

Example: What is the per cent efficiency of a 12-hp electric motor that requires 9.95 kw of electric power when running at full load?

Analysis: The units of power input and power output must both be the same in order to calculate efficiency. We shall convert 12 hp to kilowatts and compute the ratio of power output to power input.

Solution: Power output in kw = (power output in hp)(0.746)
= (12)(0.746)
= 8.95 kw output

$$\text{Per cent efficiency} = \frac{\text{power output}}{\text{power input}} (100 \text{ per cent})$$

$$= \frac{8.95}{9.95} (100 \text{ per cent})$$

$$= 90.0 \text{ per cent efficiency}$$

The result would be the same if the power input in kilowatts had been converted to horsepower, and efficiency had been obtained as a ratio of horsepower output to horsepower input.

The power rating of motors and engines is the maximum output power that they are expected to deliver constantly, unless specifically stated otherwise. The input power will always be greater than the output power. For instance, a 100-hp electric motor can develop 100 hp at its pulley, but more than 100 hp will have to be supplied by the electric power line connected to the motor.

In some situations account must be taken of the efficiency of several machines as we trace the flow of power through them. As an example, let us consider a case in which an electric motor is connected to a pump which is pumping water. The motor obtains its power from electric lines which run through a switchboard. The data are given in Fig. 15-5, in which blocks are used to represent parts of the system.

Example: Power supplied to the system, as indicated by electric meters, is 22.1 kw. Find the amount of water delivered by the pump in cubic feet per second.

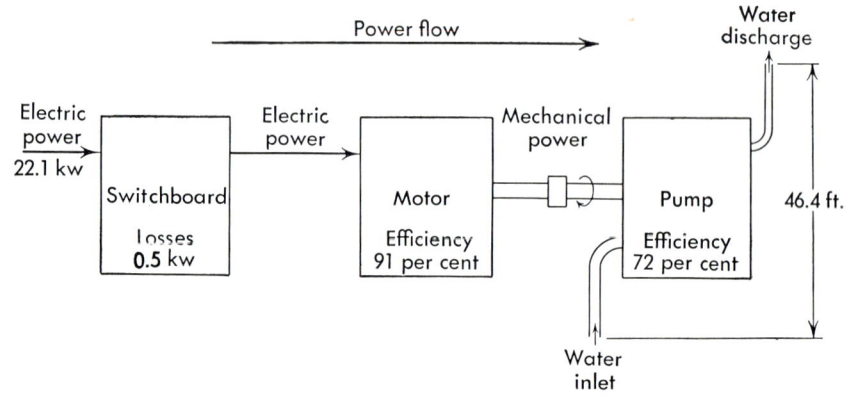

Fig. 15-5

Analysis: Compute the output power of each part of the system in order, beginning with the switchboard.

Solution:

Power supplied to the motor = 22.1 − 0.5
= 21.6 kw   (This is the power input to the motor.)

Power output of the motor = (21.6)(0.91)
= 19.66 kw

If we assume no losses in the coupling between the motor and the pump, the power output of the motor is the same as the power input to the pump.

$$\text{Power output of the pump} = (19.66)(0.72) = 14.16 \text{ kw}$$

Converting 14.16 kw to foot-pounds per second:

$$\text{Power} = \frac{(14.16)(550)}{0.746} = 10{,}420 \text{ ft-lb}_f/\text{sec}$$

The amount of water delivered now may be found if we remember that

$$\text{Power} = \frac{\text{work}}{\text{time}}$$

Analysis in Work, Power, and Energy 339

Then
$$\text{Weight of water/unit time} = \frac{10{,}420}{46.4} \qquad \left[\frac{\text{ft-lb}_f/\text{sec}}{\text{ft}} = \frac{\text{lb}}{\text{sec}}\right]$$
$$= 225 \text{ lb}_f \text{ per sec}$$

Converting 225 lb$_f$ per second to cubic feet per second:
$$\text{Volume of water/second} = \frac{225}{62.4} \qquad \left[\frac{\text{lb}_f/\text{sec}}{\text{lb}_f/\text{ft}^3}\right]$$
$$= \underline{\underline{3.60 \text{ cu ft/sec}}}$$

One additional item of information should be called to the student's attention. We notice that the efficiency of the motor is 91 per cent and the efficiency of the pump is 72 per cent. Considering the over-all efficiency of

Courtesy General Motors Corporation

Fig. 15-6. The engineer must design equipment to perform unusual tasks such as this large press which is used to form steel sheets into automobile bodies.

both machines, the input to the motor is 21.6 kw, and the output of the pump is 14.16 kw. The over-all efficiency of both machines can be found as follows:

$$\text{Over-all efficiency} = \frac{\text{output}}{\text{input}} (100 \text{ per cent})$$

$$= \frac{14.16}{21.6} (100 \text{ per cent})$$

$$= \underline{\underline{65.5 \text{ per cent}}}$$

The over-all efficiency of both machines could also be determined by finding the product of the individual efficiencies:

$$\text{Over-all efficiency} = (0.91)(0.72)(100 \text{ per cent})$$

$$= \underline{\underline{65.5 \text{ per cent}}}$$

As an additional problem, the student may solve for the over-all efficiency of the switchboard, motor, and pump, and compare the answer with the result obtained in the example problem above.

Problems on Power

15-26. A certain electric motor is rated at 25 hp. Calculate the power output in watts and in kilowatts.

15-27. Convert 330 kwh to foot-pounds.

15-28. An automobile requires 47 hp to maintain a speed of 55 mph. What force is being exerted on it by the engine?

15-29. In a recent experiment a student weighing 168 lb_f ran from the first floor to the third floor of a building, a vertical distance of 26 ft, in 9 sec. How much horsepower did he develop?

15-30. If a horse can actually develop 1 hp while pulling a loaded wagon at 3.5 mph, what force does he exert on the wagon?

15-31. A car weighing 2900 lb_f is moving at constant speed up a hill having a slope of 17 per cent. Neglecting friction, how fast will the car be moving when it is developing 25 hp?

15-32. An elevator and its load weigh 3300 lb_f. What will be the maximum upward velocity of the elevator when the driving motor is developing 12 hp.

15-33. A belt that drives a pulley is moving with a velocity of 38 fps. The tension in the belt on one side of the pulley is 88 lb_f and on the other side is 15 lb_f. How much power is being transmitted by the belt?

15-34. A diesel engine runs a pump which pumps 18,400 gal of water per hour into a tank 65 ft above the supply. How many horsepower is required at the pump?

15-35. A bulldozer exerts a force of 7200 lb_f on its blade while moving 2.5 mph. What horsepower is necessary?

Analysis in Work, Power, and Energy

15-36. A car weighing 3900 lb$_f$ is being towed by another car at a rate of 35 mph. The average force exerted by the tow cable is 200 lb$_f$. What horsepower is necessary to tow the car?

15-37. A tank holding 3500 gal of water is to be emptied by a small centrifugal pump. The water is 6 ft deep and is to be pumped to a height of 18.5 ft above the bottom of the tank. The pump is 68 per cent efficient and is driven by a motor which develops 1/4 hp. How long will it take to empty the tank?

15-38. A belt conveyor is used to carry crushed coal into a hopper. The belt carries 28 tons per hour up a 13 per cent slope 55 ft long. The friction losses in the belt and rollers amounts to 23 per cent of the power supplied. How many horsepower are needed to operate the belt?

15-39. An airplane engine which develops 2000 hp is driving the plane at a speed of 250 mph. What thrust is developed by the propeller?

15-40. A bucket elevator is used to unload wheat. The elevator moves 1000 bu of wheat an hour a vertical distance of 38 ft. How many horsepower is required?

15-41. A 1/2-hp electric motor drives a pump that lifts 1200 gal of water each hour to a height of 45 ft. What is the efficiency of the pump? While running, the motor requires 440 watts of power. What is the efficiency of the motor? What is the over-all efficiency of the motor-pump combination?

15-42. A pump having an efficiency of 59 per cent is used to pump gasoline. If the pump delivers 50 gal of gasoline per minute through an average height of 38 ft, what horsepower is needed to run the pump?

*15-43. A pulley 10 in. in diameter is on the shaft of a motor which is running 1750 rpm. If the motor is developing 25 hp, what is the difference in tension on the sides of the belt that passes over the pulley?

*15-44. The piston of a steam engine is 12 in. in diameter and moves through a distance of 20 in. each stroke. The average pressure on the piston is 75 lb$_f$ per square inch and the piston makes 250 power strokes per minute. How much horsepower is developed?

*15-45. In a certain industrial plant it was necessary to pump 120,000 gal of water per day an average height of 12 ft. The pump used was 68 per cent efficient and was directly connected to an electric motor having an efficiency of 85 per cent. While running, the motor develops 1 hp. (a) How many hours per day would the pump need to run? (b) What would be the kilowatt input to the motor? (c) Electrical energy costs 2 cents per kilowatthour. What will it cost to operate the pump for 30 days each month?

ENERGY

Another expression much used in mechanics is the term *energy*. The energy of a body is its ability to do work. Energy is measured in terms of work and has the same dimensions and units. Of all the various ways in which energy is produced, such as chemical, electrical, light, heat, sound, and mechanical, the forms in which we shall be concerned are *potential* and *kinetic*.

The potential energy (*PE*) of a body is its ability or capacity to do work because of its position or location.

$$\text{Potential energy } (PE) = (\text{weight})(\text{vertical height})$$

Example: A 100-lb$_f$ box (Fig. 15-7) is on a platform 10 ft above the ground. What is its potential energy with respect to the ground?

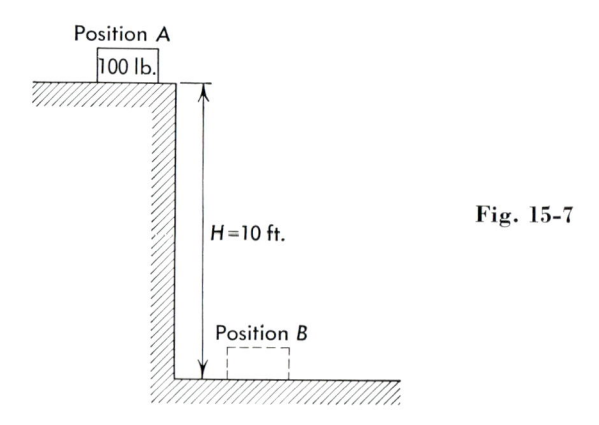

Fig. 15-7

To analyze the above problem, let us assume the box is initially in position *B*. The work necessary to raise the box to position *A* is (10 ft)(100 lb$_f$) or 1000 ft-lb$_f$. Since energy and work are convertible, the work of lifting the box evidently has gone to increasing its *PE*. The *PE* can then be found as the product of weight and the vertical distance above some reference plane. In this problem:

$$PE = (W)(H)$$
$$PE = (100 \text{ lb}_f)(10 \text{ ft})$$
$$PE = 1000 \text{ ft-lb}_f$$

The kinetic energy of a body is its ability to do work because of its motion. The dimensions of kinetic energy must be the dimensions of work. The usual expression for determining *KE* is

$$KE = \frac{(\text{mass})(\text{velocity})^2}{2}$$

The derivation of this expression is as follows: If a force acts on a body that is free to move, the body will accelerate. From Newton's laws this

Analysis in Work, Power, and Energy

force will produce an acceleration which is proportional to the mass of the body.*

$$F = (\text{mass})(\text{acceleration}) = Ma$$

If the force is constant and acts through a distance S while the body is accelerating, the work done is $(F)(S)$. Substituting the above value of F in the expression for work:

$$\text{Work} = (Ma)S$$

From the expression of accelerated motion,** the velocity acquired by a body starting from rest is $V^2 = 2aS$, or $S = V^2/2a$. Substituting this value of S in the expression for work we get

$$\text{Work} = (Ma)\left(\frac{V^2}{2a}\right) = \frac{MV^2}{2}$$

Since this is the work to give the body a velocity V, the work must have gone into increasing its KE, so

$$KE = \frac{MV^2}{2}$$

The dimensional equation using FPS gravitational units is

$$KE = \left[\frac{\text{lb}_f \text{ sec}^2}{\text{ft}}\right]\left[\frac{\text{ft}}{\text{sec}}\right]^2 = \text{ft-lb}_f$$

The units of KE are identical with units of work. It should be remembered that in the FPS gravitational system of units, the mass of a body in slugs can be calculated by dividing the weight of the body in pounds by the local acceleration of gravity in ft/sec².

Example: A 10-lb$_f$ box (Fig. 15-8) is moving with a velocity of 12 fps. What is its kinetic energy?

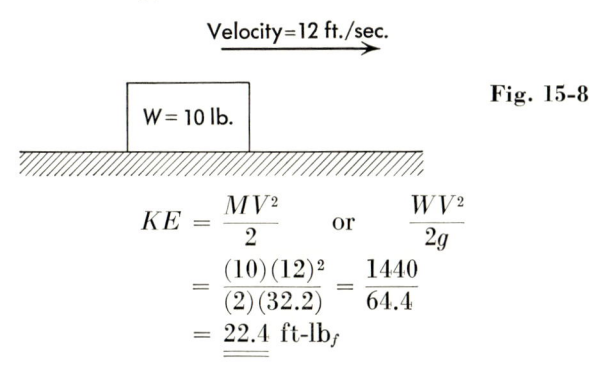

Velocity = 12 ft./sec.

W = 10 lb.

Fig. 15-8

$$KE = \frac{MV^2}{2} \quad \text{or} \quad \frac{WV^2}{2g}$$
$$= \frac{(10)(12)^2}{(2)(32.2)} = \frac{1440}{64.4}$$
$$= 22.4 \text{ ft-lb}_f$$

* For a discussion of *unit homogeneity* refer to page 217 and page 221.
** Refer to page 373.

Engineering: Elementary Problem Analysis

These relations of the equivalence of work and energy can be summed up in what is known as the Law of *Conservation of Energy*. This principle states that energy can neither be created nor destroyed but is only transformed from one kind to another (neglecting mass-energy transformations). As an example, let us take a problem which was previously solved.

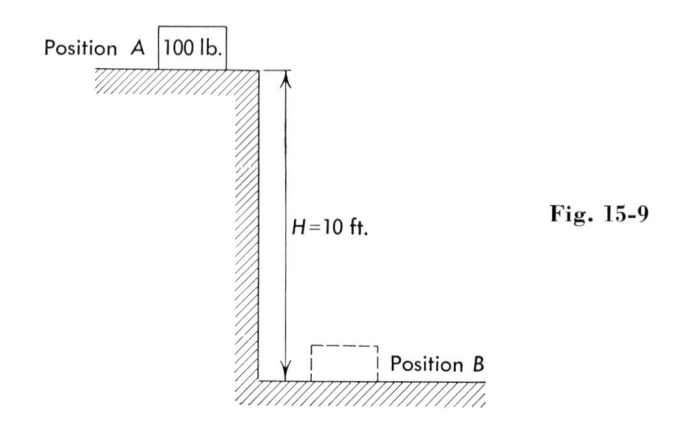

Fig. 15-9

The 100-lb$_f$ box (Fig. 15-9) when in position A has a PE of 1000 ft-lb$_f$. Its KE is zero because it is not moving. However, if we push the box to the edge of the platform so that it falls, we can see that just as the box reaches position B, the height of the box above the ground is zero and its PE is zero. Let us calculate its KE as the box reaches position B. From the expression for motion of a freely falling object starting from rest, the velocity of the box after falling 10 ft will be

$$V^2 = 2gS \qquad V = \sqrt{664 \; \frac{\text{ft}^2}{\text{sec}^2}}$$
$$V^2 = (2)(32.2)(10) \qquad V = 25.4 \text{ ft/sec}$$

Then, solving for the KE of the box as it reaches position B,

$$KE = \frac{MV^2}{2} \quad \text{or} \quad \frac{WV^2}{2g}$$
$$= \frac{(100)(644)}{(2)(32.2)}$$
$$= \underline{\underline{1000 \text{ ft-lb}_f}}$$

which is the same as the potential energy in position A.

Example: A 1000-lb$_f$ pile-driving hammer falls 16 ft onto a pile and drives the pile 3 in. What is the average force exerted?

Analysis in Work, Power, and Energy

Analysis: Using the equivalence of energy and work, the energy of the moving hammer was transformed into work by moving the pile 3/12 ft.

$$KE \text{ (of hammer)} = \text{work of driving pile}$$
$$KE = \frac{WV^2}{2g}$$

Let $S_1 = 16$ ft and $S_2 = \frac{3}{12}$ ft

Solution: Since the hammer is assumed to fall freely

$$V^2 = 2gS$$
$$= (2)(32.2)(16)$$
$$= 1030 \frac{\text{ft}^2}{\text{sec}^2}$$
$$KE = \frac{(1000)(1030)}{(2)(32.2)}$$
$$= 16{,}000 \text{ ft-lb}_f = \text{work of driving the pile}$$

Let FS_2 represent the work of driving the pile. Then

$$16{,}000 = (F)(\tfrac{3}{12})$$

or
$$F = (16{,}000)(\tfrac{4}{1}) = 64{,}000\text{-lb}_f \text{ average force}$$

It may be seen also in the above example that the PE of the hammer at the beginning of the 16-ft drop is equal to the KE at the end of the travel of the hammer.

Another example of an energy-work conversion is in the use of springs. Using a coil spring as an example, if we compress a coil spring in our hands, we exert a force in order to shorten the spring. This means we have exerted force through a distance and have done work. Also we have stored energy in the spring owing to its change in shape. This energy is in the form of potential energy. We know from experience that as the spring is compressed more and more, an increasing amount of force is required. The work done, then, evidently must be the average of the initial and final forces multiplied by the distance the average force has acted.

In diagram A in Fig. 15-10, there is no force on the 6-in. spring. As we slowly add weight to the spring, it will shorten. In diagram B the weight has been increased to 12 lb$_f$, and the spring has been compressed until it is only 4 in. long. The applied force, which initially was zero, has been increased to 12 lb$_f$, which is an average force of 6 lb$_f$.

We may take the average force, 6 lb$_f$, times the 2-in. movement of the spring as the work done, rather than take the small change of length due to each increase of force from zero pounds to 12 lb$_f$, and then add all the small increments of work. It can be shown by advanced mathematics that the increment method may be used, but for our purpose we shall use the average

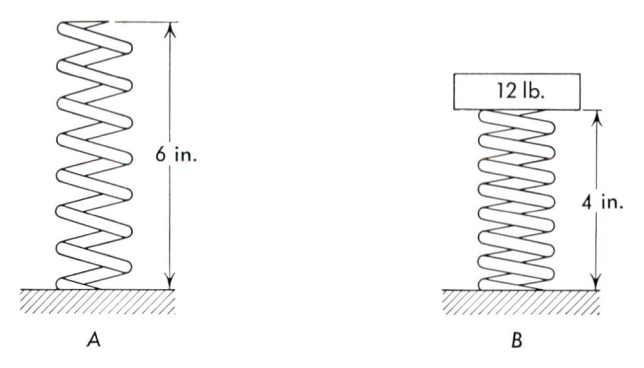

Fig. 15-10

force multiplied by the distance the average force will act. The expression for work will then be

Work = (average force)(distance) = energy in the spring

Using the data in Fig. 15-10,

$$\begin{aligned} \text{Work} &= (F_{\text{avg}})(S) \\ &= \frac{(F_1 + F_2)}{2}(S) \\ &= \frac{0 + 12 \text{ lb}_f}{2}(2) \text{ in.} \\ &= 12 \text{ in.-lb}_f \end{aligned}$$

In diagrams A and B it is shown that a force of 12 lb$_f$ changes the length of the spring 2 in. A common way of rating springs is by giving the force necessary to change their length a unit distance, such as an inch. In the example used, it will take 6 lb$_f$ to compress the spring 1 in. so we speak of the spring as being a 6-lb$_f$ spring. This value of 6 lb$_f$ per inch is called the *force constant* or the *spring rate* of the spring and is substantially independent of the applied force if the elastic limit of the material is not exceeded. If we let K represent the force constant of the spring, then

$$K = \frac{F}{S}$$

where F is the force applied and S is the distance the end of the spring moves. Rearranging the above expression

$$F = KS$$

In the expression for work when the initial force is zero

$$\text{Work} = \frac{F}{2}(S)$$

Analysis in Work, Power, and Energy

Substituting KS for F

$$\text{Work} = \frac{KS}{2}(S)$$
$$= \frac{KS^2}{2}$$

This shows that we can find the work done on a given spring if we know its force constant and the distance through which a given force has moved it.

Example: A spring has a scale (force constant) of 600 lb$_f$ per foot. How much work is done by a force that stretches it 3 in.? What force was acting to stretch the spring 3 in.?

Analysis: We must convert our different units of distance into the same units. A distance of 3 in. is 3/12 or 1/4 ft.

Solution: The work done is

$$\text{Work} = \frac{KS^2}{2}$$
$$= \frac{600 \text{ (lb}_f\text{/ft)}}{2}(0.25 \text{ ft})^2$$
$$= 300 \text{ lb/ft } (0.0625 \text{ ft}^2)$$
$$W = 18.75 \text{ ft-lb}_f$$

The force to stretch the spring 3 in., or 0.25 ft, is found as follows:

$$F = KS$$
$$= (600 \text{ lb}_f/\text{ft})(0.25 \text{ ft})$$
$$F = \underline{\underline{150 \text{ lb}_f}}$$

Problems on Energy

15-46. (a) A box weighing 1866 lb$_f$ is resting on a platform 6 ft from the ground. What is its potential energy with respect to the ground? (b) If the box is pushed off the platform, what is its potential energy just before it reaches the ground? What is its kinetic energy just before it reaches the ground?

15-47. A car weighing 3800 lb$_f$ is moving 27 mph. What is its kinetic energy? If the speed is doubled, by how much will the kinetic energy be increased?

15-48. A box weighing 150 lb$_f$ starts from rest and slides down an inclined plane with an acceleration of 7.1 fps per second. What will be its kinetic energy at the end of the first, second, third, and tenth seconds?

15-49. How much potential energy is lost when a cake of ice weighing 300 lb$_f$ slides down an incline 30 ft long that makes an angle of 29° with the horizontal?

15-50. A train weighing 1100 tons is moving fast enough to possess $(1.5)(10^8)$ ft-lb$_f$ of kinetic energy. What is its speed in miles per hour?

15-51. A hammer weighing 1 lb$_f$ moving 30 fps strikes a nail and drives it 3/4 in. into a block of wood. What was the average force exerted on the nail?

15-52. A car weighing 2600 lb$_f$ is moving with a speed of 30 mph. What average force is needed to stop it in 62 ft?

15-53. A 22-caliber rifle fires a bullet weighing 1/15 of an ounce with a muzzle velocity 1020 fps. The barrel is 28 in. long. Assuming the force on the bullet is constant while it moves down the barrel, what force was exerted on the bullet? What is the kinetic energy of the bullet as it leaves the muzzle?

15-54. A ball weighing 12.5 lb$_f$ is dropped from the top of a building 307 ft above the ground. After the ball is dropped, how long will it take for the kinetic energy and potential energy to be equal?

15-55. It requires a force of 2.5 lb$_f$ to stretch a spring 1 in. How much work is done in stretching the spring 3 in.?

15-56. A coil spring has a scale of 70 lb$_f$ per inch. A weight on it has shortened it 2.5 in., and when some more weight is added, it is shortened by an additional 0.75 in. What work was done by the added weight?

15-57. The floor of a car is 13.6 in. from level ground when no one is in the car. When several people, whose combined weight is 573 lb$_f$, get in the car, the floor is 11.9 in. from the ground. Assuming that the load was equally distributed to the front and rear wheels, what would be the force constant of the front spring system?

15-58. The recoil springs on a large gun have a combined force constant of 38,000 lb$_f$ per inch. What energy is stored in the springs when the gun is fired and the recoil compresses the springs 15.9 in.?

*15-59. A weight of 30 lb$_f$ stretches a spring 0.63 in. What energy is stored in the spring? What is the scale of the spring?

*15-60. One end of a screen door spring is fastened to the door 17 in. from the hinge side of the door, and the other end is fastened on the door jamb 2.5 in. from the screen door. It requires a force of 11 oz on the door 32 in. from the hinge side to start the door to open. What is the initial tension in the spring? If the force constant of the spring is 12 lb$_f$ per inch, what force is necessary to open the door through an angle of 65°?

*15-61. An iron ball weighing 7.5 lb$_f$ is dropped on a spring from a height of 10 ft. The spring has a force constant of 70 lb$_f$ per inch. How far is the end of the spring deflected?

Analysis in Work, Power, and Energy

THE GENERAL LAW OF WORK AND ENERGY

A generalization of work and energy relationships may be stated in what is known as the *law of work and energy* and is general enough to apply to almost any problem involving accelerated motion. The law of work and energy may be stated as:

$$\begin{bmatrix} \text{The initial} \\ KE \text{ of a} \\ \text{body.} \end{bmatrix} + \begin{bmatrix} \text{Work done by} \\ \text{forces tending} \\ \text{to increase the} \\ \text{velocity of the} \\ \text{body.} \end{bmatrix} - \begin{bmatrix} \text{Work done by} \\ \text{forces tending} \\ \text{to decrease the} \\ \text{velocity of the} \\ \text{body.} \end{bmatrix} = \begin{bmatrix} \text{Final } KE \text{ of} \\ \text{the body.} \end{bmatrix}$$

Example: A box weighing 200 lb$_f$ is on a plane which makes an angle of 20° with the horizontal. A force of 90 lb$_f$ is applied parallel to the plane and moves the box up the plane. Friction between the box and the plane is 10 lb$_f$. If the box starts from rest, what will be its velocity at the end of 5 sec?

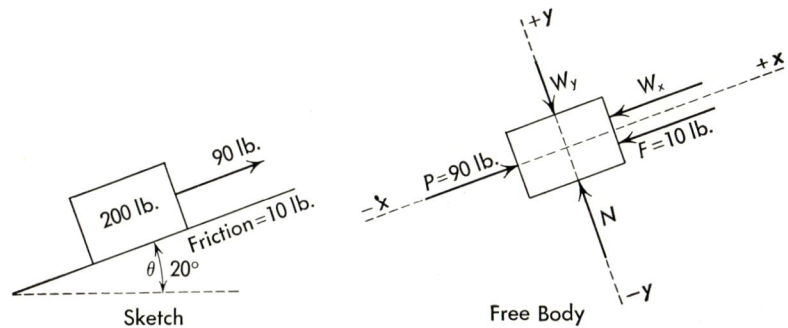

Fig. 15-11

Let us first solve for the weight components W_x and W_y.

$$W_x = W \sin \theta \qquad W_y = W \cos \theta$$
$$= (200) \sin 20° \qquad = (200) \cos 20°$$
$$= (200)(0.342) \qquad = (200)(0.94)$$
$$= 68.4 \text{ lb}_f \qquad = 188 \text{ lb}_f$$

The component W_y is perpendicular to the plane and therefore cannot produce motion along the plane. The work done by the component W_y will be zero. The other forces may produce motion parallel to the plane and must be included in the work and energy law expression.

Taking one term at a time:

Initial kinetic energy = 0 (since the body is starting from rest).

Work done by forces tending to increase the velocity. This will be the work done by the 90-lb$_f$ force, as it is the only one that tends to make the body increase its speed up the plane. This work is

$$\text{Work} = (90)(S)$$

Since the numerical value of S is not known, it will have to be included as a letter symbol and solved for later.

Work done by forces tending to decrease the velocity. The component W_x and friction both tend to slow the box as it moves up the plane. The work due to these forces is

$$\text{Work} = (68.4)(S) + (10)(S)$$
$$= (78.4)(S)$$

Final kinetic energy of the box is

$$KE = \frac{MV^2}{2} \quad \text{or} \quad \frac{WV^2}{2g}$$
$$= \frac{(200)(V^2)}{(2)(32.2)}$$

Note that the kinetic energy of the box is found by using all the weight of the box and not just a component of the weight.

Combining all the terms into a single expression, we have

$$0 + (90)(S) - (78.4)(S) = \frac{(200)(V^2)}{(2)(32.2)}$$
$$11.6S = 3.11 V^2$$

In the initial statement of the problem, the velocity at the end of 5 secs was required. From the expressions of motion of a body:

$$S = (\text{average velocity})(\text{time}) = \frac{V_1 + V_2}{2}(t)$$

Since the initial velocity V_1 is zero,

$$S = \left(\frac{V_2}{2}\right)(t)$$

and since $t = 5$ sec,

$$S = \left(\frac{V}{2}\right)(5)$$

Substituting for S in the expression $11.6S = 3.11 V^2$

$$(11.6)\left[\left(\frac{V}{2}\right)(5)\right] = 3.11 V^2$$
$$29 V = 3.11 V^2$$
$$29 = 3.11 V$$
$$V = 9.33 \text{ ft/sec}$$

Analysis in Work, Power, and Energy

Example: A cart and its contents (Fig. 15-12) weigh 4260 lb$_f$. It is sitting on a ramp that makes an angle of 11° with the horizontal. The coefficient of friction between the cart and the ramp is 0.2. What horizontal force will be needed to give the loaded cart an acceleration of 3.70 fps per second up the ramp?

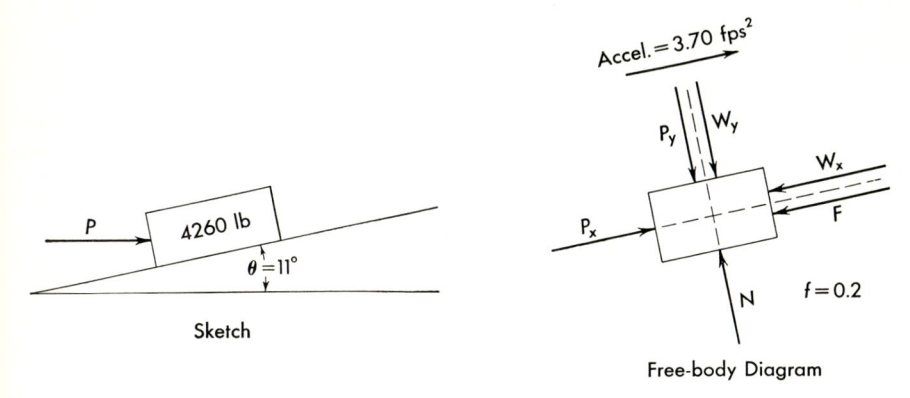

Fig. 15-12

Analysis: Determine the components of forces parallel and perpendicular to the ramp and solve, using the work and energy law.

Solution: Solve for the weight components W_x and W_y.

$$\begin{aligned} W_x &= W \sin \theta & W_y &= W \cos \theta \\ &= (4260)(\sin 11°) & &= (4260)(\cos 11°) \\ &= (4260)(0.1908) & &= (4260)(0.982) \\ &= 812 \text{ lb} & &= 4190 \text{ lb} \end{aligned}$$

From $\Sigma F_y = 0$, $N = W_y + P_y$

and friction force
$$\begin{aligned} F &= 0.2N \\ &= 0.2(4260 + P_y) \\ &= 852 + 0.2P_y \end{aligned}$$

Since velocities are not given, we should solve for a velocity at some assumed time to provide a value of velocity from which to solve for work and energy relations. Assume that the cart starts from rest and travels for 1 sec.

$$\begin{aligned} \text{Velocity} &= at \\ &= (3.7)(1) \\ V &= 3.7 \text{ ft/sec} \end{aligned}$$

Similiarly solve for the distance traveled in 1 sec.

$$S = \tfrac{1}{2}at^2$$
$$= \frac{(3.7)(1^2)}{2}$$
$$= 1.85 \text{ ft}$$

Substitute in each part of the work and energy equation.
The *initial kinetic energy* is zero, since the cart starts from rest.
Work done by forces tending to increase the velocity:

$$\text{Work} = (P_x)(1.85)$$

Since the value of P_x is not known, it will be solved for later.
Work done by forces tending to decrease the velocity:

$$\text{Work} = (W_x)(S) + (F)(S)$$
$$= (812)(1.85) + (1.85)(852 + 0.2P_y)$$
$$= 1502 + 1578 + 0.37P_y$$

Final kinetic energy of the cart is

$$KE = \frac{MV^2}{2} \quad \text{or} \quad \frac{WV^2}{2g}$$
$$= \frac{(4260)(3.7)^2}{(2)(32.2)}$$
$$= 907 \text{ ft-lb}_f$$

Combining all the terms into a single expression, we have

$$0 + (P_x)(1.85) - 1502 - 1578 - 0.37(P_y) = 907$$

To solve for the force P:

$$P_x = P(\cos\theta) \quad \text{and} \quad P_y = P(\sin\theta)$$
$$= P(0.982) \quad\quad\quad\quad\quad = P(0.1908)$$

Substituting:

$$P(1.85)(0.982) - P(0.37)(0.1908) = 3987$$
$$P = \underline{\underline{2285 \text{ lb}_f}}$$

General Problems on Work, Power, and Energy

15-62. An electric motor is delivering 48 hp to a water pump. How many gallons of water per minute will be pumped to a height of 32 ft if the efficiency of the motor is 70 per cent and the efficiency of the pump is 55 per cent?

15-63. A 200-lb$_f$ man runs up a flight of stairs a vertical distance of 13 ft in 2.5 sec. Assuming that the only resistance that he overcomes is the pull

Analysis in Work, Power, and Energy

of gravity and that he runs at constant velocity, find (a) the work the man does, (b) how much horsepower he was developing while ascending the stairs.

15-64. What horsepower will be necessary to pump 420 gal of gasoline per minute to a height of 65 ft?

15-65. A bullet weighing 0.065 lb_f and traveling with a velocity of 1100 fps strikes a large tree. Assuming the bullet meets a constant resistance to motion of 4000 lb_f, how far will the bullet go into the tree?

15-66. What motor horsepower is necessary to raise a 1200-lb_f elevator at a constant velocity of 12 fps? (Assume no loss of power in the hoisting cables.) If the motor is 85 per cent efficient, what is the kilowatt input?

15-67. A wooden box weighing 458 lb_f starts from rest and slides down a wooden inclined plane with an acceleration of 5.3 fps per second. What will be its kinetic energy when it reaches a speed of 22 fps?

15-68. A 3200 lb_f elevator is raised 40 ft vertically at a constant velocity of 1.6 fps. (a) How much work is done? (b) If the elevator hoist is 90 per cent efficient, what motor horsepower is required to operate the hoist?

15-69. A 750-ton train is being pulled up a 2 per cent grade. The drawbar pull is 15,000 lb_f. The track resistance is 13 lb_f per ton. What horsepower is necessary at the instant the velocity is 60 mph?

15-70. How much energy does a 2-lb_f hammer have, if it is moving 52 fps? How far will it drive a nail into a piece of wood if the nail meets a constant resistance of 3000 lb_f?

15-71. A block weighing 773 lb_f is setting on an incline that makes an angle of 28° with the horizontal. What force parallel to the incline is necessary to give the block an acceleration of 4.1 fps^2 up the incline? Friction amounts to 12.3 lb_f.

15-72. A pump having an efficiency of 55 per cent is pumping 748 gal of kerosene to a height of 120 ft in one minute. What horsepower is required to run the pump?

15-73. An electric motor is driving a centrifugal pump which is pumping crude petroleum against a head of 12 ft into the top of a cylindrical tank 6 ft in diameter and 18 ft long. Motor efficiency is 92 per cent and pump efficiency is 87 per cent. (a) What power in kilowatts must be supplied to the motor if the tank is filled in 26 min? (b) What will be the cost of filling the tank if energy costs 3 cents per kilowatt-hour?

15-74. Water flows into a mine which is 300 ft deep at the rate of 160 cfm. What horsepower should be supplied to a pump that is 60 per cent efficient if it is to keep the mine pumped out?

15-75. A bullet weighing 1/10 oz, traveling 1500 fps, strikes a large tree. If it meets a constant resistance to motion of 2500 lb_f, how far into the tree will it go?

15-76. A 5-hp electric motor having an efficiency of 84 per cent is directly coupled to a centrifugal pump having an efficiency of 70 per cent. (a) If the pump is delivering 630 gal of water per minute against a head of 18.1 ft, what horsepower is being supplied by the motor? (b) If the amount of water delivered by the pump is changed so that the motor takes 3.2 kw, what horsepower is the motor putting out at its shaft?

15-77. A cylindrical water tank 15 ft high and 10 ft in diameter is filled in 2 1/2 hr by a pump located 30 ft below the bottom of the tank. What motor horsepower is required to operate the pump if the pump is 72 per cent efficient? The water is pumped into the tank through a 4-in. pipe opening into the tank at the top. Neglect friction in the pipe and all other friction and head losses.

15-78. An electric motor is driving a pump which is delivering 750 gal of water per minute to a height of 83 ft. The motor has an efficiency of 87 per cent and the pump has an efficiency of 73 per cent. What power in kilowatts is supplied to the motor?

15-79. A train is running on a horizontal track at 50 mph. The average track resistance is 4000 lb_f and the air resistance is 300 lb_f. What horsepower is developed by the locomotive?

15-80. A freight train consisting of sixty cars, each weighing 50 tons, starts up a 1.5 per cent grade with an initial speed of 15 mph. The drawbar pull is 90 tons, and the train resistance including rolling resistance and air resistance is 15 lb_f per ton of weight. At the top of the grade the speed is 30 mph. (a) How long is the grade? (b) How much is the work of the drawbar pull? (c) How much work is done against gravity?

15-81. Water runs into a mine shaft that is 312 ft deep and must be pumped out at a rate of 106 gpm. (a) The motor-driven pump has an over-all efficiency of 61 per cent. What is the input to the motor in kilowatts? (b) While the water is being pumped out, what is the pressure at the lower end of the pipe in pounds per square inch?

15-82. It is desired to install a hydroelectric station on a certain stream. The cross-sectional area of the stream is 800 ft^2. There is a fall of 48 ft obtainable, and the velocity of the stream is 5 mph. What would be the horsepower output, assuming an over-all efficiency of 75 per cent?

15-83. A 1.75-ton car coasting at 15 mph comes to the foot of a 2 per cent slope. If it meets a resistance of 12 lb_f per ton on the slope caused by friction and windage, how far up the slope will it go before it stops?

15-84. A 3400-lb_f automobile is traveling 63 mph up a 3 per cent grade. The brakes are suddenly applied and the car is brought to a standstill. If the average air resistance is 54 lb_f and the rolling resistance is 20 lb_f per ton, what must the braking force be to stop the car in 300 ft?

15-85. A 3000-lb_f car is moving with a speed of 88 fps over level ground. The car is brought to a stop in a distance of 300 ft. Consider the frictional force to be 50 lb_f. Find the braking force.

Analysis in Work, Power, and Energy

15-86. What acceleration will be given an elevator weighing 4650 lb$_f$ if the pull on the supporting cables is 5300 lb$_f$?

15-87. The electric rates of a utility are as follows:

> First 10 kwh 10¢ per kwh
> Next 40 kwh 4.9¢ per kwh
> Next 40 kwh 3.7¢ per kwh
> All above this, 2.0¢ per kwh

(a) Compute the monthly bill for a customer whose meter readings show a reading of 33 kwh. (b) Calculate the monthly bill for a consumption of 126 kwh.

15-88. A 5-hp motor is operated at full load for 6.3 hr per day, 25 days out of each month. How many kilowatt-hours will be consumed in a month if the motor is 75 per cent efficient?

15-89. An electric iron requires 550 watts of electric power. How much will it cost to operate the iron for an hour if energy costs 3.5 cents per kilowatt-hour?

15-90. What total force is required to increase the speed of a 1288-lb$_f$ box on a horizontal plane from 10 fps to 30 fps in a distance of 20 ft? Coefficient of friction is 0.2.

15-91. A machine weighing 774 lb$_f$ is being pulled across a floor by a force of 328 lb$_f$ pulling at an angle of 25° above the floor. If the coefficient of sliding friction between the base of the machine and the floor is 0.20, what acceleration will the machine have? If it starts from an initial velocity of 4.6 fps, what will be its velocity at the end of 5 sec?

15-92. A car weighing 3000 lb$_f$ starts from rest and increases its speed uniformly on a horizontal road. After covering a distance of 876 ft, the speed is 48 mph. (a) What is the acceleration of the car? (b) What time did it take to cover this distance? (c) What resultant force was moving the car forward?

15-93. A 655-lb$_f$ body starts from the top of a 20° incline which is 46 ft long. The body has an initial speed of 3.1 fps, and the coefficient of sliding friction is 0.33. (a) What is the speed of the body when it reaches the foot of the incline? (b) What is the change of potential energy?

15-94. What force parallel to an inclined plane making an angle of 25° with the horizontal will be necessary to give a 36-lb$_f$ block an acceleration of 7 fps per second up the plane? Coefficient of friction is 0.25.

15-95. A trailer weighing 1250 lb$_f$ is being pulled along by a chain making an angle of 15° above the ground. The coefficient of rolling friction is 0.1. What pull on the chain will increase the speed uniformly from 10 mph to 40 mph in 12 sec?

15-96. A block weighing 320 lb$_f$ is resting on an inclined plane having a slope of 38 per cent. The coefficient of friction between the block and the plane is 0.2. (a) Calculate the horizontal force necessary to prevent slipping down the plane. (b) If the block is released and allowed to slide freely down the plane, what will be its acceleration?

15-97. A mine hoist and its load weigh 4500 lb$_f$. What will be the tension in the supporting cables when the upward acceleration of the hoist is 13.5 fps^2?

15-98. A truck weighing 6500 lb$_f$ has a velocity of 45 mph when the brakes are applied. The truck is brought to rest in a distance of 310 ft after the brakes are applied. How much force was slowing down the truck?

15-99. A 32-lb$_f$ sled is being pulled behind an automobile at 22 mph, when it is cut loose and allowed to slide uniformly to a stop. If the coefficient of friction between the sled and the street is 0.12, how far will the sled slide before it comes to rest?

15-100. A body weighing 112 lb$_f$, sitting on a horizontal plane, is acted upon by a force of 42 lb$_f$ pulling upward at an angle of 30° with the horizontal. Coefficient of friction between the body and plane is 0.2. The initial velocity of the body is 3 fps. If the body moves 25 ft, find (a) the final velocity of the body, (b) the time required to move the body 25 ft, (c) the acceleration of the body.

15-101. A 480-lb$_f$ body is being pushed along a horizontal surface by a horizontal 55-lb$_f$ force. The frictional force between the body and the horizontal surface is 12.2 lb$_f$. What is the acceleration of the body?

15-102. A box weighing 500 lb$_f$ is moving horizontally with a speed of 14 fps. A force is applied in the direction of motion which increases the speed to 28.5 fps in 4 sec. What is the average force acting?

15-103. A train weighing 200 tons starting from rest reaches a speed of 0.12 mph in 30 sec. If friction is 50 lb$_f$ per ton weight, what force is required to produce this motion?

15-104. A wood block which weighs 16.5 lb$_f$ is sitting at the top of a wood plane 10 ft long which makes an angle of 36° with the horizontal. Coefficient of friction is 0.2. (a) How long will it take for the block to slide to the bottom of the plane? (b) If the weight is doubled, how long will it take to slide to the bottom of the plane?

15-105. A 3,800-lb$_f$ automobile coasts down a 12 per cent grade and increases its speed uniformly from 5 mph to 15 mph in a distance of 350 ft. Find the retarding force on the car.

15-106. A car weighing 3000 lb$_f$ and having a velocity of 26 mph coasts to a stop in 1 min on a horizontal road. (a) What is the average retarding force? (b) What distance was covered?

15-107. A force of 25 lb$_f$ parallel to a plane gives a 42-lb$_f$ box an acceleration of 2 fps per second up the plane, which makes an angle of 28° with the horizontal. What is the coefficient of friction between the box and the plane?

Analysis in Work, Power, and Energy

15-108. A steel billet weighing 520 lb$_f$ is allowed to start sliding down a plane that makes an angle of 35° with the horizontal. What will be the speed of the billet after moving 20 ft down the plane if the coefficient of friction is 0.3?

15-109. A 3600-lb$_f$ elevator which is ascending is brought to a stop uniformly in a distance of 11 ft during a time of 2 sec. Find the force in the cables supporting it while the elevator is stopping.

15-110. A 4200-lb$_f$ automobile starts from rest and accelerates uniformly at a rate of 5.7 fps per second. (a) How far will the car go in 18.4 sec? (b) If the tires have a diameter of 31 in., what is the angular acceleration of the wheels? (c) What driving force is required to produce this acceleration if the wind and rolling resistance average 112 lb$_f$?

15-111. A body weighing 125 lb$_f$ is pushed up an 18° plane, for which the coefficient of sliding friction is 0.1, by a horizontal force of 60 lb$_f$. If the initial velocity is 8 fps, what will be the velocity after the body has moved 38 ft? If the force is then removed, how much farther will the body slide?

15-112. How much force parallel to the plane will it take to give a 60-lb$_f$ block an acceleration of 8 fps per second up a 40° plane, where the coefficient of friction is 0.25?

15-113. A 300-lb$_f$ box is sitting at the top of a 40 ft long inclined plane which makes an angle of 33° with the horizontal. If the box is allowed to begin to slide freely down the incline of its own accord, and it reaches the bottom with a velocity of 34 fps, what work was done in overcoming friction?

15-114. A 42-lb$_f$ box is being pulled across a horizontal floor by a rope which is parallel to the floor. If the box is being accelerated at the rate of 35 fps per second by a pull in the rope of 12 lb$_f$, what is the frictional force?

15-115. A small boat is powered by a 12-hp outboard motor. At full throttle the speed is 15 mph. Find the resistance to motion of the boat.

15-116. A car weighing 3000 lb$_f$ is moving 30 mph on a level road. Traction resistance and wind resistance amount to 50 lb$_f$. What power is required to keep the car moving at uniform speed?

15-117. A certain city has a water consumption of 5,600,000 gal per 24-hr day, and a pressure gauge on the delivery side of the water pump reads 135-psi pressure. If the efficiency of the pump is 80 per cent, and if the motor is 90 per cent efficient, how many kilowatts of electric power are supplied to the motor?

15-118. Water is supplied to a Pelton water wheel from a lake whose surface is 810 ft above the wheel. Water from the lake flows through a conduit and discharges through a nozzle, and 10 per cent of the energy of the flowing water is lost in the conduit and nozzle. When the flow of water is 7.75 cfs, the efficiency of the water wheel is 80.0 per cent. The water wheel drives an electric generator on the same shaft, and the generator efficiency is 90.0 per cent. How much electric power in kilowatts is delivered by the generator under the above conditions?

15-119. A certain city has a water consumption of 2,500,000 gal per 24-hr day. The average pressure on the discharge side of the pump is 125 lb$_f$ per square inch. If the efficiency of the pump and engine together is 60 per cent, what is the horsepower supplied to the motor driving the pump? If electric current costs 2 cents per kilowatt-hour, how much does the electricity for running the motor cost per 30-day month?

15-120. The readings on a customer's electric meter are as shown in Fig. 15-13. Compute the bill for a month. Use data from Problem 15-87.

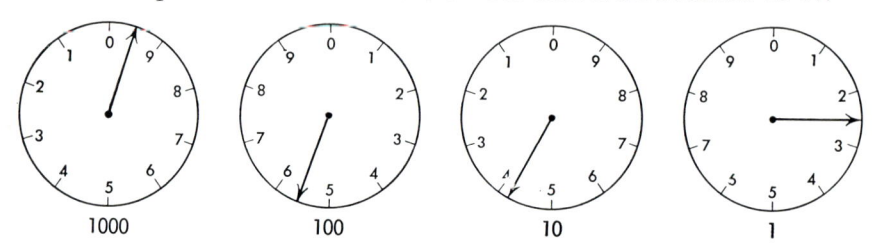

Fig. 15-13

Reading on March 20
Kilowatt-hours

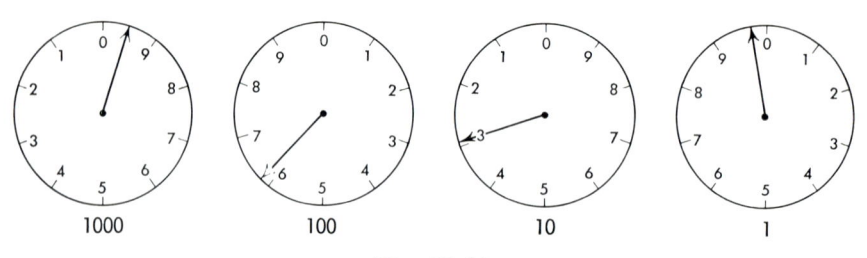

Fig. 15-14

Reading on April 20
Kilowatt-hours

15-121. A box weighing 24 lb$_f$ is sitting on a horizontal floor. A horizontal pull of 8.5 lb$_f$ is applied to the box. (a) If the frictional force is negligible, what will be the acceleration of the box? (b) If the frictional force is 6.7 lb$_f$, what will be the acceleration?

15-122. An elevator and its load weigh 4755 lb$_f$. (a) If the tension in the supporting cables is 5320 lb$_f$, what acceleration will the elevator have? (b) If the tension in the supporting cables is 4600 lb$_f$, what acceleration will the elevator have?

*15-123. A street car weighing 6.6 tons is moving 21 mph when the power is turned off and a braking force of 1250 lb$_f$ is applied. (a) What will be the

Analysis in Work, Power, and Energy

acceleration of the street car? (b) How long will it take to stop? (c) How far will it travel before stopping?

*15-124. A 150-lb_f box slides 91 ft down a 35° inclined plane onto a horizontal plane. The initial velocity at the top of the incline was 5 fps. The coefficient of friction is 0.2 for both planes. Find (a) the velocity at the foot of the incline, (b) total distance the body slides on both planes assuming no loss in velocity as the box reaches the foot of the incline.

*15-125. An elevator and its load weighs 4500 lb_f. The hoisting cable gives it an upward acceleration of 9.2 fps per second. What is the tension in the cable? Determine from data in a reference book, what size of plow-steel cable will be needed to withstand this load. Assume the working load will be one-eighth the breaking strength of the cable.

*15-126. A man weighing 185 lb_f is standing on some scales in an elevator. (a) What will the scales read when the elevator has an acceleration of 8 fps^2 upward? (b) What will the scales read when there is an acceleration of 3.5 fps^2 downward? (c) What will the scales read when the elevator is traveling at a uniform speed upward of 6.6 fps?

*15-127. A flexible cord passes over a pulley. A weight of 5 lb_f hangs on one end of the cord and a weight of 4 lb_f on the other end. (a) What will be the acceleration of each weight? (b) What will be the tension in the cord?

*15-128. A safe weighing 7.4 tons is sitting in a truck. The safe is 4.5 ft wide, 4.5 ft long, and 5.8 ft high. Assuming the wheels on the bottom of the safe touch the truck bed at points 4.5 ft apart but do not roll, and the center of gravity of the safe is at a point 2.9 ft above the truck bed, how much force is tending to tip the safe over when the truck has an acceleration of 7.7 fps^2? Will the safe tip under these conditions?

*15-129. A cylindrical piece of pipe 6 ft long and 10 in. outside diameter and weighing 44 lb_f is standing on end on a cart. What is the greatest acceleration the cart may have without tipping over the pipe?

*15-130. A man jumps from an airplane in flight. Just before he opens his parachute, his acceleration is 26 fps^2. What is the air resistance force that is slowing him down?

appendix

Courtesy E. I. du Pont de Nemours & Company

Modern electronic computers have revolutionized the facility with which data may be stored and retrieved. Tables and repetitious data are stored on magnetic tape or punched cards for almost instantaneous retrieval.

appendix

Methods of Measurement

VERNIERS

A common way of determining fractional parts of a division on a scale is to estimate by eye the value of the fractional division. Frequently there is attached to scientific equipment using divided scales a device called a *vernier*. The vernier is an auxiliary scale placed alongside the main scale which enables one to estimate the fractional divisions of the main scale accurately.

The graduations on the vernier scale are different from those on the main scale but bear a simple relation to the main scale divisions. The scale of the usual vernier that is used to estimate tenths is divided so that ten graduations on the vernier scale correspond to nine graduations on the main scale, which will make a vernier graduation shorter than a main scale graduation by one-tenth of a division.

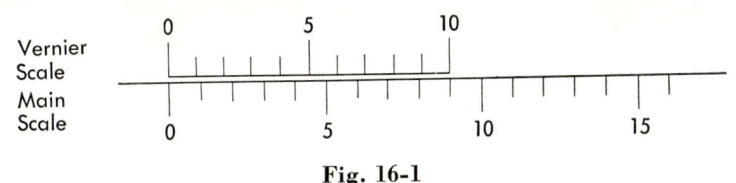

Fig. 16-1

The zero of the vernier is the index, and its position on the main scale will indicate the main scale graduation to be read. As an example, suppose the position of the vernier and main scale are as shown in Fig. 16-2.

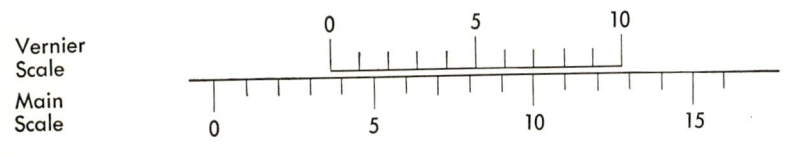

Fig. 16-2

It is readily seen that the index of the vernier lies between 3 and 4 on the main scale. The fractional part of the division can be found by determining which vernier division coincides with a main scale division. On inspection, the eighth vernier division is seen to coincide with a main scale division. Since the vernier has a 1:10 ratio, the reading indicated by the vernier index is 3.8 divisions. The direct reading is obtained from the main scale and the estimated part from the vernier scale.

For verniers having ratios different from 1:10, the value of the vernier ratio, called the *least count*, can be obtained by the following formula:

$$\text{Least count} = \left(\frac{1}{n}\right)(S)$$

where n = number of divisions on the vernier scale
S = numerical value of the smallest main scale division

For example, a vernier scale having eight divisions sliding against a scale divided into sixteenths of an inch would have a least count of (1/8) (1/16) = 1/128 in. This means that the smallest distance that could be estimated using the vernier is 1/128 in.; or that we can estimate reliably an inch into 128 parts.

PLANIMETER

The polar planimeter (Fig. 16-3) is a device used for the rapid and accurate determination of the areas of plane surfaces. The planimeter consists essentially of three parts, the pole arm, the tracer arm, and a carriage. The pole arm and tracer arm

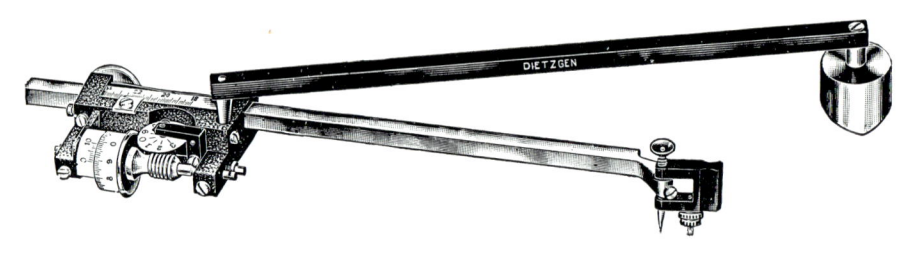

Fig. 16-3

are pivoted together and are free to rotate about a weighted needle point or pole which holds that end of the pole arm at a fixed point on the paper. The tracer arm carries a tracer point at one end and the carriage at the other end. The carriage supports a measuring wheel that turns on a horizontal axis and is parallel to the tracer arm.

In operation, the rim of the measuring wheel is in contact with the paper so that as the tracing point is moved around a given area, the wheel drags along, sometimes slipping and sometimes rolling, and the difference between the readings of the scale on the wheel at the beginning and end of the circuit of the tracing point represents the area of the figure.

Where possible, the pole should be set outside the boundary of the figure to be measured at a place so that an angle of about 90° is formed between the pole arm and tracing arm when the tracing arm is in the approximate center of the figure, as shown in Fig. 16-4.

The tracing point is then moved to the boundary of the figure and the reading of the wheel is recorded. The tracing point is then moved around the outline of the area, being careful to follow the line accurately, until the starting point is reached again. The wheel is again read, and the difference of the initial and final readings is the area expressed in units which depend on the calibration of the instrument. In the usual type of planimeter the wheel is calibrated to read area directly in tenths of square inches, and by means of a vernier, readings may be obtained to hundredths of square inches.

Various other methods can be used to determine areas by graphical or semi-graphical means by dividing the area into approximate triangles, rectangles, or

Appendix 363

trapezoids. A more complete discussion of these methods can be found in texts on surveying and calculus.

Another means used to obtain the area of a figure makes use of what is called the *jackknife method*. A pocket knife having blades at either end, or a piece of wire bent in the shape of an inverted U, may be used. In either case one end of the device used should have a sharp edge rather than a point, as shown in Fig. 16-5.

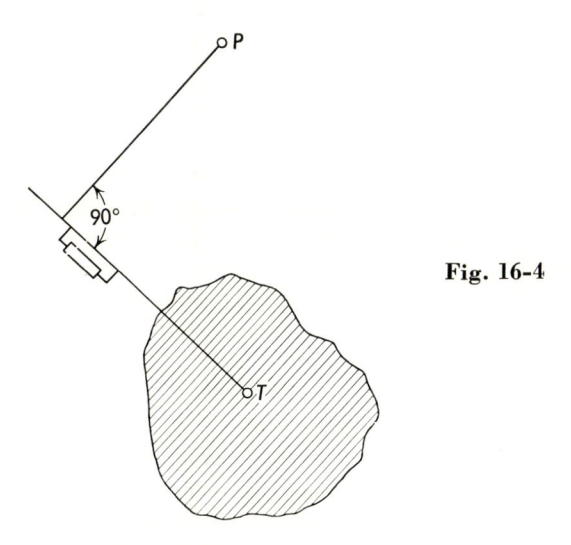

Fig. 16-4

To use this method, draw a tangent line to the boundary of the area to be measured. Set the edge E on the tangent line and the tracing point T at the point of tangency. Trace around the figure with the tracing point, letting the edge slide where it will. When the tracing point returns to the beginning, measure the distance of the edge from the tangent line. Repeat the tracing as above but go around the figure in the opposite direction. Measure the distance of the edge from the tangent line. The

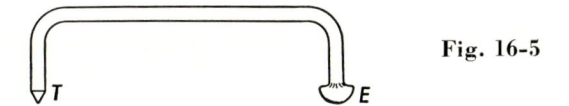

Fig. 16-5

average of the two distances multiplied by the length between the tracing point and the edge will give the area of the figure in the units in which the distances were measured. A convenient length for the arm of the device is 10 in.

Crude as this method may appear, it will give surprisingly good results if carefully performed. A modification of the procedure, which sometimes will improve precision, is to draw the line for the knife-edge through the center of gravity of the figure. Start the tracing point at the center of gravity of the figure, pass out to the perimeter along a line, traverse the perimeter, and then return to the center of gravity on the same line. The area is found as before by multiplying the distance of the edge from the line by the length of the tracing arm.

GEOMETRIC FIGURES

RECTANGLE

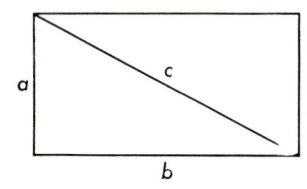

RECTANGLE

Area = (base)(altitude) = ab
Diagonal = $\sqrt{(\text{altitude})^2 + (\text{base})^2}$
$C = \sqrt{a^2 + b^2}$

RIGHT TRIANGLE

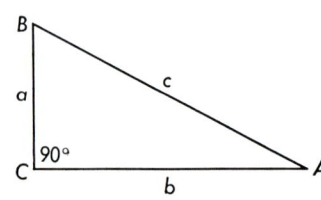

RIGHT TRIANGLE

Angle A + angle B = angle C = 90°
Area = ½ (base)(altitude)
Hypotenuse = $\sqrt{(\text{altitude})^2 + (\text{base})^2}$
$C = \sqrt{a^2 + b^2}$

ANY TRIANGLE

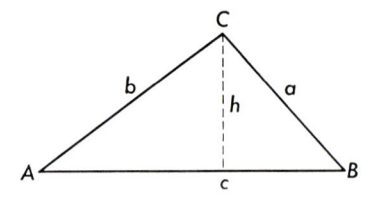

ANY TRIANGLE

Angles $A + B + C$ = 180°
(Altitude h is perpendicular to base c)
Area = ½ (base)(altitude)

PARALLELOGRAM

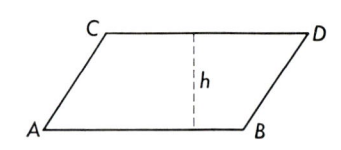

PARALLELOGRAM

Area = (base)(altitude)
Altitude h is perpendicular to base AB.
Angles $A + B + C + D$ = 360°

TRAPEZOID

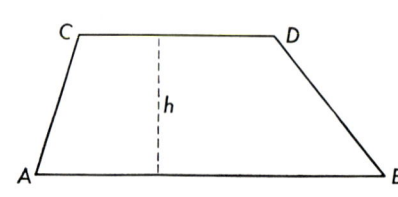

TRAPEZOID

Area = ½ (altitude)(sum of bases)
(Altitude h is perpendicular to sides AB and CD. Side AB is parallel to side CD.

Appendix

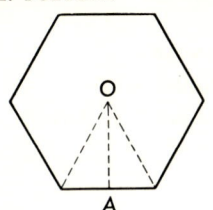

REGULAR POLYGON

$$\text{Area} = \tfrac{1}{2} \begin{bmatrix} \text{length of} \\ \text{one side} \end{bmatrix} \begin{bmatrix} \text{Number} \\ \text{of sides} \end{bmatrix} \begin{bmatrix} \text{Distance} \\ OA \text{ to} \\ \text{center} \end{bmatrix}$$

A regular polygon has equal angles and equal sides and can be inscribed in or circumscribed about a circle.

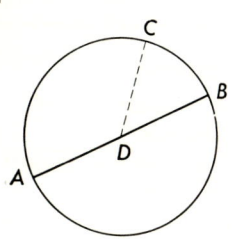

CIRCLE

AB = diameter, CD = radius

$$\text{Area} = \pi(\text{radius})^2 = \frac{\pi(\text{diameter})^2}{4}$$

Circumference = π(diameter)

$C = 2\pi(\text{radius})$

$$\frac{\text{arc } BC}{\text{circumference}} = \frac{\text{angle } BDC}{360°}$$

$$1 \text{ radian} = \frac{180°}{\pi} = 57.2958°$$

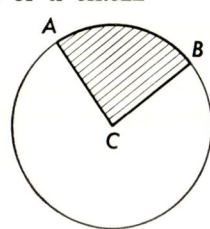

SECTOR OF A CIRCLE

$$\text{Area} = \frac{(\text{arc } AB)(\text{radius})}{2}$$

$$= \pi \frac{(\text{radius})^2(\text{angle } ACB)}{360°}$$

$$= \frac{(\text{radius})^2(\text{angle } ACB \text{ in radians})}{2}$$

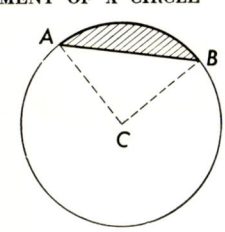

SEGMENT OF A CIRCLE

$$\text{Area} = \frac{(\text{radius})^2}{2} \left[\frac{\pi(\sphericalangle ACB°)}{180} - \sin ACB° \right]$$

$$\text{Area} = \frac{(\text{radius})^2}{2} (\sphericalangle ACB \text{ in radians} - \sin ACB°)$$

Area = area of sector ACB − area of triangle ABC

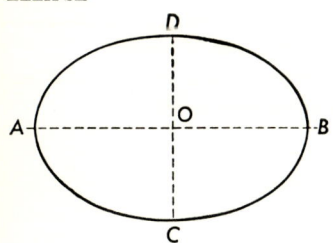

ELLIPSE

Area = π(long radius OA)(short radius OC)

Area = $\dfrac{\pi}{4}$ (long diameter AB)(short diameter CD)

RECTANGULAR PRISM

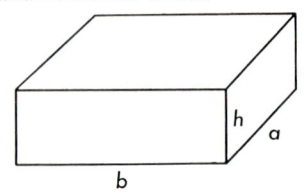

RECTANGULAR PRISM

Volume = length × width × height
Volume = area of base × altitude

ANY PRISM

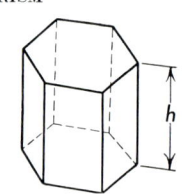

ANY PRISM

(Axis either perpendicular or inclined to base)
Volume = (area of base)(perpendicular height)
Volume = (lateral length)(area of perpendicular cross-section)

ANY CYLINDER

ANY CYLINDER

(Axis either perpendicular or inclined to base)
Volume = (area of base)(perpendicular height)
Volume = (length of axis)(area of section perpendicular to axis)
Area of cylindrical surface
   = (perimeter of base)(perpendicular height)

PYRAMID

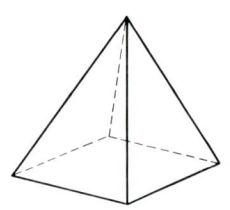

PYRAMID

(Axis either perpendicular or inclined to base)
Volume = ⅓ (area of base)(perpendicular height)

CONE

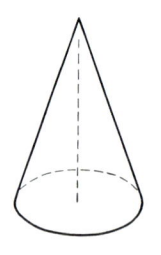

CONE

(Axis either inclined or perpendicular to base)
Volume = ⅓ (area of base)(perpendicular height)
Area of conical surface (right cone)
   = ½ (circumference of base) × (slant height)

SPHERE

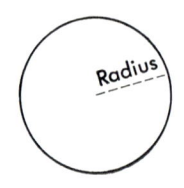

SPHERE

$$\text{Volume} = \frac{4\pi(\text{radius})^3}{3} = \frac{\pi(\text{diameter})^3}{6}$$

Area of surface = $4\pi(\text{radius})^2$
                = $\pi(\text{diameter})^2$

Appendix

Tables of Weights and Measures

AVOIRDUPOIS WEIGHT

1 grain (avdp)	1 grain	1 grain (troy)
$27^{11}/_{32}$ grain	1 dram	
16 dram	1 ounce (oz)	
16 ounces	1 pound (lb)	
100 pounds	1 hundredweight (cwt)	
2000 pounds	1 short ton (T)	
2240 pounds	1 long ton	

METRIC WEIGHT

10 milligram (mg)	1 centigram (cg)
10 centigram	1 decigram (dg)
10 decigram	1 gram (g)
10 gram	1 dekagram (Dg)
10 dekagram	1 hectogram (hg)
10 hectogram	1 kilogram (kg)

MASS AND FORCE EQUIVALENTS

1 gram	0.03527 ounce	980.6 dynes	
1 kilogram	2.2046 pound	9.807 newton	$(6.852)(10^{-2})$ slug
1 metric ton	2205 pound		
1 pound	453.6 gram	0.4536 kilogram	4.448 newton
1 ounce	28.35 gram		
1 newton	10^5 dynes	0.2248 pounds	

DRY MEASURE

2 pints	1 quart (qt)	67.2 cubic inches (in.^{3})
8 quarts	1 peck	
4 pecks	1 bushel (bu)	

LIQUID MEASURE

4 gill	1 pint (pt)	16 fluid ounces 2 cups
2 pints	1 quart	
4 quarts	1 gallon (gal)	231 cubic inches
7.48 gallons	1 cubic foot (ft^3)	
31½ gallons	1 barrel (bbl)	
1 British Imperial gallon	1.200 U.S. gallons	

LINEAR MEASURE

1 mil	0.001 inch (in.)
12 inches	1 foot (ft)
3 feet	1 yard (yd)
5½ yards	1 rod

40 rods	1 furlong		
320 rods	1 mile	5280 ft	1760 yards
3 miles	1 league		

LINEAR MEASURE EQUIVALENTS

6.08 feet — 1 fathom
6080.2 feet — 1 nautical mile
1 nautical mile — 1.15 statute mile
1 knot is a speed of 1 nautical mile per hour

METRIC LINEAR MEASURE

10 millimeter (mm) — 1 centimeter (cm)
10 centimeter — 1 decimeter (dm)
10 decimeter — 1 meter (m)
10 meter — 1 dekameter (Dm)
10 dekameter — 1 hectometer (hm)
10 hectometer — 1 kilometer (km)

METRIC LINEAR EQUIVALENTS

1 centimeter	0.3937 inch	10^{-5} kilometer	
1 meter	39.37 inches	1.0936 yard	3.281 feet
1 kilometer	0.62137 mile (approximately ⅝ mile)		3281 feet
1 inch	2.540 centimeter		
1 foot	30.48 centimeter	0.3048 meter	
1 mile	1.6093 kilometer		
1 Angstrom	10^{-10} meter		
1 micron (μ)	10^{-6} meter		

AREA MEASURE

144 square inches (in.^{2})	1 square foot (ft^2)		
9 square feet	1 square yard (yd.^{2})		
30¼ square yards	1 square rod		
160 square rods	1 acre	4840 square yards	43,560 square feet
640 acres	1 square mile 1 section		
2.47 acres	1 hectare (metric)		
0.7854 square mils	1 circular mil 7.854(10^{-7}) square inches		

VOLUME MEASURE

1728 cubic inches — 1 cubic foot (ft^3)
27 cubic feet — 1 cubic yard (yd^3)
231 cubic inches — 1 standard gallon (U.S.)
2150.42 cubic inches — 1 standard bushel
144 cubic inches — 1 board foot
61.02 cubic inches — 1 liter (metric)

Appendix

CONVERSION EQUIVALENTS

1 atmosphere	14.69 pounds per square inch (psi)
	29.92 inches of mercury
	406.8 inches of water
1 British thermal unit	252 calories (gram, at 15°C)
1 British thermal unit	778 foot-pounds (ft-lb) 0.00039 horsepower-hour
1 calorie	0.003968 British thermal unit
1 cubic inch	16.39 cubic centimeters 0.01639 liters
1 foot-pound per second	0.001818 horsepower (hp)
1 horsepower	746 watts 33,000 foot-pounds per minute
	550 foot-pounds per second
1 kilowatt	1.34 horsepower
Hydrostatic water pressure in pounds per square inch = (height in feet) (0.4332)	
1 inch Hg (mercury)	0.491 pound per square inch
1 Joule	1 watt second 0.737 foot-pound 10^7 ergs
	$9.48(10^{-4})$ Btu
1 kilowatt-hour	3413 British thermal unit 1.341 hp-hr
	$3.6(10^6)$ Joule
1 radian	57.2958 degrees
1 million electron volts (Mev)	$1.602(10^{-13})$ joule

COEFFICIENTS OF FRICTION

AVERAGE VALUES

SURFACES	STATIC	KINETIC
Metals on wood	0.4 —0.63	0.35—0.60
Wood on wood	0.3 —0.5	0.25—0.4
Leather on wood	0.38—0.45	0.3 —0.35
Iron on iron (wrought)	0.4 —0.5	0.4 —0.5
Glass on glass	0.23—0.25	0.20—0.25
Leather on glass	0.35—0.38	0.33—0.35
Wood on glass	0.35—0.40	0.28—0.31
Wood on sheet iron	0.43—0.50	0.38—0.45
Leather on sheet iron	0.45—0.50	0.35—0.40
Brass on wrought iron	0.35—0.45	0.30—0.35
Babbitt on steel	0.35—0.40	0.30—0.35
Steel on ice	0.03—0.04	0.03—0.04

SPECIFIC GRAVITIES AND SPECIFIC WEIGHTS

AVERAGE VALUES

MATERIAL	SPECIFIC GRAVITY	AVERAGE SPECIFIC WEIGHT IN LB_f/FT^3	MATERIAL	SPECIFIC GRAVITY	AVERAGE SPECIFIC WEIGHT IN LB_f/FT^3
Alcohol, ethyl	0.792	49.6	Limestone, crushed	1.4—1.6	95
Aluminum, cast	2.65	166	Marble	2.5—2.8	166
Air, S.T.P.	0.001293	0.0806	Mercury	13.56	845
Babbit metal, soft	9.75—10.65	625	Nickel	8.90	558
Brass, cast, red	8.4—8.7	530	Oil, lubricating	0.91	57
Brick, common	1.8—2.0	119	Paraffin	0.90	56
Cement, portland, bags	1.44	90	Petroleum, crude	0.88	55
Chalk	2.25	140	Rubber	1.25	78
Clay, loose, wet	1.7—1.8	110	Sand, loose, wet	1.9	120
Coal, anthracite, solid	1.4—1.8	95	Sandstone, solid	2.3	144
Coal, bituminous, solid	1.2—1.5	85	Sea water	1.03	64
			Silver	10.5	655
			Steel, structural	7.9	490
			Sulfur	1.9—2.1	125
			Tin	7.3	456
Concrete, gravel, sand	2.2—2.4	142	Turpentine	0.865	54
Copper, wire	8.93	560	Water, 4°C (39.2°F)	1.000	62.43
Cork	0.18—0.25	12.5	Water, 100°C (212°F)	0.96	59.83
Earth	1.45—2.2	90—130	Wood seasoned:		
Gasoline	0.68—0.72	44	Cedar	0.35—0.65	31
Glass, crown	2.5—2.7	161	Cypress	0.48—0.57	32
Glass, flint	3.0—3.6	205	Ebony	1.2—1.3	78
Glycerine	1.25	78	Fir	0.51—0.60	35
Gold	19.3	1205	Hickory	0.70—0.93	51
Granite, solid	2.5—3.0	172	Mahogany	0.56—0.85	44
Gravel, loose, wet	1.45—1.90	105	Maple	0.68—0.80	45
Ice	0.911	57	Oak	0.70—0.90	50
Iron, gray cast	7.00—7.12	450	Pine, white	0.38—0.48	28
Iron, wrought	7.6—7.9	480	Pine, yellow	0.65—0.75	44
Kerosene	0.8	50	Walnut	0.60—0.70	41
Lead	11.34	710	Zinc	7.14	445
Limestone, solid	2.5—2.9	168			

NOTE: The value for the density of water, which is usually used in problem solutions, is 62.4 lb_f/ft^3 or 8.34 lb_f per gallon.

Appendix

TRIGONOMETRIC FUNCTIONS

$\sin(-\alpha) = -\sin\alpha$
$\cos(-\alpha) = \cos\alpha$
$\tan(-\alpha) = -\tan\alpha$
$\sin^2\alpha = \tfrac{1}{2} - \tfrac{1}{2}\cos 2\alpha$
$\cos^2\alpha = \tfrac{1}{2} + \tfrac{1}{2}\cos 2\alpha$

$\sin^2\alpha + \cos^2\alpha = 1$
$\sec^2\alpha = 1 + \tan^2\alpha$
$\csc^2\alpha = 1 + \mathrm{ctn}^2\alpha$
$\sin 2\alpha = 2\sin\alpha\cos\alpha$
$\cos 2\alpha = \cos^2\alpha - \sin^2\alpha = 1 - 2\sin^2\alpha = 2\cos^2\alpha - 1$

$$\sin\alpha = \alpha - \frac{\alpha^3}{3!} + \frac{\alpha^5}{5!} - \frac{\alpha^7}{7!} + \frac{\alpha^9}{9!} \cdots$$

$$\cos\alpha = 1 - \frac{\alpha^2}{2!} + \frac{\alpha^4}{4!} - \frac{\alpha^6}{6!} + \frac{\alpha^8}{8!} \cdots$$

$\sin(\alpha \pm \theta) = \sin\alpha\cos\theta \pm \cos\alpha\sin\theta$
$\cos(\alpha \pm \theta) = \cos\alpha\cos\theta \mp \sin\alpha\sin\theta$

DIFFERENTIALS AND INTEGRALS

$$\frac{dx^n}{dx} = nx^{n-1}$$

$$\frac{d(uv)}{dx} = U\frac{dv}{dx} + V\frac{du}{dx}$$

$$\frac{d(u/v)}{dx} = \frac{V(du/dx) - U(dv/dx)}{v^2}$$

$$\int x^n\,dx = \frac{x^{n+1}}{n+1} + C$$

$$\int u\,dv = uv - \int v\,du$$

$$\int \frac{dx}{x} = \log_e x + C$$

$$\int \sin x\,dx = -\cos x + C$$

$$\int \cos x\,dx = \sin x + C$$

$$\int \sin^2 x\,dx = \frac{x}{2} - \frac{\sin 2x}{4} + C$$

$$\int \cos^2 x\,dx = \frac{x}{2} + \frac{\sin 2x}{4} + C$$

SPECIAL PURPOSE FORMULAS USEFUL IN SOLVING UNIFORM MOTION PROBLEMS

GIVEN	TO FIND	SUGGESTED FORMULAS
V_1, V_2, t	S	$S = \left(\dfrac{V_1 + V_2}{2}\right) t$
V_1, V_2, a	S	$S = \dfrac{V_2^2 - V_1^2}{2a}$
V_1, a, t	S	$S = V_1 t + \dfrac{at^2}{2}$
V_1, V_2	V_{av}	$V_{av} = \dfrac{V_1 + V_2}{2}$
S, t	V_{av}	$V_{av} = \dfrac{S}{t}$
V_2, a, t	V_1	$V_1 = V_2 - at$
V_2, a, S	V_1	$V_1 = \sqrt{V_2^2 - 2aS}$
S, a, t	V_1	$V_1 = \dfrac{S}{t} - \dfrac{at}{2}$
V_1, a, t	V_2	$V_2 = V_1 + at$
V_1, a, S	V_2	$V_2 = \sqrt{V_1^2 + 2aS}$
V_1, S, t	V_2	$V_2 = \dfrac{2S}{t} - V_1$
V_1, V_2, S	t	$t = \dfrac{2S}{V_1 + V_2}$
V_1, a, S	t	$t = \dfrac{-V_1 \pm \sqrt{V_1^2 + 2aS}}{a}$
V_1, V_2, a	t	$t = \dfrac{V_2 - V_1}{a}$
V_1, V_2, t	a	$a = \dfrac{V_2 - V_1}{t}$
V_1, V_2, S	a	$a = \dfrac{V_2^2 - V_1^2}{2S}$
V_1, S, t	a	$a = \dfrac{2S}{t^2} - \dfrac{2V_1}{t}$

THE GREEK ALPHABET

A	α	Alpha	N	ν	Nu
B	β	Bēta	Ξ	ξ	Xī
Γ	γ	Gamma	O	o	Ōmicron
Δ	δ	Delta	Π	π	Pī
E	ϵ	Epsilon	P	ρ	Rhō
Z	ζ	Zēta	Σ	$\sigma\,s$	Sigma
H	η	Ēta	T	τ	Tau
Θ	θ	Thēta	Υ	υ	Upsilon
I	ι	Iōta	Φ	ϕ	Phī
K	κ	Kappa	X	χ	Chī
Λ	λ	Lambda	Ψ	ψ	Psī
M	μ	Mu	Ω	ω	Ōmega

DIMENSIONAL PREFIXES

mega units = 10^6 units
kilo units = 10^3 units
hecto units = 10^2 units
deci units = 10^{-1} units
centi units = 10^{-2} units
milli units = 10^{-3} units
micro units = 10^{-6} units
milli micro units = 10^{-9} units
micro micro units = 10^{-12} units

374   *Appendix*

HIGH ALTITUDE CHART

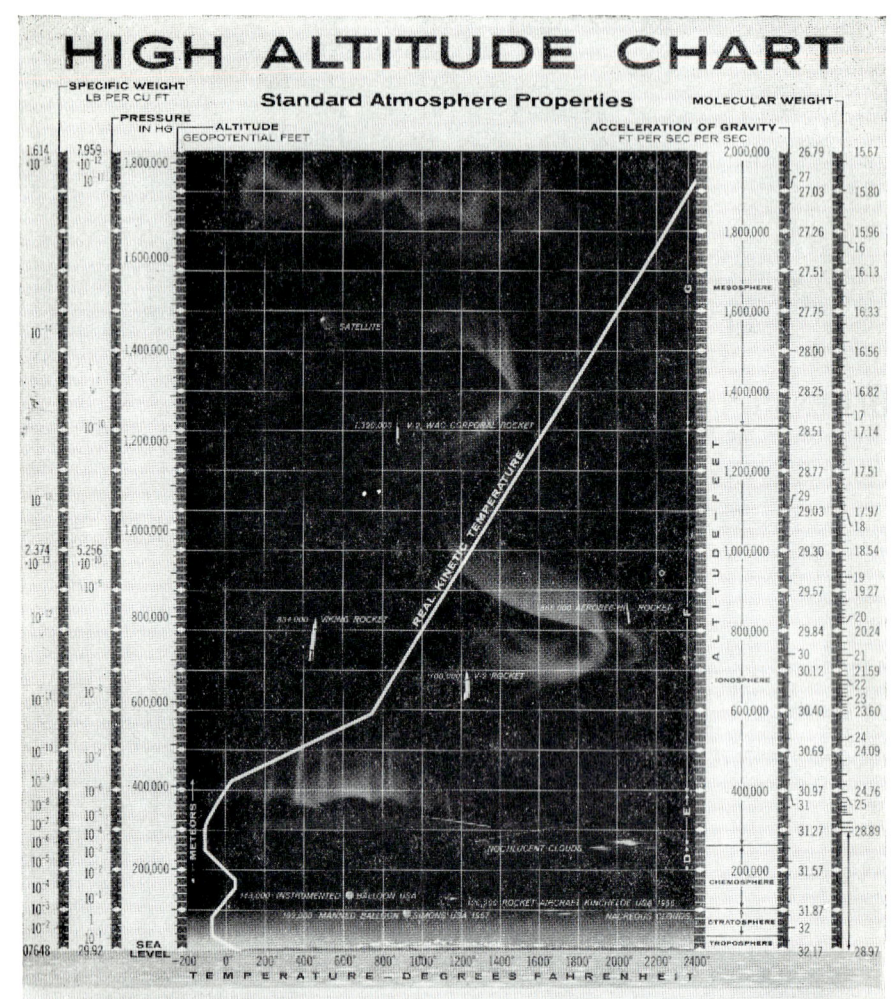

Used by permission of The Garrett Corporation. Copyright, 1958.

Appendix 375

ATMOSPHERE CHART

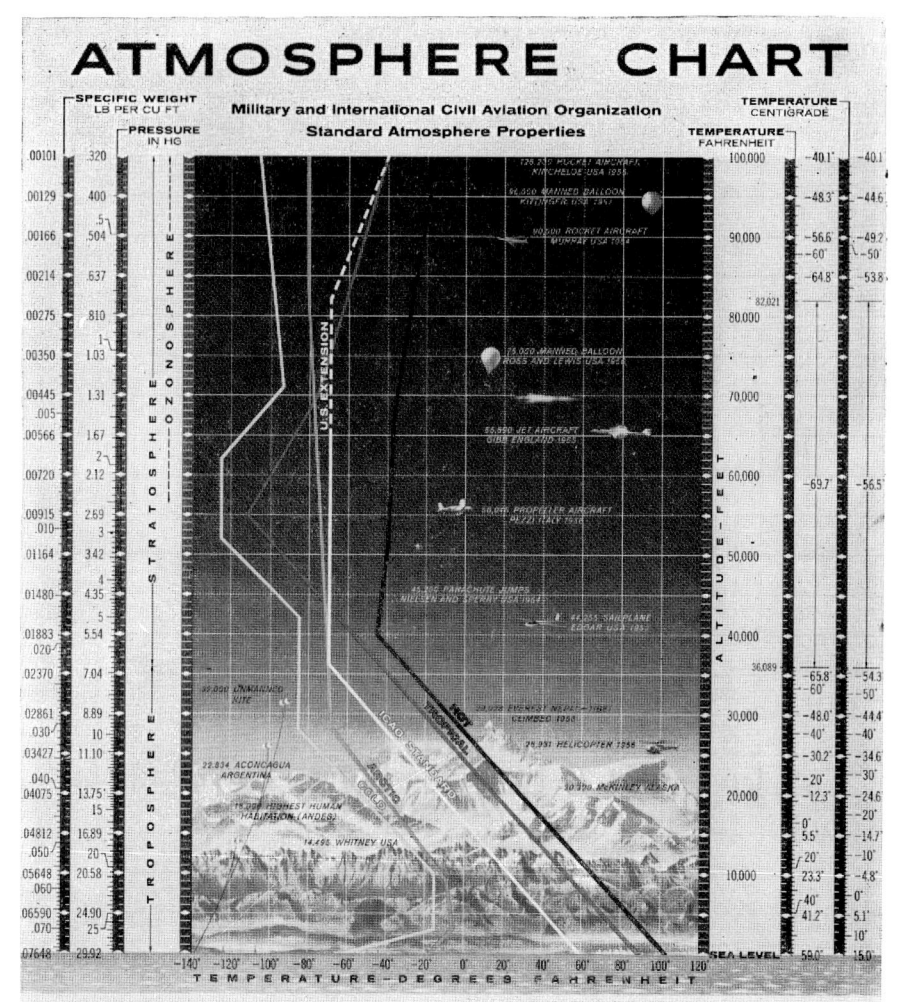

This chart presents the latest recognized standard values of temperature, pressure and specific weight of the air for altitudes up to 100,000 feet. The pictorial inserts represent steps in man's achievement in learning to reach and to exist at high altitudes. From sea level to 65,800 feet the columns on the sides and the central profile all refer to the International Civil Aviation Organization Standard Atmosphere. The NACA Standard Atmosphere, 1955, and the ARDC Model Atmosphere, 1956, are consistent with the ICAO Standard Atmosphere up to 65,800 feet. Above that altitude the data in the columns and the dashed portion of the central profile are taken from the U. S. Extension to the ICAO Standard Atmosphere and the ARDC Model Atmosphere, 1956, which are in agreement. The pressure and specific weight values shown are consistent only with the Standard temperature profile. The hot and cold profiles represent U. S. Military extreme temperature criteria. The tropical and arctic profiles represent U.S. Military homogeneous atmospheres for the tropical and arctic regions.

Used by permission of the Garrett Corporation. Copyright, 1958.

LOGARITHMS

	0	1	2	3	4	5	6	7	8	9
10	0000	0043	0086	0128	0170	0212	0253	0294	0334	0374
11	0414	0453	0492	0531	0569	0607	0645	0682	0719	0755
12	0792	0828	0864	0899	0934	0969	1004	1038	1072	1106
13	1139	1173	1206	1239	1271	1303	1335	1367	1399	1430
14	1461	1492	1523	1553	1584	1614	1644	1673	1703	1732
15	1761	1790	1818	1847	1875	1903	1931	1959	1987	2014
16	2041	2068	2095	2122	2148	2175	2201	2227	2253	2279
17	2304	2330	2355	2380	2405	2430	2455	2480	2504	2529
18	2553	2577	2601	2625	2648	2672	2695	2718	2742	2765
19	2788	2810	2833	2856	2878	2900	2923	2945	2967	2989
20	3010	3032	3054	3075	3096	3118	3139	3160	3181	3201
21	3222	3243	3263	3284	3304	3324	3345	3365	3385	3404
22	3424	3444	3464	3483	3502	3522	3541	3560	3579	3598
23	3617	3636	3655	3674	3692	3711	3729	3747	3766	3784
24	3802	3820	3838	3856	3874	3892	3909	3927	3945	3962
25	3979	3997	4014	4031	4048	4065	4082	4099	4116	4133
26	4150	4166	4183	4200	4216	4232	4249	4265	4281	4298
27	4314	4330	4346	4362	4378	4393	4409	4425	4440	4456
28	4472	4487	4502	4518	4533	4548	4564	4579	4594	4609
29	4624	4639	4654	4669	4683	4698	4713	4728	4742	4757
30	4771	4786	4800	4814	4829	4843	4857	4871	4886	4900
31	4914	4928	4942	4955	4969	4983	4997	5011	5024	5038
32	5051	5065	5079	5092	5105	5119	5132	5145	5159	5172
33	5185	5198	5211	5224	5237	5250	5263	5276	5289	5302
34	5315	5328	5340	5353	5366	5378	5391	5403	5416	5428
35	5441	5453	5465	5478	5490	5502	5514	5527	5539	5551
36	5563	5575	5587	5599	5611	5623	5635	5647	5658	5670
37	5682	5694	5705	5717	5729	5740	5752	5763	5775	5786
38	5798	5809	5821	5832	5843	5855	5866	5877	5888	5899
39	5911	5922	5933	5944	5955	5966	5977	5988	5999	6010
40	6021	6031	6042	6053	6064	6075	6085	6096	6107	6117
41	6128	6138	6149	6160	6170	6180	6191	6201	6212	6222
42	6232	6243	6253	6263	6274	6284	6294	6304	6314	6325
43	6335	6345	6355	6365	6375	6385	6395	6405	6415	6425
44	6435	6444	6454	6464	6474	6484	6493	6503	6513	6522
45	6532	6542	6551	6561	6571	6580	6590	6599	6609	6618
46	6628	6637	6646	6656	6665	6675	6684	6693	6702	6712
47	6721	6730	6739	6749	6758	6767	6776	6785	6794	6803
48	6812	6821	6830	6839	6848	6857	6866	6875	6884	6893
49	6902	6911	6920	6928	6937	6946	6955	6964	6972	6981
50	6990	6998	7007	7016	7024	7033	7042	7050	7059	7067
51	7076	7084	7093	7101	7110	7118	7126	7135	7143	7152
52	7160	7168	7177	7185	7193	7202	7210	7218	7226	7235
53	7243	7251	7259	7267	7275	7284	7292	7300	7308	7316
54	7324	7332	7340	7348	7356	7364	7372	7380	7388	7396

LOGARITHMS

	0	1	2	3	4	5	6	7	8	9
55	7404	7412	7419	7427	7435	7443	7451	7459	7466	7474
56	7482	7490	7497	7505	7513	7520	7528	7536	7543	7551
57	7559	7566	7574	7582	7589	7597	7604	7612	7619	7627
58	7634	7642	7649	7657	7664	7672	7679	7686	7694	7701
59	7709	7716	7723	7731	7738	7745	7752	7760	7767	7774
60	7782	7789	7796	7803	7810	7818	7825	7832	7839	7846
61	7853	7860	7868	7875	7882	7889	7896	7903	7910	7917
62	7924	7931	7938	7945	7952	7959	7966	7973	7980	7987
63	7993	8000	8007	8014	8021	8028	8035	8041	8048	8055
64	8062	8069	8075	8082	8089	8096	8102	8109	8116	8122
65	8129	8136	8142	8149	8156	8162	8169	8176	8182	8189
66	8195	8202	8209	8215	8222	8228	8235	8241	8248	8254
67	8261	8267	8274	8280	8287	8293	8299	8306	8312	8319
68	8325	8331	8338	8344	8351	8357	8363	8370	8376	8382
69	8388	8395	8401	8407	8414	8420	8426	8432	8439	8445
70	8451	8457	8463	8470	8476	8482	8488	8494	8500	8506
71	8513	8519	8525	8531	8537	8543	8549	8555	8561	8567
72	8573	8579	8585	8591	8597	8603	8609	8615	8621	8627
73	8633	8639	8645	8651	8657	8663	8669	8675	8681	8686
74	8692	8698	8704	8710	8716	8722	8727	8733	8739	8745
75	8751	8756	8762	8768	8774	8779	8785	8791	8797	8802
76	8808	8814	8820	8825	8831	8837	8842	8848	8854	8859
77	8865	8871	8876	8882	8887	8893	8899	8904	8910	8915
78	8921	8927	8932	8938	8943	8949	8954	8960	8965	8971
79	8976	8982	8987	8993	8998	9004	9009	9015	9020	9025
80	9031	9036	9042	9047	9053	9058	9063	9069	9074	9079
81	9085	9090	9096	9101	9106	9112	9117	9122	9128	9133
82	9138	9143	9149	9154	9159	9165	9170	9175	9180	9186
83	9191	9196	9201	9206	9212	9217	9222	9227	9232	9238
84	9243	9248	9253	9258	9263	9269	9274	9279	9284	9289
85	9294	9299	9304	9309	9315	9320	9325	9330	9335	9340
86	9345	9350	9355	9360	9365	9370	9375	9380	9385	9390
87	9395	9400	9405	9410	9415	9420	9425	9430	9435	9440
88	9445	9450	9455	9460	9465	9469	9474	9479	9484	9489
89	9494	9499	9504	9509	9513	9518	9523	9528	9533	9538
90	9542	9547	9552	9557	9562	9566	9571	9576	9581	9586
91	9590	9595	9600	9605	9609	9614	9619	9624	9628	9633
92	9638	9643	9647	9652	9657	9661	9666	9671	9675	9680
93	9685	9689	9694	9699	9703	9708	9713	9717	9722	9727
94	9731	9736	9741	9745	9750	9754	9759	9763	9768	9773
95	9777	9782	9786	9791	9795	9800	9805	9809	9814	9818
96	9823	9827	9832	9835	9841	9845	9850	9854	9859	9863
97	9868	9872	9877	9881	9886	9890	9894	9899	9903	9908
98	9912	9917	9921	9926	9930	9934	9939	9943	9948	9952
99	9956	9961	9965	9969	9974	9978	9983	9987	9991	9996

FOUR PLACE TRIGONOMETRIC FUNCTIONS*

[Characteristics of Logarithms omitted—determine by the usual rule from the value]

Radians	Degrees	Sine Value	Sine Log₁₀	Tangent Value	Tangent Log₁₀	Cotangent Value	Cotangent Log₁₀	Cosine Value	Cosine Log₁₀		
.0000	0° 00′	.0000	—	.0000	—	—	—	1.0000	.0000	90° 00′	1.5708
.0029	10	.0029	.4637	.0029	.4637	343.77	.5363	1.0000	.0000	50	1.5679
.0058	20	.0058	.7648	.0058	.7648	171.89	.2352	1.0000	.0000	40	1.5650
.0087	30	.0087	.9408	.0087	.9409	114.59	.0591	1.0000	.0000	30	1.5621
.0116	40	.0116	.0658	.0116	.0658	85.940	.9342	.9999	.0000	20	1.5592
.0145	50	.0145	.1627	.0145	.1627	68.750	.8373	.9999	.0000	10	1.5563
.0175	1° 00′	.0175	.2419	.0175	.2419	57.290	.7581	.9998	.9999	89° 00′	1.5533
.0204	10	.0204	.3088	.0204	.3089	49.104	.6911	.9998	.9999	50	1.5504
.0233	20	.0233	.3668	.0233	.3669	42.964	.6331	.9997	.9999	40	1.5475
.0262	30	.0262	.4179	.0262	.4181	38.188	.5819	.9997	.9999	30	1.5446
.0291	40	.0291	.4637	.0291	.4638	34.368	.5362	.9996	.9998	20	1.5417
.0320	50	.0320	.5050	.0320	.5053	31.242	.4947	.9995	.9998	10	1.5388
.0349	2° 00′	.0349	.5428	.0349	.5431	28.636	.4569	.9994	.9997	88° 00′	1.5359
.0378	10	.0378	.5776	.0378	.5779	26.432	.4221	.9993	.9997	50	1.5330
.0407	20	.0407	.6097	.0407	.6101	24.542	.3899	.9992	.9996	40	1.5301
.0436	30	.0436	.6397	.0437	.6401	22.904	.3599	.9990	.9996	30	1.5272
.0465	40	.0465	.6677	.0466	.6682	21.470	.3318	.9989	.9995	20	1.5243
.0495	50	.0494	.6940	.0495	.6945	20.206	.3055	.9988	.9995	10	1.5213
.0524	3° 00′	.0523	.7188	.0524	.7194	19.081	.2806	.9986	.9994	87° 00′	1.5184
.0553	10	.0552	.7423	.0553	.7429	18.075	.2571	.9985	.9993	50	1.5155
.0582	20	.0581	.7645	.0582	.7652	17.169	.2348	.9983	.9993	40	1.5126
.0611	30	.0610	.7857	.0612	.7865	16.350	.2135	.9981	.9992	30	1.5097
.0640	40	.0640	.8059	.0641	.8067	15.605	.1933	.9980	.9991	20	1.5068
.0669	50	.0669	.8251	.0670	.8261	14.924	.1739	.9978	.9990	10	1.5039
.0698	4° 00′	.0698	.8436	.0699	.8446	14.301	.1554	.9976	.9989	86° 00′	1.5010
.0727	10	.0727	.8613	.0729	.8624	13.727	.1376	.9974	.9989	50	1.4981
.0756	20	.0756	.8783	.0758	.8795	13.197	.1205	.9971	.9988	40	1.4952
.0785	30	.0785	.8946	.0787	.8960	12.706	.1040	.9969	.9987	30	1.4923
.0814	40	.0814	.9104	.0816	.9118	12.251	.0882	.9967	.9986	20	1.4893
.0844	50	.0843	.9256	.0846	.9272	11.826	.0728	.9964	.9985	10	1.4864
.0873	5° 00′	.0872	.9403	.0875	.9420	11.430	.0580	.9962	.9983	85° 00′	1.4835
.0902	10	.0901	.9545	.0904	.9563	11.059	.0437	.9959	.9982	50	1.4806
.0931	20	.0929	.9682	.0934	.9701	10.712	.0299	.9957	.9981	40	1.4777
.0960	30	.0958	.9816	.0963	.9836	10.385	.0164	.9954	.9980	30	1.4748
.0989	40	.0987	.9945	.0992	.9966	10.078	.0034	.9951	.9979	20	1.4719
.1018	50	.1016	.0070	.1022	.0093	9.7882	.9907	.9948	.9977	10	1.4690
.1047	6° 00′	.1045	.0192	.1051	.0216	9.5144	.9784	.9945	.9976	84° 00′	1.4661
.1076	10	.1074	.0311	.1080	.0336	9.2553	.9664	.9942	.9975	50	1.4632
.1105	20	.1103	.0426	.1110	.0453	9.0098	.9547	.9939	.9973	40	1.4603
.1134	30	.1132	.0539	.1139	.0567	8.7769	.9433	.9936	.9972	30	1.4573
.1164	40	.1161	.0648	.1169	.0678	8.5555	.9322	.9932	.9971	20	1.4544
.1193	50	.1190	.0755	.1198	.0786	8.3450	.9214	.9929	.9969	10	1.4515
.1222	7° 00′	.1219	.0859	.1228	.0891	8.1443	.9109	.9925	.9968	83° 00′	1.4486
.1251	10	.1248	.0961	.1257	.0995	7.9530	.9005	.9922	.9966	50	1.4457
.1280	20	.1276	.1060	.1287	.1096	7.7704	.8904	.9918	.9964	40	1.4428
.1309	30	.1305	.1157	.1317	.1194	7.5958	.8806	.9914	.9963	30	1.4399
.1338	40	.1334	.1252	.1346	.1291	7.4287	.8709	.9911	.9961	20	1.4370
.1367	50	.1363	.1345	.1376	.1385	7.2687	.8615	.9907	.9959	10	1.4341
.1396	8° 00′	.1392	.1436	.1405	.1478	7.1154	.8522	.9903	.9958	82° 00′	1.4312
.1425	10	.1421	.1525	.1435	.1569	6.9682	.8431	.9899	.9956	50	1.4283
.1454	20	.1449	.1612	.1465	.1658	6.8269	.8342	.9894	.9954	40	1.4254
.1484	30	.1478	.1697	.1495	.1745	6.6912	.8255	.9890	.9952	30	1.4224
.1513	40	.1507	.1781	.1524	.1831	6.5606	.8169	.9886	.9950	20	1.4195
.1542	50	.1536	.1863	.1554	.1915	6.4348	.8085	.9881	.9948	10	1.4166
.1571	9° 00′	.1564	.1943	.1584	.1997	6.3138	.8003	.9877	.9946	81° 00′	1.4137
		Value Log₁₀ Cosine		Value Log₁₀ Cotangent		Value Log₁₀ Tangent		Value Log₁₀ Sine		Degrees	Radians

* The following table is from *The Macmillan Logarithmic and Trigonometric Tables*, Revised Edition, prepared under the direction of Earle Raymond Hedrick. Copyright 1913 and 1920 by the Macmillan Company; 1941 by Grace G. Kenyon and Stanley Ingold; 1948 by Helen B. Hedrick. Reproduced by permission of the publisher.

Appendix

FOUR PLACE TRIGONOMETRIC FUNCTIONS

[Characteristics of Logarithms omitted—determine by the usual rule from the value]

Radians	Degrees	Sine Value	Sine Log₁₀	Tangent Value	Tangent Log₁₀	Cotangent Value	Cotangent Log₁₀	Cosine Value	Cosine Log₁₀	Degrees	Radians
.1571	9° 00′	.1564	.1943	.1584	.1997	6.3138	.8003	.9877	.9946	81° 00′	1.4137
.1600	10	.1593	.2022	.1614	.2078	6.1970	.7922	.9872	.9944	50	1.4108
.1629	20	.1622	.2100	.1644	.2158	6.0844	.7842	.9868	.9942	40	1.4079
.1658	30	.1650	.2176	.1673	.2236	5.9758	.7764	.9863	.9940	30	1.4050
.1687	40	.1679	.2251	.1703	.2313	5.8708	.7687	.9858	.9938	20	1.4021
.1716	50	.1708	.2324	.1733	.2389	5.7694	.7611	.9853	.9936	10	1.3992
.1745	10° 00′	.1736	.2397	.1763	.2463	5.6713	.7537	.9848	.9934	80° 00′	1.3963
.1774	10	.1765	.2468	.1793	.2536	5.5764	.7464	.9843	.9931	50	1.3934
.1804	20	.1794	.2538	.1823	.2609	5.4845	.7391	.9838	.9929	40	1.3904
.1833	30	.1822	.2606	.1853	.2680	5.3955	.7320	.9833	.9927	30	1.3875
.1862	40	.1851	.2674	.1883	.2750	5.3093	.7250	.9827	.9924	20	1.3846
.1891	50	.1880	.2740	.1914	.2819	5.2257	.7181	.9822	.9922	10	1.3817
.1920	11° 00′	.1908	.2806	.1944	.2887	5.1446	.7113	.9816	.9919	79° 00′	1.3788
.1949	10	.1937	.2870	.1974	.2953	5.0658	.7047	.9811	.9917	50	1.3759
.1978	20	.1965	.2934	.2004	.3020	4.9894	.6980	.9805	.9914	40	1.3730
.2007	30	.1994	.2997	.2035	.3085	4.9152	.6915	.9799	.9912	30	1.3701
.2036	40	.2022	.3058	.2065	.3149	4.8430	.6851	.9793	.9909	20	1.3672
.2065	50	.2051	.3119	.2095	.3212	4.7729	.6788	.9787	.9907	10	1.3643
.2094	12° 00′	.2079	.3179	.2126	.3275	4.7046	.6725	.9781	.9904	78° 00′	1.3614
.2123	10	.2108	.3238	.2156	.3336	4.6382	.6664	.9775	.9901	50	1.3584
.2153	20	.2136	.3296	.2186	.3397	4.5736	.6603	.9769	.9899	40	1.3555
.2182	30	.2164	.3353	.2217	.3458	4.5107	.6542	.9763	.9896	30	1.3526
.2211	40	.2193	.3410	.2247	.3517	4.4494	.6483	.9757	.9893	20	1.3497
.2240	50	.2221	.3466	.2278	.3576	4.3897	.6424	.9750	.9890	10	1.3468
.2269	13° 00′	.2250	.3521	.2309	.3634	4.3315	.6366	.9744	.9887	77° 00′	1.3439
.2298	10	.2278	.3575	.2339	.3691	4.2747	.6309	.9737	.9884	50	1.3410
.2327	20	.2306	.3629	.2370	.3748	4.2193	.6252	.9730	.9881	40	1.3381
.2356	30	.2334	.3682	.2401	.3804	4.1653	.6196	.9724	.9878	30	1.3352
.2385	40	.2363	.3734	.2432	.3859	4.1126	.6141	.9717	.9875	20	1.3323
.2414	50	.2391	.3786	.2462	.3914	4.0611	.6086	.9710	.9872	10	1.3294
.2443	14° 00′	.2419	.3837	.2493	.3968	4.0108	.6032	.9703	.9869	76° 00′	1.3265
.2473	10	.2447	.3887	.2524	.4021	3.9617	.5979	.9696	.9866	50	1.3235
.2502	20	.2476	.3937	.2555	.4074	3.9136	.5926	.9689	.9863	40	1.3206
.2531	30	.2504	.3986	.2586	.4127	3.8667	.5873	.9681	.9859	30	1.3177
.2560	40	.2532	.4035	.2617	.4178	3.8208	.5822	.9674	.9856	20	1.3148
.2589	50	.2560	.4083	.2648	.4230	3.7760	.5770	.9667	.9853	10	1.3119
.2618	15° 00′	.2588	.4130	.2679	.4281	3.7321	.5719	.9659	.9849	75° 00′	1.3090
.2647	10	.2616	.4177	.2711	.4331	3.6891	.5669	.9652	.9846	50	1.3061
.2676	20	.2644	.4223	.2742	.4381	3.6470	.5619	.9644	.9843	40	1.3032
.2705	30	.2672	.4269	.2773	.4430	3.6059	.5570	.9636	.9839	30	1.3003
.2734	40	.2700	.4314	.2805	.4479	3.5656	.5521	.9628	.9836	20	1.2974
.2763	50	.2728	.4359	.2836	.4527	3.5261	.5473	.9621	.9832	10	1.2945
.2793	16° 00′	.2756	.4403	.2867	.4575	3.4874	.5425	.9613	.9828	74° 00′	1.2915
.2822	10	.2784	.4447	.2899	.4622	3.4495	.5378	.9605	.9825	50	1.2886
.2851	20	.2812	.4491	.2931	.4669	3.4124	.5331	.9596	.9821	40	1.2857
.2880	30	.2840	.4533	.2962	.4716	3.3759	.5284	.9588	.9817	30	1.2828
.2909	40	.2868	.4576	.2994	.4762	3.3402	.5238	.9580	.9814	20	1.2799
.2938	50	.2896	.4618	.3026	.4808	3.3052	.5192	.9572	.9810	10	1.2770
.2967	17° 00′	.2924	.4659	.3057	.4853	3.2709	.5147	.9563	.9806	73° 00′	1.2741
.2996	10	.2952	.4700	.3089	.4898	3.2371	.5102	.9555	.9802	50	1.2712
.3025	20	.2979	.4741	.3121	.4943	3.2041	.5057	.9546	.9798	40	1.2683
.3054	30	.3007	.4781	.3153	.4987	3.1716	.5013	.9537	.9794	30	1.2654
.3083	40	.3035	.4821	.3185	.5031	3.1397	.4969	.9528	.9790	20	1.2625
.3113	50	.3062	.4861	.3217	.5075	3.1084	.4925	.9520	.9786	10	1.2595
.3142	18° 00′	.3090	.4900	.3249	.5118	3.0777	.4882	.9511	.9782	72° 00′	1.2566
		Value Cosine	Log₁₀	Value Cotangent	Log₁₀	Value Tangent	Log₁₀	Value Sine	Log₁₀	Degrees	Radians

FOUR PLACE TRIGONOMETRIC FUNCTIONS

[Characteristics of Logarithms omitted—determine by the usual rule from the value]

Radians	Degrees	Sine Value	Sine Log₁₀	Tangent Value	Tangent Log₁₀	Cotangent Value	Cotangent Log₁₀	Cosine Value	Cosine Log₁₀		
.3142	18° 00′	.3090	.4900	.3249	.5118	3.0777	.4882	.9511	.9782	72° 00′	1.2566
.3171	10	.3118	.4939	.3281	.5161	3.0475	.4839	.9502	.9778	50	1.2537
.3200	20	.3145	.4977	.3314	.5203	3.0178	.4797	.9492	.9774	40	1.2508
.3229	30	.3173	.5015	.3346	.5245	2.9887	.4755	.9483	.9770	30	1.2479
.3258	40	.3201	.5052	.3378	.5287	2.9600	.4713	.9474	.9765	20	1.2450
.3287	50	.3228	.5090	.3411	.5329	2.9319	.4671	.9465	.9761	10	1.2421
.3316	19° 00′	.3256	.5126	.3443	.5370	2.9042	.4630	.9455	.9757	71° 00′	1.2392
.3345	10	.3283	.5163	.3476	.5411	2.8770	.4589	.9446	.9752	50	1.2363
.3374	20	.3311	.5199	.3508	.5451	2.8502	.4549	.9436	.9748	40	1.2334
.3403	30	.3338	.5235	.3541	.5491	2.8239	.4509	.9426	.9743	30	1.2305
.3432	40	.3365	.5270	.3574	.5531	2.7980	.4469	.9417	.9739	20	1.2275
.3462	50	.3393	.5306	.3607	.5571	2.7725	.4429	.9407	.9734	10	1.2246
.3491	20° 00′	.3420	.5341	.3640	.5611	2.7475	.4389	.9397	.9730	70° 00′	1.2217
.3520	10	.3448	.5375	.3673	.5650	2.7228	.4350	.9387	.9725	50	1.2188
.3549	20	.3475	.5409	.3706	.5689	2.6985	.4311	.9377	.9721	40	1.2159
.3578	30	.3502	.5443	.3739	.5727	2.6746	.4273	.9367	.9716	30	1.2130
.3607	40	.3529	.5477	.3772	.576	2.6511	.4234	.9356	.9711	20	1.2101
.3636	50	.3557	.5510	.3805	.5804	2.6279	.4196	.9346	.9706	10	1.2072
.3665	21° 00′	.3584	.5543	.3839	.5842	2.6051	.4158	.9336	.9702	69° 00′	1.2043
.3694	10	.3611	.5576	.3872	.5879	2.5826	.4121	.9325	.9697	50	1.2014
.3723	20	.3638	.5609	.3906	.5917	2.5605	.4083	.9315	.9692	40	1.1985
.3752	30	.3665	.5641	.3939	.5954	2.5386	.4046	.9304	.9687	30	1.1956
.3782	40	.3692	.5673	.3973	.5991	2.5172	.4009	.9293	.9682	20	1.1926
.3811	50	.3719	.5704	.4006	.6028	2.4960	.3972	.9283	.9677	10	1.1897
.3840	22° 00′	.3746	.5736	.4040	.6064	2.4751	.3936	.9272	.9672	68° 00′	1.1868
.3869	10	.3773	.5767	.4074	.6100	2.4545	.3900	.9261	.9667	50	1.1839
.3898	20	.3800	.5798	.4108	.6136	2.4342	.3864	.9250	.9661	40	1.1810
.3927	30	.3827	.5828	.4142	.6172	2.4142	.3828	.9239	.9656	30	1.1781
.3956	40	.3854	.5859	.4176	.6208	2.3945	.3792	.9228	.9651	20	1.1752
.3985	50	.3881	.5889	.4210	.6243	2.3750	.3757	.9216	.9646	10	1.1723
.4014	23° 00′	.3907	.5919	.4245	.6279	2.3559	.3721	.9205	.9640	67° 00′	1.1694
.4043	10	.3934	.5948	.4279	.6314	2.3369	.3686	.9194	.9635	50	1.1665
.4072	20	.3961	.5978	.4314	.6348	2.3183	.3652	.9182	.9629	40	1.1636
.4102	30	.3987	.6007	.4348	.6383	2.2998	.3617	.9171	.9624	30	1.1606
.4131	40	.4014	.6036	.4383	.6417	2.2817	.3583	.9159	.9618	20	1.1577
.4160	50	.4041	.6065	.4417	.6452	2.2637	.3548	.9147	.9613	10	1.1548
.4189	24° 00′	.4067	.6093	.4452	.6486	2.2460	.3514	.9135	.9607	66° 00′	1.1519
.4218	10	.4094	.6121	.4487	.6520	2.2286	.3480	.9124	.9602	50	1.1490
.4247	20	.4120	.6149	.4522	.6553	2.2113	.3447	.9112	.9596	40	1.1461
.4276	30	.4147	.6177	.4557	.6587	2.1943	.3413	.9100	.9590	30	1.1432
.4305	40	.4173	.6205	.4592	.6620	2.1775	.3380	.9088	.9584	20	1.1403
.4334	50	.4200	.6232	.4628	.6654	2.1609	.3346	.9075	.9579	10	1.1374
.4363	25° 00′	.4226	.6259	.4663	.6687	2.1445	.3313	.9063	.9573	65° 00′	1.1345
.4392	10	.4253	.6286	.4699	.6720	2.1283	.3280	.9051	.9567	50	1.1316
.4422	20	.4279	.6313	.4734	.6752	2.1123	.3248	.9038	.9561	40	1.1286
.4451	30	.4305	.6340	.4770	.6785	2.0965	.3215	.9026	.9555	30	1.1257
.4480	40	.4331	.6366	.4806	.6817	2.0809	.3183	.9013	.9549	20	1.1228
.4509	50	.4358	.6392	.4841	.6850	2.0655	.3150	.9001	.9543	10	1.1199
.4538	26° 00′	.4384	.6418	.4877	.6882	2.0503	.3118	.8988	.9537	64° 00′	1.1170
.4567	10	.4410	.6444	.4913	.6914	2.0353	.3086	.8975	.9530	50	1.1141
.4596	20	.4436	.6470	.4950	.6946	2.0204	.3054	.8962	.9524	40	1.1112
.4625	30	.4462	.6495	.4986	.6977	2.0057	.3023	.8949	.9518	30	1.1083
.4654	40	.4488	.6521	.5022	.7009	1.9912	.2991	.8936	.9512	20	1.1054
.4683	50	.4514	.6546	.5059	.7040	1.9768	.2960	.8923	.9505	10	1.1025
.4712	27° 00′	.4540	.6570	.5095	.7072	1.9626	.2928	.8910	.9499	63° 00′	1.0996
		Value Log₁₀ Cosine		Value Log₁₀ Cotangent		Value Log₁₀ Tangent		Value Log₁₀ Sine		Degrees	Radians

Appendix

FOUR PLACE TRIGONOMETRIC FUNCTIONS

[Characteristics of Logarithms omitted—determine by the usual rule from the **value**]

Radians	Degrees	Sine Value	Sine Log₁₀	Tangent Value	Tangent Log₁₀	Cotangent Value	Cotangent Log₁₀	Cosine Value	Cosine Log₁₀		
.4712	27° 00'	.4540	.6570	.5095	.7072	1.9626	.2928	.8910	.9499	63° 00'	1.0996
.4741	10	.4566	.6595	.5132	.7103	1.9486	.2897	.8897	.9492	50	1.0966
.4771	20	.4592	.6620	.5169	.7134	1.9347	.2866	.8884	.9486	40	1.0937
.4800	30	.4617	.6644	.5206	.7165	1.9210	.2835	.8870	.9479	30	1.0908
.4829	40	.4643	.6668	.5243	.7196	1.9074	.2804	.8857	.9473	20	1.0879
.4858	50	.4669	.6692	.5280	.7226	1.8940	.2774	.8843	.9466	10	1.0850
.4887	28° 00'	.4695	.6716	.5317	.7257	1.8807	.2743	.8829	.9459	62° 00'	1.0821
.4916	10	.4720	.6740	.5354	.7287	1.8676	.2713	.8816	.9453	50	1.0792
.4945	20	.4746	.6763	.5392	.7317	1.8546	.2683	.8802	.9446	40	1.0763
.4974	30	.4772	.6787	.5430	.7348	1.8418	.2652	.8788	.9439	30	1.0734
.5003	40	.4797	.6810	.5467	.7378	1.8291	.2622	.8774	.9432	20	1.0705
.5032	50	.4823	.6833	.5505	.7408	1.8165	.2592	.8760	.9425	10	1.0676
.5061	29° 00'	.4848	.6856	.5543	.7438	1.8040	.2562	.8746	.9418	61° 00'	1.0647
.5091	10	.4874	.6878	.5581	.7467	1.7917	.2533	.8732	.9411	50	1.0617
.5120	20	.4899	.6901	.5619	.7497	1.7796	.2503	.8718	.9404	40	1.0588
.5149	30	.4924	.6923	.5658	.7526	1.7675	.2474	.8704	.9397	30	1.0559
.5178	40	.4950	.6946	.5696	.7556	1.7556	.2444	.8689	.9390	20	1.0530
.5207	50	.4975	.6968	.5735	.7585	1.7437	.2415	.8675	.9383	10	1.0501
.5236	30° 00'	.5000	.6990	.5774	.7614	1.7321	.2386	.8660	.9375	60° 00'	1.0472
.5265	10	.5025	.7012	.5812	.7644	1.7205	.2356	.8646	.9368	50	1.0443
.5294	20	.5050	.7033	.5851	.7673	1.7090	.2327	.8631	.9361	40	1.0414
.5323	30	.5075	.7055	.5890	.7701	1.6977	.2299	.8616	.9353	30	1.0385
.5352	40	.5100	.7076	.5930	.7730	1.6864	.2270	.8601	.9346	20	1.0356
.5381	50	.5125	.7097	.5969	.7759	1.6753	.2241	.8587	.9338	10	1.0327
.5411	31° 00'	.5150	.7118	.6009	.7788	1.6643	.2212	.8572	.9331	59° 00'	1.0297
.5440	10	.5175	.7139	.6048	.7816	1.6534	.2184	.8557	.9323	50	1.0268
.5469	20	.5200	.7160	.6088	.7845	1.6426	.2155	.8542	.9315	40	1.0239
.5498	30	.5225	.7181	.6128	.7873	1.6319	.2127	.8526	.9308	30	1.0210
.5527	40	.5250	.7201	.6168	.7902	1.6212	.2098	.8511	.9300	20	1.0181
.5556	50	.5275	.7222	.6208	.7930	1.6107	.2070	.8496	.9292	10	1.0152
.5585	32° 00'	.5299	.7242	.6249	.7958	1.6003	.2042	.8480	.9284	58° 00'	1.0123
.5614	10	.5324	.7262	.6289	.7986	1.5900	.2014	.8465	.9276	50	1.0094
.5643	20	.5348	.7282	.6330	.8014	1.5798	.1986	.8450	.9268	40	1.0065
.5672	30	.5373	.7302	.6371	.8042	1.5697	.1958	.8434	.9260	30	1.0036
.5701	40	.5398	.7322	.6412	.8070	1.5597	.1930	.8418	.9252	20	1.0007
.5730	50	.5422	.7342	.6453	.8097	1.5497	.1903	.8403	.9244	10	.9977
.5760	33° 00'	.5446	.7361	.6494	.8125	1.5399	.1875	.8387	.9236	57° 00'	.9948
.5789	10	.5471	.7380	.6536	.8153	1.5301	.1847	.8371	.9228	50	.9919
.5818	20	.5495	.7400	.6577	.8180	1.5204	.1820	.8355	.9219	40	.9890
.5847	30	.5519	.7419	.6619	.8208	1.5108	.1792	.8339	.9211	30	.9861
.5876	40	.5544	.7438	.6661	.8235	1.5013	.1765	.8323	.9203	20	.9832
.5905	50	.5568	.7457	.6703	.8263	1.4919	.1737	.8307	.9194	10	.9803
.5934	34° 00'	.5592	.7476	.6745	.8290	1.4826	.1710	.8290	.9186	56° 00'	.9774
.5963	10	.5616	.7494	.6787	.8317	1.4733	.1683	.8274	.9177	50	.9745
.5992	20	.5640	.7513	.6830	.8344	1.4641	.1656	.8258	.9169	40	.9716
.6021	30	.5664	.7531	.6873	.8371	1.4550	.1629	.8241	.9160	30	.9687
.6050	40	.5688	.7550	.6916	.8398	1.4460	.1602	.8225	.9151	20	.9657
.6080	50	.5712	.7568	.6959	.8425	1.4370	.1575	.8208	.9142	10	.9628
.6109	35° 00'	.5736	.7586	.7002	.8452	1.4281	.1548	.8192	.9134	55° 00'	.9599
.6138	10	.5760	.7604	.7046	.8479	1.4193	.1521	.8175	.9125	50	.9570
.6167	20	.5783	.7622	.7089	.8506	1.4106	.1494	.8158	.9116	40	.9541
.6196	30	.5807	.7640	.7133	.8533	1.4019	.1467	.8141	.9107	30	.9512
.6225	40	.5831	.7657	.7177	.8559	1.3934	.1441	.8124	.9098	20	.9483
.6254	50	.5854	.7675	.7221	.8586	1.3848	.1414	.8107	.9089	10	.9454
.6283	36° 00'	.5878	.7692	.7265	.8613	1.3764	.1387	.8090	.9080	54° 00'	.9425
		Value Log₁₀ Cosine		Value Log₁₀ Cotangent		Value Log₁₀ Tangent		Value Log₁₀ Sine		Degrees	Radians

FOUR PLACE TRIGONOMETRIC FUNCTIONS

[Characteristics of Logarithms omitted—determine by the usual rule from the value]

Radians	Degrees	Sine Value	Sine Log₁₀	Tangent Value	Tangent Log₁₀	Cotangent Value	Cotangent Log₁₀	Cosine Value	Cosine Log₁₀		
.6283	36° 00′	.5878	.7692	.7265	.8613	1.3764	.1387	.8090	.9080	54° 00′	.9425
.6312	10	.5901	.7710	.7310	.8639	1.3680	.1361	.8073	.9070	50	.9396
.6341	20	.5925	.7727	.7355	.8666	1.3597	.1334	.8056	.9061	40	.9367
.6370	30	.5948	.7744	.7400	.8692	1.3514	.1308	.8039	.9052	30	.9338
.6400	40	.5972	.7761	.7445	.8718	1.3432	.1282	.8021	.9042	20	.9308
.6429	50	.5995	.7778	.7490	.8745	1.3351	.1255	.8004	.9033	10	.9279
.6458	37° 00′	.6018	.7795	.7536	.8771	1.3270	.1229	.7986	.9023	53° 00′	.9250
.6487	10	.6041	.7811	.7581	.8797	1.3190	.1203	.7969	.9014	50	.9221
.6516	20	.6065	.7828	.7627	.8824	1.3111	.1176	.7951	.9004	40	.9192
.6545	30	.6088	.7844	.7673	.8850	1.3032	.1150	.7934	.8995	30	.9163
.6574	40	.6111	.7861	.7720	.8876	1.2954	.1124	.7916	.8985	20	.9134
.6603	50	.6134	.7877	.7766	.8902	1.2876	.1098	.7898	.8975	10	.9105
.6632	38° 00′	.6157	.7893	.7813	.8928	1.2799	.1072	.7880	.8965	52° 00′	.9076
.6661	10	.6180	.7910	.7860	.8954	1.2723	.1046	.7862	.8955	50	.9047
.6690	20	.6202	.7926	.7907	.8980	1.2647	.1020	.7844	.8945	40	.9018
.6720	30	.6225	.7941	.7954	.9006	1.2572	.0994	.7826	.8935	30	.8988
.6749	40	.6248	.7957	.8002	.9032	1.2497	.0968	.7808	.8925	20	.8959
.6778	50	.6271	.7973	.8050	.9058	1.2423	.0942	.7790	.8915	10	.8930
.6807	39° 00′	.6293	.7989	.8098	.9084	1.2349	.0916	.7771	.8905	51° 00′	.8901
.6836	10	.6316	.8004	.8146	.9110	1.2276	.0890	.7753	.8895	50	.8872
.6865	20	.6338	.8020	.8195	.9135	1.2203	.0865	.7735	.8884	40	.8843
.6894	30	.6361	.8035	.8243	.9161	1.2131	.0839	.7716	.8874	30	.8814
.6923	40	.6383	.8050	.8292	.9187	1.2059	.0813	.7698	.8864	20	.8785
.6952	50	.6406	.8066	.8342	.9212	1.1988	.0788	.7679	.8853	10	.8756
.6981	40° 00′	.6428	.8081	.8391	.9238	1.1918	.0762	.7660	.8843	50° 00′	.8727
.7010	10	.6450	.8096	.8441	.9264	1.1847	.0736	.7642	.8832	50	.8698
.7039	20	.6472	.8111	.8491	.9289	1.1778	.0711	.7623	.8821	40	.8668
.7069	30	.6494	.8125	.8541	.9315	1.1708	.0685	.7604	.8810	30	.8639
.7098	40	.6517	.8140	.8591	.9341	1.1640	.0659	.7585	.8800	20	.8610
.7127	50	.6539	.8155	.8642	.9366	1.1571	.0634	.7566	.8789	10	.8581
.7156	41° 00′	.6561	.8169	.8693	.9392	1.1504	.0608	.7547	.8778	49° 00′	.8552
.7185	10	.6583	.8184	.8744	.9417	1.1436	.0583	.7528	.8767	50	.8523
.7214	20	.6604	.8198	.8796	.9443	1.1369	.0557	.7509	.8756	40	.8494
.7243	30	.6626	.8213	.8847	.9468	1.1303	.0532	.7490	.8745	30	.8465
.7272	40	.6648	.8227	.8899	.9494	1.1237	.0506	.7470	.8733	20	.8436
.7301	50	.6670	.8241	.8952	.9519	1.1171	.0481	.7451	.8722	10	.8407
.7330	42° 00′	.6691	.8255	.9004	.9544	1.1106	.0456	.7431	.8711	48° 00′	.8378
.7359	10	.6713	.8269	.9057	.9570	1.1041	.0430	.7412	.8699	50	.8348
.7389	20	.6734	.8283	.9110	.9595	1.0977	.0405	.7392	.8688	40	.8319
.7418	30	.6756	.8297	.9163	.9621	1.0913	.0379	.7373	.8676	30	.8290
.7447	40	.6777	.8311	.9217	.9646	1.0850	.0354	.7353	.8665	20	.8261
.7476	50	.6799	.8324	.9271	.9671	1.0786	.0329	.7333	.8653	10	.8232
.7505	43° 00′	.6820	.8338	.9325	.9697	1.0724	.0303	.7314	.8641	47° 00′	.8203
.7534	10	.6841	.8351	.9380	.9722	1.0661	.0278	.7294	.8629	50	.8174
.7563	20	.6862	.8365	.9435	.9747	1.0599	.0253	.7274	.8618	40	.8145
.7592	30	.6884	.8378	.9490	.9772	1.0538	.0228	.7254	.8606	30	.8116
.7621	40	.6905	.8391	.9545	.9798	1.0477	.0202	.7234	.8594	20	.8087
.7650	50	.6926	.8405	.9601	.9823	1.0416	.0177	.7214	.8582	10	.8058
.7679	44° 00′	.6947	.8418	.9657	.9848	1.0355	.0152	.7193	.8569	46° 00′	.8029
.7709	10	.6967	.8431	.9713	.9874	1.0295	.0126	.7173	.8557	50	.7999
.7738	20	.6988	.8444	.9770	.9899	1.0235	.0101	.7153	.8545	40	.7970
.7767	30	.7009	.8457	.9827	.9924	1.0176	.0076	.7133	.8532	30	.7941
.7796	40	.7030	.8469	.9884	.9949	1.0117	.0051	.7112	.8520	20	.7912
.7825	50	.7050	.8482	.9942	.9975	1.0058	.0025	.7092	.8507	10	.7883
.7854	45° 00′	.7071	.8495	1.0000	.0000	1.0000	.0000	.7071	.8495	45° 00′	.7854
		Value Log₁₀ Cosine		Value Log₁₀ Cotangent		Value Log₁₀ Tangent		Value Log₁₀ Sine		Degrees	Radians

*Abbreviations for Engineering Terms**

absolute	abs
acre	spell out
acre-foot	acre-ft
air horsepower	air hp
alternating-current (as adjective)	a-c
ampere	amp
ampere-hour	amp-hr
amplitude, an elliptic function	am.
Angstrom unit	A
antilogarithm	antilog
atmosphere	atm
atomic weight	at. wt
average	avg
avoirdupois	avdp
azimuth	az or α
barometer	bar.
barrel	bbl
Baumé	Bé
board feet (feet board measure)	fbm
boiler pressure	spell out
boiling point	bp
brake horsepower	bhp
brake horsepower-hour	bhp-hr
Brinell hardness number	Bhn
British thermal unit	Btu or B
bushel	bu
calorie	cal
candle	c
candle-hour	c-hr
candlepower	cp
cent	c or ¢
center to center	c to c
centigram	cg
centiliter	cl
centimeter	cm
centimeter-gram-second (system)	cgs
chemical	chem
chemically pure	cp
circular	cir
circular mils	cir mils
coefficient	coef
cologarithm	colog
conductivity	cond
constant	const
cord	cd
cosecant	csc
cosine	cos
cosine of the amplitude, an elliptic function	cn
cotangent	cot
coulomb	spell out
cubic	cu
cubic centimeter	cu cm, cm^3
cubic feet per minute	cfm or ft^3/min
cubic feet per second	cfs or ft^3/sec
cubic foot	cu ft or ft^3
cubic inch	cu in. or in.^{3}
cubic meter	cu m or m^3
cubic micron	cu μ or cu mu or μ^3
cubic millimeter	cu mm or mm^3
cubic yard	cu yd or yd^3
cylinder	cyl
decibel	db
degree	deg or °
degree centigrade	C
degree Fahrenheit	F
degree Kelvin	K
degree Réaumur	R
diameter	diam
direct-current (as adjective)	d-c
dollar	$
dozen	doz
dram	dr
efficiency	eff
electric	elec
electromotive force	emf
elevation	el
equation	eq
external	ext
farad	spell out or f
feet board measure (board feet)	fbm

* This list of abbreviations is revised from *Abbreviations for Scientific and Engineering Terms*, approved by the American Standards Association, and published by the American Society of Mechanical Engineers, New York City.

feet per minute..........ft/min or fpm
feet per second............ft/sec or fps
fluid................................fl
foot................................ft
foot-candle.......................ft-c
foot-Lambert....................ft-L
foot-pound......................ft-lb
foot-second (see cubic feet per second)
freezing point....................fp
fusion point.....................fnp

gallon............................gal
gallons per minute......gal/min or gpm
gallons per second........gal/sec or gps
gram................................g
gram-calorie.....................g-cal

haversine........................hav
hectare...........................ha
henry..............................h
high-pressure (adjective)...........h-p
hogshead.........................hhd
horsepower........................hp
horsepower-hour................hp-hr
hour...............................hr
hundred............................C
hundredweight (112 lb)............cwt
hyperbolic cosine................cosh
hyperbolic sine..................sinh
hyperbolic tangent...............tanh

inch..............................in.
inch-pound....................in.-lb
inches per second.........in./sec or ips
indicated horsepower..............ihp
indicated horsepower-hour.......ihp-hr
inside diameter....................ID
internal..........................int

joule..............................j

kilocalorie......................kcal
kilogram...........................kg
kilogram-calorie................kg-cal
kilogram-meter...................kg-m
kilograms per cubic meter
    ....kg per cu m or kg/m^3

kilograms per second....kg/sec or kgps
kiloliter..........................kl
kilometer..........................km
kilometers per second............kmps
kilovolt...........................kv
kilovolt-ampere..................kva
kilowatt..........................kw
kilowatthour....................kwhr

latitude.....................lat or ϕ
linear foot....................lin ft
liter...............................l
logarithm (common)...............log
logarithm (natural)........$\log_e$ or ln
longitude..................long. or λ
low-pressure (as adjective).........l-p
lumen...............................l
lumen-hour......................l-hr
lumens per watt..................lpw

mass....................m or spell out
maximum..........................max
mean effective pressure..........mep
melting point.....................mp
meter...............................m
meter-kilogram..................m-kg
microampere.............μa or mu a
microfarad.......................μf
microinch.......................μin.
micromicrofarad.................$\mu\mu$f
micromicron............$\mu\mu$ or mu mu
micron....................μ or mu
microvolt........................μv
microwatt..............μw or mu w
mile.................mi or spell out
miles per hour..........mi/hr or mph
miles per hour per second
    ....mi/hr/sec or mphps
milliampere......................ma
milligram........................mg
millihenry.......................mh
millilambert.....................mL
milliliter........................ml
millimeter.......................mm
millimicron............mμ or m mu
million......................spell out
million gallons per day..........mgd

Appendix

millivolt.........................mv
minute..........................min
minute (angular measure)............'
mole.......................spell out
molecular weight..............mol. wt
month......................spell out

National Electrical Code.........NEC

ohm....................spell out or Ω
ohm-centimeter..............ohm-cm
ounce............................oz
ounce-foot.....................oz-ft
ounce-inch.....................oz-in.
outside diameter..................OD

parts per million.................ppm
peck.............................pk
penny (pence)......................d
pennyweight....................dwt
pint..............................pt
pound.............................lb
pound-foot.....................lb-ft
pound-inch.....................lb-in.
pound sterling.....................£
pounds per brake horsepower-hour
　　　　.........lb/bph-hr or lb per bhp-hr
pounds per cubic foot
　　　　..............lb/ft³ or lb per cu ft
pounds per square foot.....lb/ft² or psf
pounds per square inch....lb/in.² or psi
pounds per square inch absolute
　　　　..................lb/in. abs. or psia
power factor............spell out or pf

quart............................qt

radian...................rad or spell out
revolutions per minute..rev/min or rpm
revolutions per second....rev/sec or rps

rod........................spell out
root mean square.................rms

secant...........................sec
second...........................sec
second (angular measure)............"
shaft horsepower..................shp
shilling...........................s
sine..............................sin
specific gravity.................sp gr
specific heat...................sp ht
square............................sq
square centimeter........sq cm or cm²
square foot..............ft² or sq ft
square inch..............in.² or sq in.
square kilometer.........sq km or km²
square meter..............sq m or m²
square micron......sq μ or sq mu or μ²
square millimeter.......sq mm or mm²
square root of mean square........rms
standard.........................std

tangent..........................tan
temperature.....................temp
thousand..........................M
thousand pound...................kip
ton........................spell out

versed sine......................vers
volt..............................v
volt-ampere.......................va
volt-coulomb...............spell out

watt..............................w
watthour.........................whr
watts per candle.................wpc
week.......................spell out
weight............................wt

yard..............................yd
year..............................yr

answers to problems

7-5. $x = 5$
7-10. $x = -3$
7-15. $x = 4$
7-20. $x = 12$
7-25. 19.6781
7-30. 7699.6
7-35. 10331
7-40. 0.223
7-45. -2.961
7-50. -29.724
7-55. -254.36
7-60. $2.6139(10^6)$
7-65. $7.46(10^1)$
7-70. $7.1045(10^3)$
7-75. $6.969(10^{-1})$
7-80. $6.856(10^1)$
7-85. $-5.984(10^{-1})$
7-90. $-1.809(10^5)$
7-95. 0.01%
7-100. 0.2%
7-105. $\pm 6(10^{-3})$
7-110. $\pm 5(10^6)$
7-115. 7.46 ft; 1.89 ft; 0.7%

9-5. $\left(b - \dfrac{1}{3}\right)\left(b + \dfrac{1}{3}\right)$

9-10. $x(-a + 3c - x)$
9-15. $(2N - 3)(N - 1)$
9-20. $6 + 12m$
9-25. $-9B + 5$
9-30. -1
9-35. $-9d - 2e$
9-40. $x = 21$
9-45. $x = 30.6$
9-50. $x = 100$
9-55. $x = -3$
9-60. $a = 0.5$
9-65. a^{12}
9-70. x^6
9-75. x^5
9-80. x^2
9-85. $\dfrac{y^5}{32}$

9-90. x^8

9-95. $-1.68(10^4)a^{15}$
9-100. $x^{3k}y^{2k}$
9-105. $3a^5x^5$
9-110. $-64a^{7n}b^{10n}$
9-115. $8 + i6$
9-120. $1 + i1$
9-125. $9 + i11$
9-130. $3 + i1$
9-135. Proof
9-140. $\log_a c = b$
9-145. $\log_R 6.3 = 25$
9-150. $\log_1 N = 10$
9-155. $\log_x N/3 = bc$
9-160. $(5)^2 = N$
9-165. $(9)^{1/3} = A$
9-170. $(64)^{1/2} = A$
9-175. $(4)^{1/2} = N$
9-180. 5.1001
9-185. 3.1804
9-190. 2.6387
9-195. 1.1458
9-200. $9.9544 - 10$
9-205. 2.9943
9-210. 5.0374
9-215. $0.4782 - 17$
9-220. $1.7433 - 10$
9-225. $0.4771 - 103$
9-230. $9.980(10^0)$
9-235. $6.380(10^4)$
9-240. $5.900(10^7)$
9-245. $2.760(10^{-4})$
9-250. $5.640(10^{-6})$
9-255. $1.148(10^3)$
9-260. $6.855(10^{-10})$
9-265. $3.022(10^{-18})$
9-270. $1.356(10^{-52})$
9-275. $1.164(10^{-42})$
9-280. $1.009(10^3)$
9-285. $8.066(10^{10})$
9-290. $5.281(10^8)$
9-295. $2.466(10^0)$
9-300. $1.512(10^{-1})$
9-305. $4.686(10^4)$
9-310. $3.804(10^{-20})$
9-315. $1.636(10^1)$

Answers to Problems

9-320. $8.724(10^{-1})$
9-325. $8.40(10^{-1})$
9-330. $1.01(10^0)$
9-335. $6.873(10^2)$
9-340. $1.198(10^0)$
9-345. $1.044(10^2)$
9-350. $2.78(10^{-17})$
9-355. $4.505(10^4)$
9-360. $8.548(10^{-3})$
9-365. $5.266(10^2)$
9-370. $(2.110)(10)^7$
9-375. $2.451(10^{15})$
9-380. -0.9970
9-385. 0.5823
9-390. 9.2203
9-395. -5.9099
9-400. -0.00806
9-405. 7.4805
9-410. -1.1039
9-415. -17.9099
9-420. 1.8043
9-425. 1.5835
9-430. $29.9°$; 4.52 ft
9-435. 11.7 ft
9-440. 52.2 ft
9-445. 115.8 ft
9-450. 282 ft
9-455. 118 ft; 108 ft
9-460. $50.1°$
9-465. 22.4 ft
9-470. a. $68.75°$; 64.5 ft; 65.0 ft
9-475. 452 ft
9-480. $1.77(10^5)$ ft^2
9-485. 214 mi; N $46°$ W
9-490. $1.44(10^5)$ ft^2
9-495. $9.642 - 10$
9-500. 2.332
9-505. 4.192
9-510. 5.742
9-515. 10.339
9-520. 1.484
9-525. $7.27(10)^2$
9-530. $1.07(10^2)$
9-535. $1.166(10^4)$
9-540. $3.12(10^3)$
9-545. $4.86(10^6)$
9-550. $1.275(10^8)$

9-555. $1.128(10^2)$
9-560. $6.94(10^{-5})$
9-565. $1.186(10^{-4})$
9-570. $3.98(10^{-3})$
9-575. $1.278(10^0)$
9-580. $2.65(10^{-2})$
9-585. $1.925(10^0)$
9-590. $1.50(10^4)$
9-595. $3.34(10^3)$
9-600. $1.01(10^0)$
9-605. $2.76(10^{-4})$
9-610. $9.21(10^{-1})$
9-615. $2.395(10^{-8})$
9-620. $4.44(10^{-2})$
9-625. $2.93(10^1)$
9-630. $6.30(10^{-2})$
9-635. $2.51(10)^3$
9-640. $5.54(10^0)$
9-645. $1.04(10^6)$
9-650. $1.905(10^1)$
9-655. $1.548(10^{-18})$
9-660. $6.94(10^2)$
9-665. $2.54(10^{-3})$
9-670. $6.75(10^{-7})$
9-675. $4.55(10^3)$
9-680. $4.20(10^9)$
9-685. $2.59(10^7)$
9-690. $1.359(10^{-1})$
9-695. $8.70(10^0)$
9-700. $3.39(10^{-1})$
9-705. $8.75(10^5)$
9-710. $3.20(10^6)$
9-715. $6.15(10^{16})$
9-720. $9.20(10^2)$
9-725. $9.02(10^1)$
9-730. $1.299(10^1)$
9-735. $4.46(10^{-1})$
9-740. $2.34(10^0)$
9-745. $5.66(10^2)$
9-750. $8.23(10)^6$
9-755. 0.242
9-760. 0.819
9-765. 0.721
9-770. 14.7
9-775. 0.236
9-780. 0.55
9-785. 1.62

Answers to Problems

9-790. 1.012
9-795. 5.44
9-800. 83.16°
9-805. 0.998
9-810. 76.2°
9-815. 38.2
9-820. 0.764
9-825. 1.88
9-830. 38.5°
9-835. 0.569
9-840. 0.0595
9-845. 0.0818
9-850. 18.7
9-855. $1.55(10)^3$
9-860. $2.44(10)^0$
9-865. $1.154(10)^0$
9-870. $3.11(10)^{-1}$
9-875. $4.53(10)^{14}$
9-880. $3.54(10^{15})$
9-885. $9.934(10^{-1})$
9-890. $1.249(10)^0$
9-895. $7.29(10^{-1})$
9-900. $9.378(10^{-1})$
9-905. $1.318(10^0)$
9-910. $1.30(10)^2$
9-915. $1.246(10^{-1})$
9-920. $2.96(10^{-1})$
9-925. $1.18(10)^{-1}$
9-930. 9.88
9-935. 2.57
9-940. −0.0888
9-945. 0.00477
9-950. 0.691
9-955. 65.0; 46.8°
9-960. 71.1; 53.7°
9-965. $9.81(10)^{-3}$; $1.00(10)^{-2}$
9-970. 87.2; 1071
9-975. $2.17(10^4)$
9-980. $3.06(10^5)$
9-985. $1.58(10^5)$
9-990. $7.64(10^3)$
9-995. $-8.54(10^3)$
9-1000. $7.00(10^{-10})$
9-1005. $1.775(10^{-3})$
9-1010. $1.56(10^1)$
9-1015. $8.52(10^{-1})$
9-1020. $4.91(10^3)$

9-1025. $4.71(10^1)$
9-1030. $5.69(10^1)$
9-1035. $3.25(10^3)$
9-1040. $5.01(10^{-1})$; $8.32(10^5)$
9-1045. $7.38(10^4)$
9-1050. $1.048(10^0)$
9-1055. $1.071(10^{-1})$
9-1060. $3.33(10^1)$
9-1065. $3.20(10^{-1})$
9-1070. $1.07(10^{-9})$

10-5. $k = \dfrac{R^8 T^3}{G^4 J N}$

10-10. $k = \dfrac{Y C^2}{R^{\frac{1}{2}} M^3}$

10-15. $M = FL$
10-20. $r = L$
10-25. $(4.44)(10)^1$ ft^3
10-30. a. $(6.66)(10)^4$ mi/hr
     b. $(9.77)(10)^4$ ft/sec
     c. $(2.98)(10)^4$ meters/sec
     d. $(1.788)(10)^3$ km/min
10-35. a. $(1.162)(10)^3$ psi
     b. $(9.45)(10)^{-3}$ ft^2
     c. 1.305 ft
     d. $(2.00)(10)^5$ lb/in^2
10-40. a. $F = (4.915)(10)^1$ newtons
     b. $F = 5.01$ kg
10-45. $F = (4.57)(10)^9$ dynes
10-50. $m_1 = (5.97)(10)^{24}$ kg
12-5. $w_T = (1.50)(10)^4$ lb$_f$
12-10. Vol $= (4.30)(10)^2$ ft^3
12-15. Time $= 9.36$ hr
12-20. $w_T = (2.32)(10)^2$ lb$_f$
12-25. a. Vol $= (2.09)(10)^6$ yd^3
     b. Time $= (1.17)(10)^4$ hr
12-30. Dia. $= 8.30$ in.
12-35. a. Vol $= (3.95)(10)^{-1}$ ft^3
     b. $w_T = (1.78)(10)^2$ lb$_f$
12-40. Vol $= 7.72$ gal
12-45. a. $(3.19)(10)^{-1}$ in.
     b. $(3.19)(10)^{-1}$ in.
     c. $(3.19)(10)^{-1}$ in.
12-50. a. $d = (3.24)(10)^1$ ft
     b. $l = (7.13)(10)^1$ ft
12-55. $h = (2.54)(10)^1$ ft
12-60. $l = (1.53)(10)^1$ in.

Answers to Problems

12-65. 2.94 in.
12-70. 65.46 min
12-75. 0.75 in./ft
12-80. 2.047 in.²
12-85. $-119.2°F$
12-90. 13.02 psi
12-95. 185°F
12-100. a. $6.19(10^{-1})$ amp
   b. $5.14(10^{-1})$ amp
12-105. $5540
13-5. $R = (6.80)(10)^4$ lb @ 10° from 45,000 lb force
13-10. $R = (6.40)(10)^2$ lb @ E 49° S
13-15. $R = (1.945)(10)^3$ lb @ N 6° E
13-20. M 3.61 @ 11° above horizontal
   M 4.09 @ 29° above horizontal
13-25. $R = (1.24)(10)^2$ lb @ E 46° N
13-30. $R = (3.06)(10)^2$ @ N 13° E
13-35. $R = (4.7)(10)^1$ lb @ N 21.5° W
13-40. $R = 5.10$ lb
   $\theta = $ S 39° W
13-45. $R = (1.837)(10)^2$ lb
   $\theta = $ E 18.4° S
13-50. $T = (3.56)(10)^2$ lb
13-55. 2.51 ft
13-60. a. $(1.375)(10)^4$ lb-ft
   $(5.25)(10)^3$ lb-ft
   $(1.75)(10)^3$ lb-ft
   $(2.25)(10)^3$ lb-ft
   $(9.45)(10)^3$ lb-ft
   b. $(2.625)(10)^4$ lb-ft
   $(1.475)(10)^4$ lb-ft
   $(9.75)(10)^3$ lb-ft
   $(9.50)(10)^3$ lb-ft
   $(1.43)(10)^4$ lb-ft
   c. $(1.25)(10)^4$ lb-ft
   $(9.50)(10)^3$ lb-ft
   $(8.00)(10)^3$ lb-ft
   $(7.25)(10)^3$ lb-ft
   $(4.85)(10)^3$ lb-ft
13-65. $(3.92)(10)^2$ lb-ft
   $(8.24)(10)^2$ lb-ft
   $(1.98)(10)^2$ lb-ft
13-70. $(2.090)(10)^3$ lb-in.
13-75. 2.58 ft from right end
13-80. $R_R = (4.60)(10)^2$ lb
   $R_L = (6.00)(10)^2$ lb

13-85. $\alpha = 13.5°$
   $AB = (5.95)(10)^1$ lb
   $C = (1.98)(10)^1$ lb
13-90. $C = (1.50)(10)^2$ lb
   $AB_x = (1.06)(10)^2$ lb
   $AB = (1.26)(10)^2$ lb
   $AB_y = (6.88)(10)^1$ lb
13-95. $A = (3.70)(10)^3$ lb T
   $B = (5.28)(10)^3$ lb C
13-100. $T = (1.145)(10)^2$ lb
13-105. $CB = (1.597)(10)^3$ lb
   $A = 1.984$ lb @ 75.5°
13-110. $N = (8.22)(10)^1$ lb
   $F = (8.22)(10)^1$ lb
   $R = (1.90)(10)^2$ lb
13-115. a. $P = (2.88)(10)^1$ lb
   b. $P = (1.56)(10)^1$ lb
13-120. $P = (2.17)(10)^2$ lb
13-125. $W = (6.37)(10)^2$ lb
13-130. a. $(2.96)(10)^{-1}$
   b. $(2.96)(10)^{-1}$; f is constant
14-5. b. $(4.00)(10)^4$ ft
   c. $(4.75)(10)^{-1}$ ft/sec²
   d. $(-5.5)(10)^{-1}$ ft/sec²
14-10. $(2.06)(10)^3$ ft
14-15. a. $(3.85)(10)^1$ ft/sec
   b. $(3.10)(10)^2$ ft
14-20. $(1.50)(10)^2$ ft
14-25. $(1.54)(10)^1$ mi/hr
14-30. a. $(1.988)(10)^3$ ft/sec²
   b. $(3.59)(10)^3$ ft
14-35. $(2.71)(10)^2$ rev/min
14-40. b. $(1.41)(10)^1$ rad/sec
   c. $(6.07)(10)^2$ rev
14-45. a. $1.80(10^2)$ rpm
   b. $1.892(10^1)$ rad/sec
   c. $1.51(10^3)$ ft/min
   d. $4.61(10^3)$ ft/min
   e. 2.29 ft
15-5. $(3.46)(10)^5$ ft-lb
15-10. $(0.94)(10)^2$ ft lb
15-15. $(3.08)(10)^6$ ft-lb
15-20. $(7.70)(10)^5$ ft-lb
15-25. a. $(5.08)(10)^3$ ft-lb
   b. $(5.08)(10)^3$ ft-lb
15-30. $(1.07)(10)^2$ lb
15-35. $(4.80)(10)^1$ hp

15-40. 1.150 hp
15-45. a. 8.91 hp
       b. $(8.79)(10)^{-1}$ kw
       c. $4.69
15-50. $(4.52)(10)^1$ mi/hr
15-55. $(1.125)(10)^1$ in-lb
15-60. a. 8.66 lb
       b. 1.43 lb
15-65. 3.67 in.
15-70. a. $(8.40)(10)^1$ ft-lb
       b. 3.36 in.
15-75. 1.05 in.
15-80. a. $3.02(10^3)$ ft
       b. $5.44(10^8)$ ft-lb
       c. $2.71(10^8)$ ft-lb
15-85. $(1.153)(10)^3$ lb
15-90. $(1.057)(10)^3$ lb
15-95. $(2.66)(10)^2$ lb
15-100. a. $(1.644)(10)^1$ ft/sec
        b. 2.57 sec
        c. 6.09 ft/sec^2
15-105. $(3.81)(10)^2$ lb
15-110. a. $(9.66)(10)^2$ ft
        b. 4.41 rad/sec^2
15-115. 3.00 (10^2) lb
15-120. $4.33
15-125. $4.64(10^4)$ lb
15-130. 19.1% of wt

Index

Abbreviations for engineering terms, 384
Absolute unit systems, 220
Acceleration, 318
Aeronautical engineering, 47
Agricultural engineering, 48
Algebra, 124
American Institute of Electrical Engineers, 71
American Institute of Mining and Metallurgical Engineers, 71
American Society of Civil Engineers, 70
American Society of Mechanical Engineers, 71
Ampere, 255
Analysis and design, engineering, 3
Analysis, processes of, 227
  static mechanics, 272
Angle of repose, 310
Angular acceleration, 325
Angular motion, 324
Angular velocity, 324
Anti-logarithms, 137
Arabian engineering, 17
Architectural engineering, 50
Average speed or velocity, 319

Babylonian engineers, 9
Beginnings of engineering, 6
Boyle's law, 251
Briggs, adaptation of logarithms, 20

Calculus, development of, 20
Canons of ethics, 76
Center of gravity, 233
Centigrade scale, 251
Ceramic engineering, 62
Characteristic of logarithms, 134
Characteristic rules, 171
Charles' law, 253
Chemical engineering, 51
Circle graph, 101
Circuit diagram, 240
Civil engineering, 53
Code of ethics, 77
Coefficient of friction, 308, 370
Colinear forces, 273

Cologarithm, 141
Communications, 38
Complex numbers, 127
  in polar form, 130
Components, force, 234
  of forces, 274
  rectangular, 280
Computer engineering, 54
Computers, development of, 42
Concurrent force system, 235
Concurrent forces, 273
Conservation of energy, 344
Coplanar forces, 273
Cosine law, 156
Coversed sine of angle, 149
Cube and cube root, slide rule, 185
Curve plotting, 100
Current electricity, 255

Decimal point location, 174
Deductive reasoning, 226
Derived dimensions, 210
Diagram, circuit, 240
  electrical, 240
  freebody, 231
  speed-time, 317
Differentials and integrals, 372
Dimensional prefixes, 374
Division on slide rule, 178

Early civilizations, 9
Economics of engineering, 258
Efficiency, 337
Egyptian engineering, 10–11
Electrical diagram, 240
Electrical discoveries, 22
Electrical engineering, 55
Electricity, 254
Electronics, developments in, 42
Empirical equations, 112
Energy, 341
Energy sources, 40
  nuclear, 41
  sun, 40
Engineer, origin of the name, 17
  work of, 1

391

Index

Engineering, analysis and design, 3
  definition of, 1
  education objectives, 2
  registration, 74
  societies, 70
  system of units, 218
  teams, 30
Engineering today, 30
Engineering tomorrow, 34
Engineering in the world of yesterday, 6
Engineers Council for Professional Development, 74
Engineers Joint Council, 73
Engineers-in-training, 75
Equilibrium of forces, 293
Error, 94
Ethics, engineering, 76
Exponents, laws of, 126

Factors, strategic, 228
Fahrenheit scale, 251
False accuracy, 89
Folded scales, slide rule, 203
Foot-pound-second system, 217
Force, 272, 316
Force components, 234
Force constant of springs, 346
Force and mass, 217
Force system, concurrent, 235
Force vectors, 273
Forces, components, 274
  coplanar, colinear, concurrent, 273
  resultant, 274
Foreign engineers, 27
Fossil fuels, 40
Free-body diagram, 231
Friction, 307
Friction force, 237
Fuels, fossil, 40
Functions, trigonometric, 147
Fundamental dimensions, 210

Galileo, 19
Gay-Lussac's law, 253
General triangle solutions, 153
Geometric figures, 365
Graphs, 100
Gravitational system, 217
Gravity, center of, 233
Greek alphabet, 374
Greek engineering, 13

Horizontal bar graph, 101
Horsepower, 335
  standardization, 22

Idealized model system, 228
Imaginary numbers, 127
Inductive reasoning, 227
Industrial engineering, 57
Industrial model, 242
Interest, simple and compound, 259
Interpolution, 137
Iron, processing, 21

Joints, pin, 235

Kilowatts, 336
Kinetic energy, 342
Kinetic friction, 307

Laboratory data, manipulation of, 91
Law, Ohm's, 256
  pressure, 251
  temperature, 253
  of work and energy, 349
Laws, of exponents, 126
  of logarithms, 139
Lettering, engineering, 80
Line graph, 101
Logarithm tables, 377
Logarithms, 132
  common, 132
  natural, 143
Log-log graph paper, 110
Log-log scales, slide rule, 194

Major premise, 226
Management engineering, 57
Mantissa of logarithms, 134
Manufacturing processes, 38
Marine engineering, 62
Materials, research in, 43
Measurement and error, 95
Mechanical engineering, 59
Mechanics of rigid bodies, 272
Members, two force, 235
  three force, 235
Mensuration, 250
Mesopotamia, 8
Metallurgical engineering, 61
Middle Ages, engineering in, 16
Mining and metallurgical engineering, 61

Index

Minor premise, 226
Model, industrial, 240
Model problem sheets, 82
Model system, idealized, 228
Modern science, 21
Moment of forces, 285
Motion, analysis, 316
    angular, 324
    formulas, 373
    laws of, 20
Multiplication, slide rule, 172

Napier, invention of logarithms, 20
National Society of Professional Engineers, 73
Natural logarithms, 143
    slide rule, 199
Naval and marine engineering, 62
Newton, Sir Isaac, 20
Newton's laws, 217, 316
Nomographs, 115
Normal force, 237
Nuclear engineering, 64
Nuclear power, 41
Numerical error, 96

Objectives of engineering education, 2
Oblique triangles, 153
Ohm's law, 256
Operations research, 32
Oughtred, development of slide rule, 20
Outer space, 35

Parallelogram method, 275
Percent error, 96
Petroleum engineering, 66
Pictograph, 101
Pin connection, 296
Pin joints, 235
Planimeter, 363
Polar form of complex numbers, 130
Polar graph paper, 112
Polygon of forces, 277
Potential energy, 342
Power, definition of, 335
Presentation of work, 81
Pressure law of gases, 251
Principle of transmissibility, 274
Problem, defining the, 228
Processes of analysis, 227

Projection rule for division, 179
Projection rule for multiplication, 177

Qualities necessary for engineering, 2

Radian, 324
Railways, development of, 23
Reaction between surfaces, 235
Reactions, force, 295
Reasoning, deductive, 226
    inductive, 227
    methods of, 226
Reciprocal scales, slide rule, 204
Rectangular components, 280
Registration of engineers, 74
Research, operations, 32
Resistance, electrical, 255
Resistances, in parallel, 257
    in series, 257
Resultant, 274
Right triangle solution, slide rule, 201
Right triangles, trigonometry, 146
Roman engineering, 14

Scaler quantity, 272
Scale of springs, 346
Scales, temperature, 251
Scientific notation, 89
Scientific presentation of data, 88
Scratch paper, 250
Semi log graph paper, 109
Seventeenth Century engineering, 19
Significant figures, 88
Sine law, 153
Slide rule, accuracy, 165
    adjustments, 164
    care of, 162
    combined multiplication and division, 180
    cube and cube root, 185
    division, 178
    folded scales, 203
    graduations, 165
    logarithms, 171
    log-log scales, 194
    manipulation of, 163
    multiplication, 172
    natural logarithms, 199
    reciprocal scales, 204
    right triangle solution, 201
    scales, 170

Slide rule [cont.]
 squares, 183
 square roots, 183
 trigonometric functions, 187
Slug, 218
Smooth surfaces, 235
Space, 272
 outer, 35
Specific gravities, 371
Speed, 316
Speed-time diagram, 317
Springs, energy in, 345
Spring rate, 346
Square and square root, slide rule, 183
Static friction, 307
Steam engine, 21
Sterile values, 210
Strategic factors, 228
Sun, energy source, 40
Syllogism, 226
System, thermodynamic, 239

Tables of weights and measures, 368
Teams, engineering, 30
Technical societies, pounding of, 27
Temperature law of gases, 253
Temperature scales, 251
Thermodynamic system, 239
Three-force members, 235
Three sides laws, 158
Transmissibility, principle of, 274

Transportation, 39
Triangle solutions, general, 153, 160
Trigonometric functions, 372
 slide rule, 187
Trigonometric tables, 379
Trigonometry, 145
True value, 95
Twentieth Century technology, 25
Two-force members, 235

Unit systems, 210, 217

Van Der Waals, 252
Varignon's theorem, 287
Vectors, force, 273
 quantity, 272
 weight, 234
Velocity, 316
Verniers, 362
Versed sine of angle, 149
Vertical bar graph, 101
Voltage, electrical, 255

Watt, James, 22
Watts, power in, 336
Weight vectors, 234
Work, definition of, 330
Work and energy, law of, 349
Work of the engineer, 46
Work, power, energy analysis, 330